# MODELS OF DISCOVERY

# SYNTHESE LIBRARY

MONOGRAPHS ON EPISTEMOLOGY,

LOGIC, METHODOLOGY, PHILOSOPHY OF SCIENCE,

SOCIOLOGY OF SCIENCE AND OF KNOWLEDGE,

AND ON THE MATHEMATICAL METHODS OF

SOCIAL AND BEHAVIORAL SCIENCES

VOLUME 114

BOSTON STUDIES IN THE PHILOSOPHY OF SCIENCE

EDITED BY R. S. COHEN AND M. W. WARTOFSKY

VOLUME LIV

# HERBERT A. SIMON

*Carnegie-Mellon University, Pittsburgh, Penn., U.S.A.*

# MODELS OF DISCOVERY

## *and Other Topics in the Methods of Science*

D. REIDEL PUBLISHING COMPANY

DORDRECHT-HOLLAND / BOSTON-U.S.A.

Library of Congress Cataloging in Publication Data

Simon, Herbert Alexander, 1916–
    Models of discovery.

    (Boston studies in the philosophy of science; v. 54)
    (Synthese library; v. 114)
        Includes bibliographical references and indexes.
        1.  Science – Philosophy.  2.  Science – Methodology.
I.  Title.  II.  Series.
Q174.B67 vol. 54 [Q175]        501'.8        77–8930
ISBN 90-277-0812-6
ISBN 90-277-0858-4 pbk.

Published by D. Reidel Publishing Company,
P. O. Box 17, Dordrecht, Holland

Sold and distributed in the U.S.A., Canada, and Mexico
by D. Reidel Publishing Company, Inc.
Lincoln Building, 160 Old Derby Street, Hingham,
Mass. 02043, U.S.A.

Printed in The Netherlands

*To the memory of my teachers,*

RUDOLF CARNAP

*and*

HENRY SCHULTZ,

*who insisted that*
*philosophy should be done scientifically,*
*and science philosophically*

# EDITORIAL PREFACE

We respect Herbert A. Simon as an established leader of empirical and logical analysis in the human sciences while we happily think of him as also the loner; of course he works with many colleagues but none can match him. He has been writing fruitfully and steadily for four decades in many fields, among them psychology, logic, decision theory, economics, computer science, management, production engineering, information and control theory, operations research, confirmation theory, and we must have omitted several. With all of them, he is at once the technical scientist and the philosophical critic and analyst. When writing of decisions and actions, he is at the interface of philosophy of science, decision theory, philosophy of the specific social sciences, and inventory theory (itself, for him, at the interface of economic theory, production engineering and information theory). When writing on causality, he is at the interface of methodology, metaphysics, logic and philosophy of physics, systems theory, and so on. Not that the interdisciplinary is his orthodoxy; we are delighted that he has chosen to include in this book both his early and little-appreciated treatment of straightforward philosophy of physics — the axioms of Newtonian mechanics, and also his fine papers on pure confirmation theory. But, of course, here too Herbert Simon is a bit beyond the norm: he found all concepts of mass messy, not sufficiently empirical, too vague in their linkage of the empirical and the theoretical, so he went directly from the physics to its logical analysis, not too patient with Mach and his aftermath. And in confirmation theory, he sees the link to decision theory promptly, and by several connections, and we in turn see his beautiful bias for heuristics as preferable to validation: what is the heuristic worth of a bit of validation?

Coming to terms with Herbert Simon should occupy the world of scientists, philosophers, engineers, and policy officials. In the much discussed age of the technological and scientific revolution, Western, Eastern and world-wide, Herbert Simon's disciplined imagination seems to us central, whether he be right, wrong, or just plainly provocative. This book of his general methodological reflections upon specific natural and social scientific puzzle-solving will lead his readers to Professor Simon's other works; and to a deepening of methodology itself.

*Center for Philosophy and History of Science*          ROBERT S. COHEN
*Boston University*                              MARX W. WARTOFSKY

# TABLE OF CONTENTS

## SECTION 4 – COMPLEXITY

## SECTION 5 – THEORY OF SCIENTIFIC DISCOVERY

## SECTION 6 – FORMALIZING SCIENTIFIC THEORIES

# ACKNOWLEDGMENTS

I am grateful to Nicholas Rescher, Albert Ando and Guy Groen for permission to republish, as Chapters 2.4, 4.2 and 6.6, respectively, papers that we wrote jointly. The assistance of many friends and colleagues who reviewed and commented upon individual chapters is acknowledged in the notes to those chapters, as is the generous research support that I have received from a number of sources. Finally, I wish to thank Robert S. Cohen and Marx W. Wartofsky for their generous help in preparing this book for publication, and for their editorial preface to it. Whatever merit may be found in these pages owes much to these friends and this support.

Finally, I want to thank the following journals and publishers for permission to reprint the papers from the original sources:

*The Annals of Mathematical Statistics*, Chapter 1.1;
*The Journal of the American Statistical Association*, Chapters 1.2 and 2.3;
*Philosophy of Science*, Chapters 1.3, 2.4, 5.4, 5.5, 6.2 and 6.5;
The North-Holland Publishing Company, Chapters 1.4, 4.3, 5.3, and 6.3;
The Yale University Press, Chapter 2.1;
*The Journal of Philosophy*, Chapter 2.2;
*The British Journal for the Philosophy of Science*, Chapters 3.1 and 6.6;
The University of Pittsburgh Press, Chapters 3.2, 5.1 and 5.2;
*Econometrica*, Chapters 4.1 and 4.2;
G. Braziller, Chapter 4.4;
*Artificial Intelligence*, Chapter 5.3;
*The Philosophical Magazine*, Chapter 6.1;
*The Journal of Symbolic Logic*, Chapter 6.4;
D. Reidel Publishing Company, Chapter 6.7.

# GENERAL INTRODUCTION

It is no new thing for a practicing scientist to be seduced into thinking and writing about the methodology and philosophy of his subject — or the philosophy of science in general. A large number of predecessors have set the example for me.

My own seduction took place at an early age. I had forgotten how early until, just this morning, I recovered from my files a three-page outline dated July 28, 1937 and titled, 'The Logical Structure of a Science of Administration'. Inspection showed it to be a progenitor of the project that emerged five years later as my dissertation, 'The Theory of Administrative Decision, and ten years later as *Administrative Behavior*.[1] Successive reformulations of the project squeezed much of the abstract methodology out of it, and transformed it into a more substantively oriented essay on the social science of decision making. What remained of the original methodological content can be seen mainly in Chapter 3 of the dissertation and Chapter 4 of *Administrative Behavior*. These later documents failed to make good the promise of the original outline to provide answers to the following three questions (among others): What is the logical structure of sentences in Newton's *Principia*? What is the logical structure of the sentences of economic price theory? What is the logical structure of the sentences of Aristotle's *Ethics*?

Evidently the unkept promises lodged somewhere in my subconscious, for throughout my scientific career I have continued to occupy a portion of my time and thoughts with methodological and philosophical issues — most of which turn out to be closely related to these three questions. In particular, Section 3 of this book is much concerned with the logics of economics and ethics, and Section 6 with the logic of physics. Thus the papers reprinted in this volume, though their dates of publication extend over more than thirty years, are not isolated fragments. Instead, they celebrate the periodic illuminations — a little less than one a year — that fitfully brightened a continuously sustained state of murky puzzlement.

Of course, even if a practicing scientist has no special interest in methodology as such, he cannot avoid taking positions on methodological issues. Substantive and methodological concerns form the warp and woof of every scientific fabric; and advances in methodology are as likely to lead to important scientific discoveries as are advances in substantive concepts. What distinguishes the scientist-turned-philosopher from his fellows is that he abstracts from the specific methodological issues that are intrinsic to his scientific work, and seeks to understand and discuss these issues in a more general context. That is what I have tried to do in this book.

## 1. APPLICATION AS A SOURCE OF PROBLEMS

The papers I have selected for this volume address general issues in the philosophy of science, somewhat detached from specific applications. This does not mean that these issues were generated in a vacuum, or even that they were mainly derived from the mainstream literature of philosophy of science. On the contrary, most of them had their origins in specific problems that I encountered in my substantive work, and were then pursued further because they appeared to have interest and significance beyond the immediate needs of application.

This strategy reflects my belief that the comparative advantage of the practicing scientist, when he invades the field of philosophy of science, lies in his constant exposure to the concrete realities of scientific endeavor. His contacts with the 'real world' of science may bring questions to his attention, or suggest ways of framing questions, that would be less likely to occur to someone living in the purer air of methodology and theory.

In the philosophy of science, as in other theoretical fields, the areas of application are an indispensable source of new problems and new ideas. And the failure of a theoretically oriented field to touch base frequently with the world of application may lead it sometimes to descend into triviality and distract it into the pursuit of formal elegance. One responsibility, then, of the practicing scientist is to try to rescue philosophy and theory, from time to time, from excessive formalism. I shall undertake to provide some examples in later chapters of this book — some having to do with statistical tests, some with modal logic, some with scientific discovery, and some with the axiomatization of scientific theories — of cases where a closer look at the actual practice of science suggests a reformulation of the questions asked by philosophy.

## 2. THE USES OF MATHEMATICS

Readers of this book will find that some of the chapters (e.g., Chapters 1.1, 2.2, 4.2, and 6.6) contain arguments that are expressed in the languages of mathematics or mathematical logic. In other chapters mathematical symbolism is nowhere to be found. My attitude toward mathematics and rigor is wholly pragmatic: an argument should be as formal and technical as it needs to be in order to achieve clarity in its statement of issues and in its arguments — and no *more* formal than it needs to be. Nor do I believe that an argument is always best stated at the greatest achievable levels of generality and abstraction.

I recognize that tastes differ widely in these matters, and I despair of persuading others to prefer my own tastes. I do find it ironic that, having done much missionary work for mathematics in fields that had been largely innocent of it, I now find myself reacting to a surfeit of formalism more often that to a deficit of it, especially in economics, statistics, and logic.

The uses of mathematics in this book will themselves illustrate a general bias that I confess to holding, and on which I will comment further below: a bias toward the processes of discovery rather than the processes of verification. Mathematics is sometimes treated as a body of technique for guaranteeing the validity of propositions that may have been arrived at without its help. Of course, mathematics does have this function, but it has another use that, on balance, is probably far more important: to guide and facilitate the discovery process itself. For the person who thinks *in* mathematics, and does not simply translate his verbal thoughts or his images *into* mathematics, mathematics is a language of discovery as well as a language of verification. At the present stage of our knowledge of the psychology of discovery (see Chapter 5.2), I would be hard-pressed to state specifically and operationally what I mean by 'thinking in mathematics' as distinguished from thinking in words, or thinking in some other way. Nevertheless, I am confident, from introspective evidence, that such a distinction exists, and I believe my faith is shared by most applied mathematicians. I doubt that I could have discovered most of the results reported in this book (note that I say 'discovered', not 'proved') without representing the problem situations in mathematical form.

However, when conclusions have been reached by mathematical thinking, they are sometimes more readily communicated after thay are translated *out* of mathematics into ordinary language. In almost all cases, I have tried to provide such interpretations. Hence, the direction of translation between mathematics and English in this book tends to run in the opposite direction from that found in highly formal treatises that stress verification rather than discovery and understanding.

## 3. ORGANIZATION OF THE BOOK

The papers brought together here have been grouped by topic into six sections, each introduced by a brief essay outlining its central issues and showing the mutual relations among its chapters. The six topics are: (1) the validation and discovery of scientific hypotheses, (2) causal ordering, (3) the logic of imperatives, (4) complex systems, (5) the theory of scientific discovery, and (6) the formalization of scientific theories.

Each of these topics deals with a set of issues that has been important in the literature of the philosophy of science. In my approach to them, however, the six topics are not mutually independent, but are closely intertwined with each other by virtue of their sharing a few major themes. These themes run through the entire volume and give it coherence. In the remainder of this introduction, I should like to comment upon them.

### 3.1. The Processes of Discovery

The philosophy of science has for many years taken as its central preoccupation how scientific theories are tested and verified, and how choices are made among competing theories. How theories are discovered in the first place has generally been much neglected, and it is sometimes even denied that the latter topic belongs at all to the philosophy of science. Although in the past few years there has been some challenge to this classical position (e.g. in the work of Hanson, Kuhn and Lakatos, to mention just three examples), the logic of discovery is still a grossly underdeveloped domain.

This emphasis upon verification rather than discovery seems to me a distortion of the actual emphases in the practice of science. As I look about at my own scientific activity and that of my colleagues, we seem to devote much more time to seeking out possible regularities in phenomena than simply to proving that regularities we have noted are really there, and are not products of our imaginations. The history and philosophy of science have been excessively fascinated with the drama of competition between theories: the wave theory of light versus the particle theory, classical mechanics versus relativity theory, phlogiston versus oxygen, and so on. Such competition occurs only occasionally. Much more often, scientists are faced with a set of phenomena and *no* theory that explains them in even a minimally acceptable way. In this more typical situation, the scientific task is not to verify or falsify theories, or to choose between alternative theories, but to *discover* candidate theories that might help explain the facts.

Researchers in psychology and some of the other behavioral sciences, where there is often a severe deficit of good candidate theories, have sometimes been misled by the literature on philosophy and methodology to exhibit in research and publication an exaggerated concern with verification, accompanied by uncritical application of statistical tests of hypotheses to situations where they don't properly apply. I would be pleased if these essays made some small contribution to stamping out these undesirable practices.

The papers in Sections 1 and 5 are particularly concerned with questions of verification and discovery of theories (more or less in that order), and serve to illustrate the progression of my own thinking on these matters. Chapters 1.1 and 1.2 argue that tests of hypotheses must be chosen in a context that takes into consideration the decisions that are to be reached and the consequences of those decisions. The position of these chapters on decision theory is crudely but distinctly Bayesian. Chapter 1.3, taking a more explicitly Bayesian viewpoint, argues that hypotheses cannot be tested without considering the processes that generated them initially – i.e. .the discovery processes. Chapter 1.4 carries this argument further, emphasizing that data precede theories more often than theories precede data. This chapter serves as a transition to the explicit examination in Section 5 of the processes of discovery. Section 5 argues for a close relation between the psychology of scientific discovery and its logic; surveys what is known of the psychological processes of discovery, and applies that knowledge to philosophical and methodological issues.

## 3.2. Model Theory and Modal Logics

Since the turn of the century, logicians and philosophers have been struggling to extend modern symbolic logic to reasoning about the modalities: causality, possibility, necessity, obligation, imperatives, and the like. The initial path that was followed was to define special logics that admitted statements like: '*A* causally implies *B*', '*A* is possible', '*A* is necessary,' 'If *A*, then *B* is obligatory', '*X* ought to do *Y*'. The standard rules of inference were then modified and extended to encompass such statements as well as ordinary declaratives and implications.

The use of specially defined *modal logics* to handle the modalities has been beset with difficulties, not the least of them being a proliferation of alternative systems of inference, each claiming some plausibility but each failing to handle some of the dilemmas that are taken care of by others. A different approach to the modalities, through the application of *model theory*, has had great success and has gained wide acceptance.[2] Model theory treats sentences and sets of sentences semantically, in terms of the set of possible worlds in which they are valid. In the hands of Kripke and Kreisel, contemporary model theory reached a high state of technical development, and Richard Montague[3] made important contributions toward its application to the modalities.

A model-theoretic treatment of causality is provided in Section 2 of this book, and a similar treatment of the imperative mode and obligation is provided in Section 3. These analyses, arrived at independently of the technical advances in symbolic logic mentioned above, require a much less formidable apparatus than is commonly deployed by model theorists. The papers in Sections 2 and 3 demonstrate, I think, that the central idea of expressing modal concepts in terms of models can be handled in a relatively simple and straightforward way with the aid of the standard predicate calculus and some conventional, and quite elementary, mathematics.

Model-theoretic ideas also play an important role in the papers of Section 6, and particularly in the demonstration (Chapter 6.6) that theoretical terms (terms denoting non-observables) are eliminable from axiomatized scientific theories.

### 3.3. Identifiability and Definability

A central issue in modern econometrics has been the identification problem: how to use observational data to estimate the parameters of a theory, and the conditions under which such estimation is possible. A central issue in axiomatizing empirical theories has been the definition problem: determining which terms in a theory are to be defined, and which are to be treated as primitives.

Section 2, and particularly Chapter 2.1, demonstrates that there is a very close relation between identification and causal ordering. Section 6 shows that there is also a very close relation between identifiability and the standard logical concept of definability (as that term has been used by Tarski[4]). Specifically, identifiability can be regarded as a weakened form of definability. Several chapters of Section 6 (in particular, Chapters 6.3, 6.4, 6.5 and 6.7) develop the idea that it is identifiability, rather than definability, that is wanted for theoretical terms in axiomatization of empirical theories.

## 3.4. Complexity

It is widely believed that the methods of analysis that have been so successful in treating 'simple' phenomena in the physical sciences may be inadequate for handling complex biological and social systems. The chapters of Section 4 explore this issue by trying to characterize the special properties that distinguish complex from simple systems. One of these properties is hierarchy, and we will see in Chapter 4.2 that causally ordered systems have a hierarchic structure that makes them amenable to analysis even when they are very large and complex.

The topic of complexity is interesting both in its own right, and also as a basis for understanding the phenomena of problem solving by heuristic search, and hence of scientific discovery. Thus, the discussion of complexity in Section 4, based in turn upon the treatment of causal ordering in Section 2, provides an introduction to the topic of scientific discovery, which is dealt with in the chapters of Section 5.

## 3.5. Summary

These, then, are some of the threads connecting the major sections of this book: concern for the processes of discovery and deemphasis of verification, treatment of the modalities in terms of model theory, use of the notion of identifiability in the interpretation of theoretical terms, a characterization of complexity, and an application of that characterization to the study of scientific discovery. Each of the six sections can be read independently of the others, but their arrangement in the book is neither accidental nor random. As we have seen, Sections 1 and 4 provide some conceptual foundations for Section 5, while Sections 2 and 3 provide underpinnings for Sections 4, 5 and 6. Apart from these ordering constraints, the sequence of topics corresponds, roughly, to the temporal sequence in which they occupied my thoughts. Where necessary, however, temporal order has been sacrificed to topical coherence in arranging the chapters and sections.

### NOTES

[1] New York: The Free Press, Third Edition, 1976.
[2] It is an unfortunate accident that the English language distinguishes orthographically between the very different notions of 'modal' and 'model' by only a single letter.
[3] 'Logical Necessity, Physical Necessity, Ethics, and Quantifiers', Chapter 1 in *Formal Philosophy* (New Haven: Yale University Press, 1974).
[4] 'Some Methodological Investigations on the Definability of Concepts', in *Logic, Semantics, and Metamathematics* (Oxford: The Clarendon Press, 1956).

# TESTING THEORIES OF EMPIRICAL PHENOMENA

The question of how scientific theories are validated (or falsified) by evidence has been perhaps the central topic in the modern literature of the philosophy of science. The four papers reprinted in this section are addressed to several aspects of that question, but neither individually nor collectively do they attempt a systematic treatment of it. Rather, they aim to show how testing the validity of a theory requires an explicit decision-theoretic formulation, and how this formulation, in turn, leads inevitably to questions of how the theory was originally generated. The processes of validation and the processes of discovery cannot be separated as they have been in the classical treatments.

Chapters 1.1 and 1.2 discuss, from a decision-theoretic point of view, the choice between two courses of action, both having uncertain outcomes, where higher costs are associated with the one action than with the other. This mundane question arose in the treatment of data from a large field experiment whose main objective was to advise the California State Relief Administration on optimal work loads for caseworkers. Analysis of the decision problem led to a statistical test that was quite unorthodox in terms of the standard textbook procedures of that time (1940). Chapter 1.3 takes up issues that were left dangling in the two previous papers — specifically, about the nature of the prior probabilities that entered into the statistical decision procedures.

Chapter 1.4 moves from the problem of choosing between two hypotheses to the problem of testing a so-called 'extreme' hypothesis, that is, a hypothesis that makes point predictions about the data. The analysis here carries us even further toward the position that testing and discovery are all part of the same process, and that the relation between them is poorly represented in the classical statistical theory of testing hypothesis. The substantive context for the analysis in this paper is provided by some information processing models of human cognition in learning and concept attainment tasks.

## 1. THE OPERATIONALIZATION OF STATISTICS

A succession of revolutions has swept over statistics since the 1930's, displacing the paradigm established by the generation of R. A. Fisher. First (about 1933) came the liberating new idea of Neyman and Pearson[1] that hypotheses are tested in order to guide decisions, that decisions lead to actions, and that actions have consequences. Neyman and Pearson divided these consequences into errors of the first kind (rejecting the null hypothesis when it is true) and errors of the second kind (accepting it when it is false). Next came Wald's (1950) introduction of a loss function to allow the two kinds of errors to be compared and of a minimax procedure for determining the most powerful test, while avoiding or evading the need for estimating the prior probability distribution of the competing hypotheses.[2] Shortly thereafter followed Savage's (1954) advocacy of subjective (or personalistic) probabilities,[3] and the subsequent Bayesian revival, which grasped the nettle that Wald had refused and explicitly built statistical inference around the prior probability distribution and Bayes' theorem.

From a forty-year perspective, we can see that all of these upheavals were almost inevitable sequels to the initial major paradigm shift produced by Neyman and Pearson. Once an explicit decision-theoretic outlook was adopted, attention had to be paid to the loss functions and the prior probabilities. But the success of a major Reformation does not prevent sectarian strife among the Reformed. Though neo-Bayesian doctrine is in the ascendance today, there is still not much agreement as to what form it should take. The essays of Section 1 advocate a particular variant, sometimes called the empirical Bayesian approach, on which I shall comment in a moment.

If I am accused of exercising hindsight in suggesting that Bayesianism was implicit in the Neyman-Pearson paradigm, I will call as defense witness Chapter 1.1, which was published in 1943, and conceived a couple of years earlier – i.e., less than a decade after the Neyman-Pearson work first appeared. (Chapter 1.2 contains a less technical treatment of the same ideas.) Sections 1 through 4 of Chapter 1.1 are a straightforward application of the Neyman-Pearson theory, leading to a new class of tests (uniformly most powerful symmetric tests) that was later extended and further developed by Bahadur and Robbins.[4] In Section 5, however, the question is raised of how the Type I and Type II errors are to be compared, and a Bayesian argument is adduced to show that the symmetric test provides an answer to the question. This paper, then, is a very early example of how the decision-theoretic approach lured one toward Bayesianism.

## 2. THE EMPIRICAL BAYES APPROACH

Bayesian statistics stems from the idea that hypotheses do not spring from the brow of Zeus, but arise, somehow, from prior information about the world. If that prior information can be used to assign probabilities to the hypotheses, then posterior probabilities — probabilities taking into account new information — can be calculated by the application of Bayes' Law.

All the difficulties centre around the 'if'. First of all, what does it mean to associate a probability distribution with a hypothesis? Hypotheses, it is argued, are either true or false; and it makes no sense to assign a probability to their being true. The subjectivists answer this objection with an evasion. For them, the probabilities are simply 'there', in a respondent's head, to be tapped by a questionnaire or an offer of betting odds. If a client asks his subjectivist statistician for advice about a decision, the statistician replies by asking the client to state his priors. No priors, no advice.

An empirical Bayesian — at least, one belonging to my sect — would give a different answer. In order to attach a prior probability to a hypothesis, he would have to view that hypothesis as having been selected by some sampling procedure, from a specified population of hypotheses. The prior probability of the hypothesis would then be derived from a probability distribution defined over the population of hypotheses.

Now there are several ways in which operational meaning can be attached to a probability distribution over a population of hypotheses. The simplest is to assume that some fraction of these hypotheses are true, and the remainder false. Then the former fraction, if known, estimates the probability that any given hypothesis drawn at random from the population is true. The population, in turn, might consist of all of the hypotheses that are produced by some specific process — all the hypotheses generated by a particular scientist, say. If we know the past batting average of the process (the scientist), then we can use it to assign a prior probability to a new hypothesis generated by the same process. By some such procedures as these, the Bayesian approach can be reconciled with a frequency interpretation of probabilities, and rescued both from subjectivism and from the notion that a particular hypothesis can be 'probably' true or false. This is the basic idea that is developed in Chapter 1.3, and which has set at rest some of my initial hesitations in adopting a Bayesian approach.

## 3. WHERE DO HYPOTHESES COME FROM?

If hypotheses do not spring from the brain of Zeus, where then do they come from? The partial answer given above is that they come from some hypothesis-generating process. A major practical advantage of Bayesian statistics is that it does not treat each experiment as an isolated world, but allows the interpretation of data to be informed by one's prior knowledge, which usually is extensive, about that world. Bayesian theory would stand on firmer ground if it were accompanied by a theory of the origins of hypotheses – that is to say, a theory of scientific discovery. Chapter 1.4, following up the argument of Chapter 1.3, has something to say about the discovery process and the relations between discovery and verification. Hence, it provides a transition and an introduction to the fuller discussion of the theory of discovery that will be found in the essays of Section 5.

## 4. THE PROBLEM OF EXTREME HYPOTHESES

At least one other charge is added to the indictment of classical statistics that is offered in this section. There is no place in classical statistics for the notion of approximate correctness. But the working scientist, even in his most optimistic moods, does not normally regard a scientific theory as embodying final and exact truth about a body of phenomena. Theories, even very good theories, contain simplified and approximate descriptions of the phenomena they purport to explain.

When classical statistical hypothesis-testing methods are applied to scientific theories of the usual kind (theories like '$F = ma$', say), they behave in a very perverse manner. Suppose that we have a model that provides a good, but *approximate* description of a phenomenon. We apply a standard test to determine whether the model fits some data. Now, the larger the number of observations, and the more precise the observations, the more likely it is that the statistical test will reject the hypothesis; the smaller the number of observations, and the less accurate, the more likely that the test will accept the hypothesis. It does not require deep analysis to conclude that there is something wrong with a procedure that behaves in this way. What is wrong is discussed more fully in Chapter 1.4.

## NOTES

[1] 'The Testing of Statistical Hypotheses in Relation to Probability a Priori', *Proceedings of the Cambridge Philosophical Society* 29, 492–510 (1933).
[2] *Statistical Decision Functions* (New York: Wiley, 1950).
[3] *The Foundations of Statistics* (New York: Wiley, 1954).
[4] 'The Problem of the Greater Mean', *Annals of Mathematical Statistics* 21, 469–487 (1950).

# SYMMETRIC TESTS OF THE HYPOTHESIS
# THAT THE MEAN OF ONE NORMAL POPULATION
# EXCEEDS THAT OF ANOTHER†

## 1. INTRODUCTION

One of the most commonly recurring statistical problems is to determine, on the basis of statistical evidence, which of two samples, drawn from different universes, came from the universe with the larger mean value of a particular variate. Let $M_y$ be the mean value which would be obtained with universe $(Y)$ and $M_x$ be the mean value which would be obtained with universe $(X)$. Then a test may be constructed [1] for the hypothesis $M_y \geqslant M_x$.

If $x_1, \ldots, x_n$ are the observed values of the variate obtained from universe $(X)$, and $y_1, \ldots, y_n$ are the observed values obtained from universe $(Y)$, then the sample space of the points $E: (x_1, \ldots, x_n; y_1, \ldots, y_n)$ may be divided into three regions $\omega_0$, $\omega_1$, and $\omega_2$. If the sample point falls in the region $\omega_0$, the hypothesis $M_y \geqslant M_x$ is accepted; if the sample point falls in the region $\omega_1$, the hypothesis $M_y \geqslant M_x$ is rejected; if the sample point falls in the region $\omega_2$, judgment is withheld on the hypothesis. Regions $\omega_0$, $\omega_1$, and $\omega_2$ are mutually exclusive and, together, fill the entire sample space. Any such set of regions $\omega_0$, $\omega_1$, and $\omega_2$ defines a test for the hypothesis $M_y \geqslant M_x$.

In those cases, then, where the experimental results fall in the region $\omega_2$, the test leads to the conclusion that there is need for additional data to establish a result beyond reasonable doubt. Under these conditions, the test does not afford any guide to an unavoidable or non-postponable choice. In the application of statistical findings to practical problems it often happens, however, that the judgment can not be held in abeyance — that *some* choice must be made, even at a risk of error. For example, when planting time comes, a choice must be made between varieties $(X)$ and $(Y)$ of grain even if neither has been conclusively demonstrated, up to that time, to yield a larger crop than the other. It is the purpose of this paper to propose a criterion which will always permit a choice between two experimental results, that is, a test in which the regions $\omega_0$ and $\omega_1$ fill the entire sample space. In the

† [*Annals of Mathematical Statistics* 14 No. 2, 149–154 (1943)].

absence of a region $\omega_2$, any observed result is interpreted as a definite acceptance or rejection of the hypothesis tested.

## 2. GENERAL CHARACTERISTICS OF THE CRITERION

Let us designate the hypothesis $M_y \geqslant M_x$ as $H_0$ and the hypothesis $M_x > M_y$ as $H_1$. Then a pair of tests, $T_0$ and $T_1$, for $H_0$ and $H_1$ respectively must, to suit our needs, have the following properties:

(1) The regions $\omega_{00}$ ($\omega_{00}$ is the region of acceptance for $H_0$, $\omega_{10}$ the region of rejection for $H_0$; $\omega_{01}$ and $\omega_{11}$ the corresponding regions for $H_1$) and $\omega_{11}$ must coincide; as must the regions $\omega_{10}$ and $\omega_{01}$. This correspondence means that when $H_0$ is accepted, $H_1$ is rejected, and vice versa. Hence, the tests $T_0$ and $T_1$ are identical, and we shall hereafter refer only to the former.

(2) There must be no regions $\omega_{20}$ and $\omega_{21}$. This means that judgment is never held in abeyance, no matter what sample is observed.

(3) The regions $\omega_{00}$ and $\omega_{10}$ must be so bounded that the probability of accepting $H_1$ when $H_0$ is true (error of the first kind for $T_0$) and the probability of accepting $H_0$ when $H_1$ is true (error of the second kind for $T_0$) are, in a certain sense, minimized. Since $H_0$ and $H_1$ are composite hypotheses, the probability that a test will accept $H_1$ when $H_0$ is true depends upon which of the simple hypotheses that make up $H_0$ is true.

Neyman and Pearson [2] have proposed that a test, $T_\alpha$ for a hypothesis be termed *uniformly more powerful* than another test, $T_\beta$, if the probability for $T_\alpha$ accepting the hypothesis if it is false, or the probability of rejecting it if it is true, does not exceed the corresponding probability for $T_\beta$ no matter which of the simple hypotheses is actually true. Since there is no test which is uniformly more powerful than all other possible tests, it is usually required that a test be uniformly most powerful (UMP) among the members of some specified class of tests.

## 3. A SYMMETRIC TEST WHEN THE TWO UNIVERSES HAVE EQUAL STANDARD DEVIATIONS

Let us consider, first, the hypothesis $M_y \geqslant M_x$ where the universes from which observations of varieties $(X)$ and $(Y)$, respectively, are drawn are normally distributed universes with equal standard deviations, $\sigma$, and means $M_x$ and $M_y$, respectively. Let us suppose a sample drawn of $n$ random observations from the universe of variety $(X)$ and a sample of $n$ independent and random observations from the universe of $(Y)$. The probability distribution of points in the sample space is given by

(1)     $p(x_1, \ldots, x_n; y_1, \ldots, y_n)$

$= (2\pi\sigma^2)^{-n} e^{-(1/2\sigma^2)[\sum_i (x_i - M_x)^2 + \sum_i (y_i - M_y)^2]}$.

In testing the hypothesis $M_y \geqslant M_x$, there is a certain symmetry between the alternatives $(X)$ and $(Y)$. If there is no *a priori* reason for choosing $(X)$ rather than $(Y)$, and if the sample point $E_1 : (a_1, \ldots, a_n; b_1, \ldots, b_n)$ falls in the region of acceptance of $H_0$: then the point $E_2 : (b_1, \ldots, b_n; a_1, \ldots, a_n)$ should fall in the region of acceptance of $H_1$. That is, if $E_1$ is taken as evidence that $M_y \geqslant M_x$; then $E_2$ can with equal plausibility be taken as evidence that $M_x \geqslant M_y$.

Any test such that $E_1 : (a_1, \ldots, a_n; b_1, \ldots, b_n)$ lies in $\omega_0$ whenever $E_2 : (b_1, \ldots, b_n; a_1, \ldots, a_n)$ lies in $\omega_1$ and vice versa, will be designated a symmetric test of the hypothesis $M_y \geqslant M_x$. Let $\Omega$ be the class of symmetric tests of $H_0$. If $T_\alpha$ is a member of $\Omega$, and is uniformly more powerful than every other $T_\beta$ which is a member of $\Omega$, then $T_\alpha$ is *the uniformly most powerful symmetric test of $H_0$*.

The hypothesis $M_y \geqslant \overline{M}_x$ possesses a UMP symmetric test. This may be shown as follows. From (1), the ratio can be calculated between the probability densities at the sample points $E : (x_1, \ldots, x_n; y_1, \ldots, y_n)$ and $E' : (y_1, \ldots, y_n; x_1, \ldots, x_n)$. We get

(2)     $\dfrac{p(E)}{p(E')} = \exp\left\{ \dfrac{n}{\sigma^2}(\bar{x} - \bar{y})(M_x - M_y) \right\}$,

where

$$\bar{x} = \frac{1}{n}\sum_i x_i, \quad \bar{y} = \frac{1}{n}\sum_i y_i.$$

Now the condition $p(E) > p(E')$ is equivalent to $n/\sigma^2 \, (\bar{x} - \bar{y})(M_x - M_y) > 0$. Hence $p(E) > p(E')$ whenever $(\bar{x} - \bar{y})$ has the same sign as $(M_x - M_y)$.

Now for any symmetric test, if $E$ lies in $\omega_0$, $E'$ lies in $\omega_1$, and *vice versa*. Suppose that, in fact, $M_y > M_x$. Consider a symmetric test, $T_\alpha$ whose region $\omega_0$ contains a sub-region $\omega_{0U}$ (of measure greater than zero) such that $\bar{y} < \bar{x}$ for every point in that sub-region. Then for every point $E'$ in $\omega_{0U}$, $p(E') < p(E)$. Hence, a more powerful test, $T_\beta$ could be constructed which would be identical with $T_\alpha$, except that $\omega_{1U}$, the sub-region symmetric to

$\omega_0 U$, would be interchanged with $\omega_0 U$ as a portion of the region of acceptance for $H_0$. Therefore, a test such that $\omega_0$ contained all points for which $\bar{y} < \bar{x}$, and no others, would be a UMP symmetric test. This result is independent of the magnitude of $(M_x - M_y)$ provided only $M_y \geqslant M_x$. We conclude that $\bar{y} > \bar{x}$ is a uniformly most powerful symmetric test for the hypothesis $M_y > M_x$.

The probability of committing an error with the UMP symmetric test is a simple function of the difference $| M_y - M_x |$. The exact value can be found by integrating (1) over the whole region of the sample space for which $\bar{y} < \bar{x}$. There is no need to distinguish errors of the first and second kind, since an error of the first kind with $T_0$ is an error of the second kind with $T_1$, and vice versa. The probability of an error is one half when $M_x = M_y$, and in all other cases is less than one half.

### 4. RELATION OF UMP SYMMETRIC TEST AND TEST WHICH IS UMP OF TESTS ABSOLUTELY EQUIVALENT TO IT

Neyman and Pearson [2] have shown the test $\bar{y} - \bar{x} > k$ to be UMP among the tests absolutely equivalent to it, for the hypothesis $M_y \geqslant M_x$. They have defined a class of tests as absolutely equivalent if, for each simple hypothesis in $H_0$, the probability of an error of the first kind is exactly the same for all the tests which are members of the class. If $k$ be set equal to zero, $\bar{y} > \bar{x}$, and their test reduces to the UMP symmetric test. What is the relation between these two classes of tests?

If $T_\alpha$ be the UMP symmetric test, then it is clear from Section 2 that there is no other symmetric test, $T_\beta$, which is absolutely equivalent to $T_\alpha$. Hence $\Omega$, the class of symmetric tests, and $\Lambda$, the class of tests absolutely equivalent to $T_\alpha$, have only one member in common – the test $T_\alpha$ itself. Neyman and Pearson have shown $T_\alpha$ to be the UMP test of $\Lambda$, while the results of Section 4 show $T_\alpha$ to be the UMP test of $\Omega$.

### 5. JUSTIFICATION FOR EMPLOYING A SYMMETRIC TEST

In introducing Section 3, a heuristic argument was advanced for the use of a symmetric, rather than an asymmetric test for the hypothesis $M_y \geqslant M_x$. This argument will now be given a precise interpretation in terms of probabilities.

Assume, not a single experiment for testing the hypothesis $M_y \geqslant M_x$, but a series of similar experiments. Suppose a judgment to be formed independently on the basis of each experiment as to the correctness of the hypothesis. Is there any test which, if applied to the evidence in each case, will maximize the probability of a correct judgment in that experiment? Such a test can be shown to exist, providing one further assumption is made: that if any criterion be applied *prior* to the experiment to test the hypothesis $M_y \geqslant M_x$, the probability of a correct decision will be one half. That is, it must be assumed that there is no evidence which, prior to the experiment, will permit the variety with the greater yield to be selected with greater-than-chance frequency.

Consider now any asymmetric test for the hypothesis $H_0$ — that, is, any test which is not symmetric. The criterion $\bar{y} - \bar{x} > k$, where $k > 0$, is an example of such a test. Unlike a symmetric test, an asymmetric test may give a different result if applied as a test of the hypothesis $H_0$ than if applied as a test of the hypothesis $H_1$. For instance, a sample point such that $\bar{y} - \bar{x} = \epsilon$, where $k > \epsilon > 0$, would be considered a rejection of $H_0$ and acceptance of $H_1$ if the above test were applied to $H_0$; but would be considered a rejection of $H_1$ and an acceptance of $H_0$ if the test were applied to $H_1$. Hence, before an asymmetric test can be applied to a problem of dichotomous choice — a problem where $H_0$ *or* $H_1$ must be determinately selected — a decision must be reached as to whether the test is to be applied to $H_0$ or to $H_1$. This decision cannot be based upon the evidence of the sample to be tested — for in this case, the complete test, which would of course include this preliminary decision, would be symmetric by definition.

Let $H_c$ be the correct hypothesis ($H_0$ or $H_1$, as the case may be) and let $H_*$ be the hypothesis to which the asymmetric test is applied Since by assumption there is no prior evidence for deciding whether $H_c$ is $H_0$ or $H_1$, we may employ any random process for deciding whether $H_*$ is to be identified with $H_0$ or $H_1$. If such a random selection is made, it follows that the probability that $H_c$ and $H_*$ are identical is one half.

We designate as the region of asymmetry of a test the region of points $E_1$: $(a_1, \ldots, a_n; b_1, \ldots, b_n)$ and $E_2$: $(b_1, \ldots, b_n; a_1, \ldots, a_n)$ of aggregate measure greater than zero such that $E_1$ and $E_2$ both fall in $\omega_0$ or both fall in $\omega_1$. Suppose $\omega_{0a}$ and $\omega_{0b}$ are a particular symmetrically disposed pair of subregions of the region of asymmetry, which fall in $\omega_0$ of a test $T_0$. Suppose that, for every point, $E_1$, in $\omega_{0a}$, $\bar{b} > \bar{a}$, and that $\omega_{0a}$ and $\omega_{0b}$ are of measure greater than zero. The sum of the probabilities that the sample point will fall in $\omega_{0a}$ or $\omega_{0b}$ is exactly the same whether or not $H_c$ and $H_*$ are the same hypothesis. In the first case $H_c$ will be accepted, in the second case $H_c$ will be rejected. These two cases are of equal probability, hence there is a probability of one half of accepting or rejecting $H_c$ if the sample point falls in the region of asymmetry of $T_0$. But from equation (2) of Section 2 above, we see that if the subregions $\omega_{0a}$ and $\omega_{0b}$ had been in a region of symmetry, and if $\omega_{0a}$ had been in $\omega_0$, the probability of accepting $H_c$ would have been greater than the probability of rejecting $H_c$.

Hence, if it is determined by random selection to which of a pair of hypotheses an asymmetric test is going to be applied, the probability of a correct judgment with the asymmetric test will be less than if there were substituted for it the UMP symmetric test. It may be concluded that the UMP symmetric test is to be preferred unless there is prior evidence which permits a tentative selection of the correct hypothesis with greater-than-chance frequency.

### 6. SYMMETRIC TEST WHEN STANDARD DEVIATIONS OF UNIVERSES ARE UNEQUAL

Thus far, we have restricted ourselves to the case where $\sigma_x = \sigma_y$. Let us now relax this condition and see whether a UMP symmetric test for $M_y \geqslant M_x$ exists in this more general case.

We now have for the ratio of $p(E)$ to $p(E')$:

$$(3) \qquad \frac{p(E)}{p(E')} = \exp\left\{ -\frac{n}{2\sigma_x^2\sigma_y^2} [(\sigma_y^2 - \sigma_x^2)(\mu_x - \mu_y) - 2(\sigma_y^2 M_x - \sigma_x^2 M_y)(\bar{x} - \bar{y})] \right\},$$

where

$$\mu_x = \sum_i x_i^2/n, \qquad \mu_y = \sum_i y_i^2/n.$$

Even if $\sigma_y$ and $\sigma_x$ are known, which is not usually the case, there is no UMP symmetric test for the hypothesis $M_y \geqslant M_x$. From (3), the symmetric critical region which has the lowest probability of errors of the first kind for the hypothesis $(M_y = k_1; M_x = k_2; k_1 > k_2)$ is the set of points $E$ such that:

$$(4) \qquad (\sigma_y^2 - \sigma_x^2)(\mu_x - \mu_y) - 2(\sigma_y^2 k_2 - \sigma_x^2 k_1)(\bar{x} - \bar{y}) > 0.$$

Since this region is not the same for all values of $k_1$ and $k_2$ such that $k_1 > k_2$, there is no UMP symmetric region for the composite hypothesis $M_y \geqslant M_x$. This result holds, *a fortiori* when $\sigma_y$ and $\sigma_x$ are not known.

If there is no UMP symmetric test for $M_y \geqslant M_x$ when $\sigma_y \neq \sigma_x$, we must be satisfied with a test which is UMP among some class of tests more restircted than the class of symmetric tests. Let us continue to restrict ourselves to the case where there are an equal number of observations, in our sample, of $(X)$

and of $(Y)$. Let us pair the observations $x_i$, $y_i$, and consider the differences $u_i = x_i - y_i$. Is there a UMP test among the tests which are symmetric with respect to the $u_i$'s for the hypothesis that $M_y - M_x = -U \geqslant 0$? By a symmetric test in this case we mean a test such that whenever the point $(u_1, \ldots, u_n)$ falls into region $\omega_0$, the point $(-u_1, \ldots, -u_n)$ falls into region $\omega_1$.

If $x_i$ and $y_i$ are distributed normally about $M_x$ and $M_y$ with standard deviations $\sigma_x$ and $\sigma_y$ respectively, then $u_i$ will be normally distributed about $U = M_x - M_y$ with standard deviation $\sigma_u = \sqrt{\sigma_x^2 + \sigma_y^2}$. The ratio of probabilities for the sample points $E_v$: $(u_1, \ldots, u_n)$ and $E_v'$: $(-u_1, \ldots, -u_n)$ is given by:

$$(5) \qquad \frac{p(E_v)}{p(E_v')} = \exp\left\{ \frac{-2n}{\sigma_u^2} \bar{u}U \right\},$$

where

$$\bar{u} = \frac{1}{n} \sum_i u_i.$$

Hence, $p(E_v) > p(E_v')$ whenever $\bar{u}$ has the same sign as $U$. Therefore, by the same process of reasoning as in Section 2, above, we may show that $\bar{u} \leqslant 0$ is a UMP test among tests symmetric in the sample space of the $u$'s for the hypothesis $U \leqslant 0$.

It should be emphasized that $\Omega_{su}$, the class of symmetric regions in the space of $E_v$: $(u_1 \ldots u_n)$, is far more restricted than $\Omega_s$, the class of symmetric regions in the sample space of $E$: $(x_1 \ldots x_n; y_1 \ldots y_n)$. In the latter class are included all regions such that:

(A) $E$: $(a_1, \ldots, a_n; b_1, \ldots, b_n)$ falls in $\omega_0$ whenever $E$: $(b_1, \ldots, b_n; a_1, \ldots, a_n)$ falls in $\omega_1$. Members of class $\Omega_{su}$ satisfy this condition together with the further condition:

(B) For all possible sets of $n$ constants $k_1, \ldots, k_n$, $E$: $(x_1 + k_1, \ldots, x_n + k_n; y_1 + k_1, \ldots, y_n + k_n)$ falls in $\omega_0$ whenever $E$: $(x_1, \ldots, x_n; y_1, \ldots, y_n)$ falls in $\omega_0$. When $\sigma_y \neq \sigma_x$, a UMP test for $M_y \geqslant M_x$ with respect to the symmetric class $\Omega_{su}$ exists, but a UMP test with respect to the symmetric class $\Omega_s$ does not exist.

## REFERENCES

[1] J. Neyman and E. S. Pearson, 'On the problem of the Most Efficient Tests of Statistical Hypotheses', *Phil. Trans. Roy. Soc.*, Series A, 702, **231**, 289–337 (1933).
[2] J. Neyman and E. S. Pearson, 'The Testing of Statistical Hypotheses in Relation to Probabilities *A Priori*', *Proc. Camb. Phil. Soc.*, 29, 492–510 (1933).

# STATISTICAL TESTS AS A BASIS FOR 'YES–NO' CHOICES†

Recent years have seen an almost universal acceptance among statisticians of the basic philosophy which underlies sampling theory: that whenever a statistic is employed to estimate some characteristic of a parent population, an estimate should be made of the sampling variation to which this statistic is subject. The estimate of 'reliability' or 'significance' may take a wide variety of forms – from the simple probable error, to the chi-square test, the $t$ test, the $z$ test and the more general Neyman-Pearson tests of hypotheses.

Because of this emphasis on sampling fluctuations, it has perhaps not been sufficiently noted that there are decisional situations, some of great importance, where a statistic should be employed as a criterion of choice regardless of its 'significance' or 'insignificance' – where, one might say, an insignificant difference is better than no difference at all. It is the purpose of this paper to examine one such situation, to explore its implications for sampling theory, and to show that such situations can be handled within the framework of Neyman's general 'operational' approach to the theory of statistical tests.

It is our aim to show that the traditional tests of significance generally become inapplicable in situations where statistical evidence is to be used as the basis for an immediate yes–no choice. Suppose that it is desired to choose between two alternatives, one involving greater cost than the other, that data have been gathered to determine which alternative is preferable, and that a non-postponable decision must be made – either alternative A or alternative B must be selected and there is no opportunity to gather additional data. It will be argued that under these circumstances the usual tests of significance are not the best criteria of choice between the two alternatives.

To make the problem concrete we will consider a situation where it is desired to choose between two agricultural treatments – two fertilizers, say – one involving greater cost than another.[1] The writer has found two references to this problem in the literature, both offering the same solution. I quote from one of these references:

As a practical application of fiducial limits, consider the case where a treatment having been applied to a crop, the expense is in question. Suppose there is some substance whose only advantage is the resulting increase in yield, and whose cost is equivalent to the value of $c$ units of the crop. Then, if the increase in yield fails to compensate the cost, the treatment is a failure. The sample must furnish evidence that the population mean difference is greater than $c$. The lower fiducial limit is used. If $\bar{x}$ is the mean difference between treated and check plots in the experiment, with standard error $s_x$ then $\bar{x} - s_{\bar{x}}t$ must be greater than $c$, $t$ being the 5% (or 1%) level for the available degrees of freedom. If $c = \bar{x} - s_{\bar{x}}t$, there is little chance that the population mean difference is less than $c$. Finally, if the population mean difference were equal to $c$, the *average* yield would be increased just enough to pay for the treatment.[2]

Professor Snedecor's solution is certainly the one which is suggested by modern sampling theory, but I submit that it is not the best solution to the problem which is posed above. To discover why it is not the best let us examine some of the underlying assumptions.

What is the purpose of the experiment described in the quoted passage? Is it to determine (a) whether the hypothesis that the new treatment is worth its cost is clear beyond a reasonable doubt, or (b) whether the new treatment should be used on the next year's crop? The suitability of the $t$ test to the first purpose will not be disputed. Whether we use Fisher's terminology of 'fiducial limits' or Neyman's terminology of 'errors of the first kind,' we will conclude that the $t$ test, as applied in the quotation, is an appropriate way to determine whether the superiority of the new treatment is clear beyond a reasonable doubt.

But what about the immediate question: shall I use the new treatment, or shall I not? Suppose that $x$ exceeds $c$, but not significantly. We conclude that further experimentation is needed to determine with the desired degree of certainty whether the superiority of the treated plots is real, that is, whether it is due to a difference between the populations from which the samples were drawn, or whether it is merely the result of random variations in samples drawn from identical populations. Hence the significance test indicates whether further experimentation is needed, but for two reasons this may not be an adequate answer to the problem at hand:

1. The cost of refining the experiment so as to determine whether or not the difference is real may be prohibitive;

2. Even if further experimentation is possible, it may be necessary to make an immediate decision to guide action until the new experimental results are available.

Every person who uses statistics as a basis for reaching decisions which lead to action constantly faces problems of this kind. Treatment A or treatment B must be used; the person responsible for the choice wishes to know which is better; statistical tests show neither treatment to be 'significantly' (say, at the 5% level) better than the other.

How should this statistical evidence be translated into a rule of decision? There are at least four possibilities. (1) 'It doesn't matter which you do.' (2) 'Take the least expensive, because the other isn't significantly better.' (3) 'Take the apparently better one, even though the superiority is in doubt.' (4) 'No recommendation can be made unless additional data are gathered and a new test applied.'

Professor Snedecor's and Dr. Van Uven's procedure leads to the second course of action. Yet it is hard to see how the $t$ test permits any conclusion to be drawn, save the fourth, and the fourth conclusion does not solve the problem — which is to make a non-postponable choice. Is there any more positive conclusion which the data permit to be drawn and which will solve the immediate problem of action? Our analysis will lead us to conclude that in this case the third course of action is the one which should be followed.

The answer is to be sought in a modification of the Neyman-Pearson theory of testing hypotheses.[3] Using this theory, a statistical test can be interpreted as a means for reaching a decision. Since this decision involves a risk of error — two kinds of error in fact[4] — it is the property of a good statistical test that it minimizes, in some sense, this risk. The various types of 'most powerful' tests which have been devised are generally designed to control the risk of rejecting a hypothesis prematurely, at the same time reducing as far as possible the risk of accepting a false hypothesis. Tests of this kind are legitimately applied to prevent the statistician from resting his conclusions on insufficient evidence. They point to the need, if that need exists, for further investigation of hypotheses when the data at hand do not permit the correctness of the hypothesis to be determined with the desired degree of certainty.

These tests have an asymmetry which is also extremely useful in cases where the consequences of accepting a false hypothesis are much more serious than the consequences of rejecting a true hypothesis. For example, in testing the proposition that 'this batch of drug does not contain a poison in lethal quantities', we would ordinarily be much more concerned that a lethal batch might be accepted than that an innocent batch might occasionally be rejected.[5]

In the specific problem with which we are dealing there is no such asymmetry. That treatment is preferable from which we may expect the greater net yield (that is, value of gross yield less cost of treatment). The risk that we will use the more expensive treatment and discover that the additional yield is insufficient to cover the additional cost is not a more serious kind of risk than the risk that we will use the cheaper treatment and discover that its inferiority is greater than the cost difference. Any asymmetry which inheres in the situation is adequately recognized when we require that the more expensive treatment give promise of at least covering its cost.[6] There is no difference between errors of the 'first' and 'second' kind which justifies the additional requirement that the advantage of the more expensive treatment exceed its cost by a 'significant' amount.

To deal with situations of this kind, the writer proposes the use of *symmetric* tests – tests which attach exactly the same significance to an observed advantage in net yield of the more expensive over the less expensive treatment as is attached to an observed advantage in net yield of the less expensive over the more expensive. In another publication, the writer has shown that, when the populations from which the observed data are drawn can be assumed to be normally distributed with equal standard deviations, there exists a uniformly most powerful symmetric test, i.e., a test which will lead to incorrect decisions less frequently than any other symmetric test no matter which of the two treatments is really the better.[7]

To put the matter another way, if a person always uses the uniformly most powerful symmetric test in making choices of the kind described here, then the expected value of net yield in plots which he manages will be greater than if he employs any other symmetric test whatever. As a matter of fact an even stronger claim can be made for the uniformly most powerful symmetric test: that a person using this test will have a greater expected value of net yield than if he uses any *asymmetric* test whatsoever which is based solely on the evidence of a single sample.[8]

In the present case, the best symmetric test would consist in computing $\bar{x} - c$, in employing the more expensive treatment when this quantity is greater than zero (instead of when $\bar{x} - c > s_{\bar{x}}t$ as Professor Snedecor proposes), and in employing the less expensive when $\bar{x} - c$ is less than zero. The symmetric test, then, designates the choice of that treatment which gives the greater net yield, regardless of the amount of difference; while the $t$ test designates the choice of the treatment with less cost, unless the higher-cost treatment has a significantly greater net yield than the other. If the decision is based on the symmetric test, the long-run net yield in a series of such decisions will have an expected value higher than if the $t$ test is used.

At first blush this use, without regard to its statistical significance of the mean value, as a criterion of decision, seems contrary to the whole direction of progress in statistical theory and practice. Further reflection shows that this procedure is a logical corollary to recent developments in testing theory. Tests of significance were originally conceived as means of measuring the 'degree of certainty' or conversely the 'degree of doubt' of statistical conclusions. In some recent work, particularly that of Neyman, tests of significance have been treated, as they are in this paper, as criteria upon which decisions are based. Now decisions are all-or-none phenomena. Even the decision 'to doubt' or 'not to doubt' represents a clear dichotomy. Hence, statistical tests must give yes-or-no answers. If the decision to be made is whether one should continue to doubt (i.e. whether further data-gathering is necessary before acceptance or rejection of a hypothesis), then those statistics which are generally called 'tests of significance' are the appropriate criteria of choice. When the question is one involving the immediate choice of a course of action, the symmetric test should be used.

One final comment may be added. Because of the ambiguity of the notion of a 'best estimate,' as that term is used in statistical literature, Professor Neyman has abandoned the idea of making a specific estimate of a population parameter in favor of his procedure of constructing a confidence interval which – it can be predicted with a definite probability – will cover the true value of the population parameter.[9] The example used in the present paper shows that in certain instances, at least, the idea of a 'best estimate' can be given operational meaning. The best estimate of the mean of a universe may then be defined as that estimate which gives the uniformly most powerful symmetric test for the hypothesis that the mean of this universe exceeds the mean of another universe. A theory of estimation based on this definition would be simply a theory of symmetric tests.

## NOTES

[1] For simplicity, an agricultural illustration is used throughout this paper. The argument is certainly not limited to that particular field of application. As a matter of fact, the author originally developed this approach in connection with a study of optimum case loads for social workers in a public welfare agency.

[2] George W. Snedecor, *Statistical Methods* (Ames, Iowa: The Collegiate Press, 1937), p. 60. Cf. Dr. M. J. Van Uven, *Mathematical Treatment of the Results of Agricultural and other Experiments* (Gronigen–Batavia: P. Noordhoff, 1935), pp. 49–51.

[3] J. Neyman and E. S. Pearson, 'On the Problem of the Most Efficient Tests of Statistical Hypotheses', *Phil. Trans. Roy. Soc.,* Series A, 702, **231**, 289–337 (1933).

[4] There is the risk that a hypothesis will be rejected when it is true (error of the first kind), and the risk that the hypothesis will be accepted when it is false (error of the second kind). In the symmetric tests to be proposed in this paper, the two types of errors become identical.

[5] J. Neyman, 'Basic Ideas and Some Results of the Theory of Testing Statistical Hypotheses', *Journal of the Royal Statistical Society* **105**, 304 (1942).

[6] It should perhaps be pointed out that the difference in cost between the two treatments should include *all* costs, not excepting interest and depreciation on investment to be made. This raises the troublesome question whether, in setting the depreciation rates, the risk should be included that after the investment has been made the treatment now thought preferable may be found the less desirable of the two on the basis of additional data, and may therefore be discontinued. Reflection convinces the writer that no allowance should be made for this risk, since in evaluating the desirability of changing a decision already made, these investments would be treated as sunk costs and would not count in the comparison.

[7] Herbert A. Simon, 'Symmetric Tests of the Hypothesis that the Mean of One Normal Population Exceeds That of Another', *Annals of Mathematical Statistics* 14, 149–154 (1943). (Reprinted as Chapter 1.1 of this volume.)

[8] *Op. cit.*, pp. 152–153.

[9] See, for instance, J. Neyman, *Lectures and Conferences on Mathematical Statistics* (Washington, D.C., Graduate School of the U.S. Department of Agriculture, 1938), *passim*.

# PREDICTION AND HINDSIGHT AS CONFIRMATORY
# EVIDENCE† *

The central concept of Carnap's probabilistic theory of induction is a triadic relation, $c(h, e)$, the probability or degree of confirmation of the hypothesis, $h$, on evidence, $e$. The relation is a purely logical one. The value of $c$ can be computed from a knowledge of $h$, of $e$, of the structure of the language, and of the inductive rule to be employed [1 and 2].

Such a definition of degree of confirmation apparently violates some of our intuitive beliefs about the dependence of the efficacy of evidence upon the time when it is discovered. Let us suppose that the hypothesis $h$ implies the two observational propositions $e_1$ and $e_2$. Scientist A makes the observation $e_1$, formulates the hypothesis $h$ to explain his observation, predicts $e_2$ in the basis of $h$, and subsequently observes $e_2$. Scientist B makes the observations $e_1$ and $e_2$, and formulates the hypothesis $h$ to explain them. Most persons whom I have questioned on the point assert that $h$ is confirmed to a higher degree in the first case than in the second. They justify their assertion by arguing that, given the evidence, it is always possible to frame a hypothesis to explain it, and that the acid test of any hypothesis is its prediction of a phenomenon that was not known when the hypothesis was formulated.

If we take as $e_1$ the Lorentz contraction, and as $e_2$ the tranformability of mass into energy, then Einstein's hypothesis of special relativity fits the first example above. The 'naive' view of our respondents implies that we would be less confident of the relativity hypothesis than we now are if $e_2$ had been known before the law was announced.

## 1. 'EXTRINSIC' EVIDENCE IN THE CONFIRMATION OF HYPOTHESES

Can a theory of inductive inference be constructed that takes account of these time relationships? In the following paragraphs I shall try to suggest how this may be done.

Let us consider a scientist who observes pieces of evidence, $e_1, e_2, \ldots$, and formulates hypotheses to explain them. If we observe him do this

† [*Philosophy of Science* **22**, 227–230 (1955)].

repeatedly, under specified circumstances, and if we have some means of determining subsequently which of his hypotheses are, in fact, correct, then we can estimate the probability that any single, randomly selected hypothesis formulated by the scientist is correct. Call this probability $P_1$.

Suppose that our scientist draws inferences from each of the hypotheses he formulates, makes predictions, and observes whether these predictions are verified. Let us consider that subset of all the hypotheses he has formulated which have yielded predictions that were subsequently verified. Then, again, we can estimate the probability that any single hypothesis, drawn at random from this subset, is correct. Call this probability $P_2$.

Now I submit that in the real world $P_2$ is (under most circumstances) very much larger than $P_1$, and that it is this difference between $P_1$ and $P_2$ that the respondent has in mind in giving greater credence to hypotheses that have been successful in prediction.

It will be objected that I have shifted the terms of the problem, that the probabilities $P_1$ and $P_2$ do not refer to the *same* set of hypotheses, with the *same* pieces of confirming evidence. The objection is admitted, but it does not go to the heart of the problem. For the objection assumes at the outset that the evidence, $e_1$ and $e_2$ , and the hypothesis, $h$, are the only data that affect the 'degree of confirmation of $h$' or the 'degree of reasonable belief in $h$.'

What is suggested here is that there is an entirely different sense in which 'degree of confirmation' can be understood. The degree of confirmation of a hypothesis can be defined so as to depend upon the process that generated (led to the assertion of) the hypothesis. Evidence regarding this process of generation we will call 'extrinsic evidence.' A definition of degree of confirmation that admits extrinsic evidence we will call an 'extrinsic definition'; a definition that does not admit such evidence we will call 'intrinsic.'[1]

Let us see how this distinction applies to our earlier example of the hypothesis of special relativity. An intrinsic definition would lead to expressions like: $c(h, e_1 \cdot e_2)$. An extrinsic definition would lead to expressions like: $c(h, e_1 \cdot e_2 \cdot e_3)$; where $e_3$ is a statement of the form: 'The Hypothesis $h$ was first enunciated by Scientist A at time $t_2$ after $e_1$ had been observed at $t_1$; and subsequently, $e_2$ was observed at time $t_3$.'

Even in the case of the extrinsic definition, then, we can speak of 'the degree of confirmation of hypothesis $h$ on evidence $e$.' But we can do so only if we include in our description of the state of the world what observations have been made and what hypotheses have been asserted, and at what times.[2]

## 2. EXTRINSIC EVIDENCE AND THE FREQUENCY CONCEPTION OF CONFIRMATION

So long as we restrict ourselves to intrinsic evidence there are almost insuperable objections to a frequency interpretation of degree of confirmation. A particular hypothesis, $h$, is either true of false — although we may not know which it is. On the other hand, we have shown above that if we regard a particular hypothesis as a member of a large class of hypotheses that have been generated by the same process, it is perfectly reasonable to attach a probability, in the frequency sense, to the correctness of the hypothesis. This probability is simply the ratio of the number of true hypotheses in the class to the total number of hypotheses in the class. How we estimate this ratio is, of course, another question.

One need not argue that either the intrinsic or the extrinsic definition is the sole possible explicandum of 'degree of confirmation.' My main assertion is an empirical one: on the basis of a limited and not particularly random sample of responses, I conclude that most persons include extrinsic considerations in their judgments of degree of confirmation.

## 3. KINDS OF EXTRINSIC EVIDENCE

Once we have admitted the possibility of an extrinsic definition of degree of confirmation, we have opened a veritable Pandora's box. For there is a very large number of ways of characterizing the 'process' that generated a particular hypothesis, and a correspondingly large number of reference classes for which probabilities like $P_1$ and $P_2$ may be calculated. We may list some of these possibilities starting with the one already discussed.

1. The order in time of the observations of the parts of $e$ and of the formulation of $h$ may be regarded as relevant. If certain observations have been made, scientists will be impelled to try to construct hypotheses to explain these observations. Since this process will be continued until it is successful, and since there is no reason to suppose that the first hypothesis that fits will often be the correct one (as tested by a wider body of evidence), we should attach a low probability to a hypothesis that is obtained in this way.

2. The degree of 'simplicity' of the hypothesis (or its opposite, the number of degrees of freedom it contains) may be regarded as relevant. This consideration is closely related to the first. It is always easier to find *ad hoc* hypotheses — those with many degrees of freedom — to fit a body of

evidence. Therefore, the *ad hoc* hypotheses are likely to be generated first, and there are likely to be many hypotheses at least as simple as the one first discovered that will fit the evidence. Hence the confidence to be attached to any one of these is low. (I believe that this argument does not make an appeal to the 'simplicity of nature,' which is on the borderline between intrinsic and extrinsic considerations.)

3. The 'reliability' (as tested by previous hypotheses) of the scientist who proposes the hypotheses may be regarded as relevant. This kind of argument of course, has a very much more respectable status in law courts and in everyday life than in logic books. When testimony is admitted as to the credibility of a witness, this kind of argument is being employed — and most people, I think, would agree that it is appropriately employed. Laplace's whole theory of the probability of testimonies is based upon it.

If we are concerned with scientists rather than law courts, we have to consider carefully what kinds of extrinsic evidence have relevance to credibility. Motivation is important, although conscious deception is so rare — Piltdown man to the contrary notwithstanding — as to be generally insignificant. Self-deception, arising out of the strong drive to find hypotheses, is of greater concern, and examples are not lacking — particularly of mathematical 'proofs' containing subtle fallacies.

But the process of generating hypotheses is so complex that we seldom possess very much of the relevant evidence — other than evidence of the previous success of a particular scientist or a particular branch of science. Hypotheses that are announced are only a small fraction of the hypotheses that are considered. The criteria that a scientist applies in judging the appropriateness of an hypothesis that has occurred to him are exceedingly subtle, and both highly personal and peculiar to his science. Under such conditions, one man's hunches may be as credible as another man's reasoned judgments; and the casual curve-fitting methods of the physicist may carry more confirmatory weight than the elaborate regression techniques of the social scientist.

I am sure that the three kinds of extrinsic considerations I have listed do not exhaust the possibilities. They do illustrate, however, the feasibility of an extrinsic, as contrasted with an intrinsic, definition of degree of confirmation.

In attaching an actual number to the probability of a hypothesis with such a definition, we would ordinarily use the extrinsic considerations to select an appropriate reference class of hypotheses with which to compare the particular hypothesis in questions. Our previous experience with the hypotheses of that reference class will generally permit us to attach an approximate numerical value — employing a frequency definition of probability — to the degree of confirmation.

## NOTES

*I am grateful to the Ford Foundation for a grant-in-aid that made this work possible.

[1] I believe that Reichenbach's 'posits' [3] are best interpreted as measures of degree of confirmation defined by extrinsic criteria. The term 'reference class' used here is accordingly borrowed from Reichenbach.

[2] I am indebted to Professor Carnap for pointing out to me, in correspondence, that his definition of degree of confirmation does not exclude extrinsic evidence. But I should like to emphasize the implications of such a procedure for the definition of 'state of the world', and consequently the practical importance of distinguishing extrinsic from intrinsic considerations. So far as I am aware, in all the concrete examples that Professor Carnap uses to illustrate his concepts the relevant evidence for a hypothesis is always intrinsic evidence. We are accustomed to think of the scientist as observing the state of the world, but not of his observing as part of the state of the world.

## REFERENCES

[1] Carnap, Rudolf, *The Continuum of Inductive Methods* (Chicago: U. of Chicago Press, 1952).
[2] Carnap, Rudolf, *Logical Foundations of Probability* (Chicago: U. of Chicago Press, 1950).
[3] Reichenbach, Hans, *Experience and Prediction* (Chicago: U. of Chicago Press, 1938).
[4] Simon, Herbert A., 'A Bayes Solution for a Non-Sequential Decision Problem', unpublished manuscript.

ON JUDGING THE PLAUSIBILITY OF THEORIES† *

It is a fact that if you arrange the cities (or, alternatively, the metropolitan districts) of the United States in the order of their population in 1940, the population of each city will be inversely proportional to its rank in the list (see Figure 1). The same fact is true of these cities at other census dates – back to the first census – and for the cities of a number of other countries of the world.

It is a fact that if you arrange the words that occur in James Joyce's *Ulysses* in the order of their frequency of occurrence in that book, the frequency of each word will be inversely proportional to its rank in the list (see Figure 2). The same fact is true of the other books in English whose word frequencies have been counted (except, possibly, *Finnegan's wake*), and it is true of books in most other languages (although not books in Chinese).

What do I mean when I say these are 'facts'? In a way, it seems incorrect to speak in this way, since none of my 'facts' is literally and exactly true. For example, since there were 2034 cities over 5000 population in the United States in 1940, the alleged 'fact' would assert that there were therefore one half as many, 1017, over 10 000 population. Actually, there were 1072. It would assert that there were one tenth as many, 203, over 50 000 population; actually, there were 198. It would assert that the largest city, New York, had a population just over ten million people; actually, its population was seven and one half million. The other 'facts' asserted above, for cities and words, hold only to comparable degrees of approximation.

At the very least, one would think, the statements of fact should be amended to read 'nearly inversely proportional' or 'approximately inversely proportional' rather than simply 'inversely proportional'. But how near is 'nearly', and how approximate is 'approximately'? What degree of deviation from the bald generalization permits us to speak of an approximation to the generalization rather than its disconfirmation? And why do we prefer the simple but approximate rule to the particular but exact facts?

† [Van Roostelaar and Staal (eds.), *Logic, Methodology and Philosophy of Sciences III*, Amsterdam, North-Holland Publ. Co., 1968].

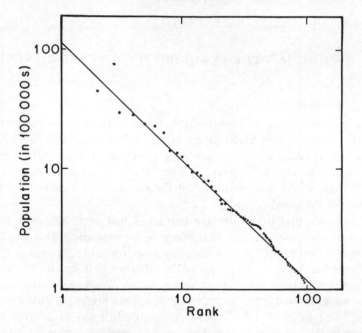

Fig. 1.    Hundred largest U.S. cities, 1940 (ranked in order of decreasing size).

## 1. SIMPLE GENERALIZATIONS

It is well known — at least among mathematical statisticians — that the theory of statistical tests gives us no real help in choosing between an approximate generalization and an invalid one.[1] By imbedding our generalization in a probability model, we can ask: If this model describes the real 'facts' what is the probability that data would have occurred at least as deviant from the generalization as those actually observed? If this probability is very low — below the magic one per cent level, say — we are still left with two alternatives: the generalization has been disconfirmed, and is invalid; or the generalization represents only a first approximation to the true, or 'exact' state of affairs.

Now such approximations abound in physics. Given adequate apparatus, any student in the college laboratory can 'disconfirm' Boyle's Law — i.e., can show that the deviations of the actual data from the generalization that the product of pressure by volume is a constant are too great to be dismissed as

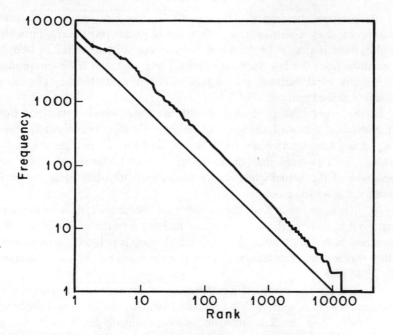

Fig. 2.   Words occurring in Joyce's *Ulysses* (ranked by frequency of occurrence).

'chance'. He can 'disconfirm' Galileo's Law of Falling Bodies even more dramatically — the most obvious way being to use a feather as the falling body.

When a physicist finds that the 'facts' summarized by a simple, powerful generalization do not fit the data exactly, his first reaction is *not* to throw away the generalization, or even to complicate it by incorporating additional terms. When the data depart from $s = \frac{1}{2}gt^2$, the physicist is not usually tempted to add a cubic term to the equation. (It took Kepler almost ten years to retreat from the 'simplicity' of a circle to the 'complexity' of an ellipse.) Instead, his explorations tend to move in two directions: (1) towards investigations of his measurement procedures as possible sources of the discrepancies; and (2) toward the identification of other variables associated with the deviations. These two directions of inquiry may, of course, be interrelated.

In his concern with other variables, the physicist is not merely or mainly concerned with 'control' in the usual sense of the term. No amount of control of air pressure, holding it, say, exactly at one atmosphere, will cause a feather to obey Galileo's Law. What the physicist must learn through his explorations is that as he decreases the air pressure on the falling body, the deviations from the law decrease in magnitude, and that if he can produce a sufficiently good vacuum, even a feather can be made to obey the law to a tolerable approximation.

In the process of producing conditions under which deviations from a generalization are small, the scope of the generalization is narrowed. Now it is only claimed to describe the facts 'for an ideal gas', or 'in a perfect vacuum'. At best, it is asserted that the deviations will go to zero in the limit as the deviation of the actual experimental conditions from the 'ideal' or 'perfect' conditions goes to zero.

At the same time that the breadth of the empirical generalization is narrowed by stating the conditions, or limiting conditions, under which it is supposed to hold, its vulnerability to falsification is reduced correspondingly. Since this is a familiar feature of theorizing in science, I will not elaborate on the point here.

Occasionally, an empirical generalization is abandoned, after innumerable attempts to tidy it up have failed. Bode's Law, that the successive distances of the planets from the Sun constitute an approximate geometric series, is an example of a regularity now regarded as perhaps 'accidental', through failure to discover limiting conditions that would regularize it, or underlying processes that would account for it. Newton's Laws are *not* an example, for they were saved (a) by limiting them to conditions where velocities are low relative to the velocity of light, and (b) by showing that just under those conditions they can be derived in the limit from the more general laws of Relativity.

From these, and many other examples, we can see what importance the physical and biological sciences attach to finding simple generalizations that will describe data approximately under some set of limiting conditions. Mendel's treatment of his sweet-pea data, as reflecting simple ratios of 3 to 1 in the second-generation hybrids, is another celebrated illustration; as is Prout's hypothesis (uneasily rejected by chemists for several generations until its exceptions were explained by the discovery of isotopes) that all atomic weights are integral multiples of the weight of the hydrogen atom. All of these examples give evidence of strong beliefs that when nature behaves in some unique fashion — deals a hand of thirteen spades, so to speak — this uniqueness, even if approximate, cannot be accidental, but must reveal underlying lawfulness.

## 2. THE GROUNDS FOR BELIEF

Let us return to city sizes and word frequencies. We have described the law-finding process in two stages:

(1) finding simple generalizations that describe the facts to some degree of approximation;

(2) finding limiting conditions under which the deviations of facts from generalization might be expected to decrease.

The process of inference from the facts (the process called 'retroduction' by Peirce and Hanson[2]) does not usually stop with this second stage, but continues to a third:

(3) explaining why the generalization 'should' fit the facts. (Examples are the statistical-mechanical explanation for Boyle's Law or Boyle's own 'spring of the air' explanation, and Newton's gravitational explanation for Galileo's Law.)

Before we go on to this third stage, we must consider whether we have really been successful in carrying out the first two for the rank-size distributions.

Does the generalization that size varies inversely with rank really fit the facts of cities and words even approximately? We plot the data on double log paper. If the generalization fits the facts, the resulting array of points will (1) fall on a straight line, (2) with a slope of minus one.

Since we earlier rejected the standard statistical tests of hypotheses as inappropriate to this situation, we are left with only judgmental processes for deciding whether the data fall on a straight line. It is not true, as is sometimes suggested, that almost *any* ranked data will fall on a straight line when graphed on doubly logarithmic paper. It is quite easy to find data that are quite curvilinear to the naked eye (see Figure 3). Since we are not committed to exact linearity but only approximate linearity, however, the conditions we are imposing on the data are quite weak, and the fact that they meet the conditions is correspondingly unimpressive. We may therefore find the evidence unconvincing that the phenomena are 'really' linear in the limiting cases. The phenomena are not striking enough in this respect to rule out coincidence and chance. Should we believe the data to be patterned?

It has often been demonstrated in the psychological laboratory that men – and even pigeons – can be made to imagine patterns in stimuli which the experimenter has carefully constructed by random processes. This behavior is sometimes called 'superstitious', because it finds causal connections where the experimenter knows none exist in fact. A less pejorative

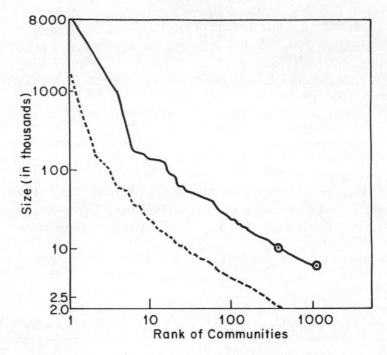

Fig. 3.    Rank-size distribution of cities in Austro-Hungarian Empire, 1910 (——) and
in Austria, 1934 (----).

term for such behavior is 'regularity-seeking' or 'law-seeking'. It can be given
a quite respectable Bayesian justification. As Jeffreys and Wrinch (1921) have
shown, if one attaches a high a priori probability to the hypothesis that the
world is simple (i.e., that the facts of the world, properly viewed, are
susceptible to simple summarization and interpretation); and if one assumes
also that simple configurations of data are sparsely distributed among all
logically possible configurations of data, then a high posterior probability
must be placed on the hypothesis that data which appear relatively linear in
fact reflect approximations to conditions under which a linear law holds.

The reason that apparent linearity, by itself, does not impress us is that it
does not meet the second condition assumed above — the sparsity of simple
configurations. A quadratic law, or an exponential, or a logarithmic, are
almost as simple as a linear one; and the data they would produce are not
always distinguishable from data produced by the latter.

What is striking about the city size and vocabulary data, however, is not just the linearity, but that the slope of the ranked data, on a log scale, is very close to minus one. Why this particular value, chosen from the whole non-denumerable infinity of alternative values? We can tolerate even sizeable deviations from this exact slope without losing our confidence that it must surely be the limiting slope for the data under some 'ideal' or 'perfect' conditions.

We might try to discover these limiting conditions empirically, or we might seek clues to them by constructing an explanatory model for the limiting generalization – the linear array with slope of minus one. In this way we combine stages two and three of the inference process described at the beginning of this section. Let us take this route, confining our discussion to city size distributions.

## 3. EXPLANATION

To 'explain' an empirical regularity is to discover a set of simple mechanisms that would produce the former in any system governed by the latter. A half dozen sets of mechanisms are known today that are capable of producing the linear rank-size distribution of city populations. Since they are all variations on one or two themes, I will sketch just one of them (Simon, 1955).

We consider a geographical area that has some urban communities as well as rural population. We assume, for the urban population, that birth rates and death rates are uncorrelated with city size. ('Rate' here always means 'number per year per 1 000 population'.) We assume that there is migration between cities, and net emigration from rural areas to cities (in addition to net immigration to cities from abroad, if we please). With respect to all migration, we assume: (1) that out-migration rates from cities are uncorrelated with city size; (2) that the probability that any migrant, chosen at random, will migrate to a city in a particular size class is proportional to total urban population in that class of cities. Finally, we assume that of the total growth of population in cities above some specified minimum size, a constant fraction is contributed by the appearance of new cities (i.e., cities newly grown to that size). The resulting steady-state rank-size distribution of cities will be approximately linear on a double log scale, and the slope of the array will approach closer to minus one as the fraction of urban population growth contributed by new cities approaches zero.

When we have satisfied ourselves of the 'reasonableness' of the assumptions incorporated in our mechanism, and of the insensitivity of the steady-state distribution to slight deviations from the assumptions as given, then we may feel, first, that the empirical generalization can now be regarded as 'fact'; and, second, that it is not merely 'brute fact' but possesses a plausible explanation.

But the explanation does even more for us; for it also suggests under what conditions the linearity of the relation should hold most exactly, and under what conditions the slope should most closely approximate to one. If the model is correct, then the rank-size law should be best approximated in geographical areas (1) where urban growth occurs largely in existing cities, (2) where all cities are receiving migration from a common 'pool'; and (3) where there is considerable, and relatively free, migration among all the cities. The United States, for example, would be an appropriate area to fit the assumptions of the model; India a less suitable area (because of the relatively weak connection between its major regions); Austria after World War I a still less suitable area (because of the fragmentation of the previous Austro-Hungarian Empire, see Figure 3). I do not wish to discuss the data here beyond observing that these inferences from the model seem generally to be borne out.

### 4. SIMPLICITY AND FALSIFIABILITY

In our account thus far, the simplicity of the empirical generalization has played a central role. Simplicity is also an important concept in Popper (1961)[3] but Popper treats simplicity in a somewhat different way than we have done. Popper (on p.140) equates simplicity with *degree of falsifiability*. A hypothesis is falsifiable to the degree that it selects out from the set of all possible worlds a very small subset, and asserts that the real world belongs to this subset.

There is a strong correlation between our intuitive notions of simplicity (e.g., that a linear relation is simpler than a polynomial of higher degree) and falsifiability. Thus, among all possible monotonic arrays, linear arrays are very rare. (They would be of measure zero, if we imposed an appropriate probability measure on the set of all monotonic arrays.) Linear arrays with slope of minus one are even rarer.

No one has provided a satisfactory general measure of the simplicity or falsifiability of hypotheses. In simple cases, the concepts have an obvious connection with degrees of freedom: the fewer the degrees of freedom, or free parameters, the simpler and more falsifiable the hypothesis. I shall not undertake to carry the formalization of the concepts beyond this intuitively appealing basis.[4]

Notice, however, that our use of simplicity is quite different from Popper's (1961). Popper's argument runs like this: it is desirable that hypotheses be simple so that, if they are false, they can be disconfirmed by empirical data as readily as possible. Our argument (apparently first introduced by Jeffreys and Wrinch, 1921) runs: a simple hypothesis that fits data to a reasonable approximation should be entertained, for it probably reveals an underlying law of nature. As Popper himself observes (Popper, 1961, p. 142, footnote*[2]), these two arguments take quite opposite positions with respect to the 'probability' or 'plausibility' of simple hypotheses. He regards such hypotheses as describing highly particular, hence improbable states of the world, and therefore as readily falsified. Jeffreys and Wrinch (1921) (and I) regard them as successfully summarizing highly unique (but actual) states of the world, therefore as highly plausible.

Which of these views is tenable would seem to depend on which came first, the generalization or the data. If I construct generalizations, with no criterion to guide my choice except that they be simple, and subsequently apply them to data, then the simpler the generalizations the more specific their description, and the less likely that they will stand up under their first empirical test. This is essentially Popper's argument.

But the argument does not apply if the generalization was constructed with the data in view. The rank-size hypothesis arises because we think to plot the data on double log paper, and when we do, it appears to be linear and to have a slope of minus one. There is no thought of using the data to falsify the generalization, for the latter has come into being only because it fits the data, at least approximately.

Now one can cite examples from the history of science of both of these alternative sequences of events. It is probably true, however, that the first sequence — generalization followed by data — seldom occurs except as a sequel to the second. The Special Theory of Relativity, for example, led to the prediction of the convertibility of mass into energy. But Special Relativity itself was based on a generalization, the Lorentz-Fitzgerald equation, that was derived to fit facts about the behavior of particles in very intense fields of force, as well as other facts about electromagnetics and the 'luminiferous ether'. Special Relativity did not commend itself to Einstein merely because of its 'simplicity' independently of the facts to be explained. (The Galilean transformations would be thought by most people to be simpler than the Lorentz.)

If the generalization is just that — an approximate summary of the data — then it is certainly not falsifiable. It becomes falsifiable, or testable, when (a) it is extended beyond the data from which it was generated, or (b) an explanatory theory is constructed, from which the generalization can be derived, and the explanatory theory has testable consequences beyond the original data.

With respect to the city size data, case (a) would arise if the rank size generalization were proposed after examining the data from the 1940 U.S. Census, and then were extrapolated to earlier and later dates, or to the cities of other countries. Case (b) would arise if we were to note that the explanatory theory of Section 4, above, has implications for patterns of migration that could be tested directly if data on points of origin and destination of migrants were available.

It should be evident that the mechanisms incorporated in the explanatory theory were not motivated by their falsifiability. They were introduced in order to provide 'plausible' premises from which the generalization summarizing the observed data could be deduced. And what does 'plausible' mean in this context? It means that the assumptions about birth and death rates and migration are not inconsistent with our everyday general knowledge of these matters. At the moment they are introduced, they are already known (or strongly suspected) to be not far from the truth. The state of affairs they describe is not rare or surprising (given what we actually know about the world); rather their subsequent empirical falsification would be rather surprising. What is *not* known at the moment they are introduced is whether they provide adequate premises for the derivation of the rank-size generalization.

Explaining the empirical generalization, that is, providing a set of mechanisms capable of producing it, therefore reintroduces new forms of testability to replace those that were lost by accepting the approximation to the data. Even without data on migration, the mechanism proposed to explain the city rank-size law can be subjected to new tests by constructing the transition matrix that compares the sizes of the same cities at two points of time (taking the 1900 population, say, as the abscissa, and the 1950 population as the ordinate (see Figure 4)). The explanatory mechanism implies that the means of the rows in this matrix fall on a straight line through the origin (or on a straight line of slope +1 on a log-log scale). The result (which we will expect to hold only approximately) is equivalent to the proposition that the expected growth rates are independent of initial city size.

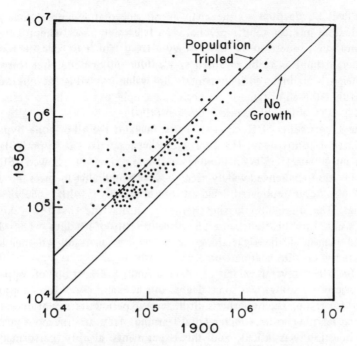

Fig. 4.   Population of U.S. metropolitan districts, 1900 and 1950.
(Only districts over 100 000 population in 1950 are shown.)

## 5. AN EXAMPLE FROM LEARNING THEORY

In the preceding sections a model has been sketched of the scientific activities of hypothesis-generation and hypothesis-testing. The model suggests that there are several distinct processes that lead to hypotheses being formulated, judged with respect to plausibility, and tested. One of these processes, the generation of simple extreme hypotheses from the 'striking' characteristics of empirical data, fits closely the idea of Jeffreys and Wrinch (1921) that simple hypotheses possess a high plausibility. A second process, the construction of explanations for these extreme hypotheses, takes us back to Popper's (1961) idea that simple hypotheses entail strong and 'improbable' consequences, hence are readily falsified (if false). There is no contradiction between these two views.

To elucidate further this model of the scientific process, and to reveal some additional characteristics it possesses, the remaining sections of this paper will be devoted to the analysis of a second example, this one of considerable interest to the psychology of learning and concept formation. An important question in psychology during the past decade has been whether learning is to be regarded as a sudden, all-or-none phenomenon, or whether it is gradual and incremental. One value in stating the question this way is that the all-or-none hypothesis is a simple, extreme hypothesis, hence is highly falsifiable in the sense of Popper (1961).

The experiments of Rock (1957) first brought the all-or-none hypothesis into intense controversy. His data strongly supported the hypothesis (even under rather strict limits on the degree of approximation allowed). Since his generalization challenged widely-acccepted incrementalist theories, his experiment was soon replicated (seldom quite literally), with widely varying findings. The discussion in the literature, during the first few years after Rock's initial publication, centered on the 'validity'of his data — i.e., whether he had measured the right things in his experiment, and whether he had measured them with adequate precision.

Only after several years of debate and publication of apparently contradictory findings was some degree of agreement reached on appropriate designs for testing the hypothesis. Still, some experimenters continued to find one-trial learning, others incremental learning. After several more years, the right question was asked, and the experiments already performed were reviewed to see what answer they gave.[5] The 'right question', of course, was: 'Under what conditions will learning have an all-or-none character?' The answer, reasonably conformable to the experimental data, commends itself to common sense. Oversimplified, the answer is that one-trial learning is likely to occur when the time per trial is relatively long, and when the items to be learned (i.e., associated) are already familiar units.[6] These are the 'ideal' or 'perfect' conditions under which one-trial learning can be expected to occur.

## 6. AN EXAMPLE FROM CONCEPT ATTAINMENT

Meanwhile, the all-or-none hypothesis was also being applied to concept attainment experiments. Important work was done in this area by Estes, by Bourne, and by Bower and Trabasso, among others. I will take as my example for discussion a well-known paper by Bower and Trabasso that Gregg and I have analysed in another context.[7]

The experiments we shall consider employ an $N$-dimensional stimulus with two possible values on each dimension, and having a single relevant dimension (i.e., simple concepts). On each trial, an instance (positive or negative) is presented to the subject; he responds 'positive' or 'negative'; and he is reinforced by 'right' or 'wrong', as the case may be.

Bower and Trabasso obtain from the data of certain of their experiments an important empirical generalization: the probability that a subject will make a correct response on any trial prior to the trial on which he makes his last error is a constant. (In their data, this constant is always very close to one half, but they do not incorporate this fact in their generalization as they usually state it.) Since the generalization that the probability of making a correct response is constant is an extreme hypothesis, the standard tests of significance are irrelevant. We must judge whether the data fit the generalization 'well enough'. Most observers, looking at the data, would agree that they do (see Figure 5).

But Bower and Trabasso go a step further. They derive the empirical generalization from a simple stochastic model of the learning process – they explain it, in the sense in which we used that term earlier. The explanation runs thus: (1) the subject tries out various hypotheses as to what is the correct concept, and responds on individual trials according to the concept he is currently holding; (2) if his response is wrong, he tries a new concept. Two important empirical quantities are associated with the model: The probability of making a correct response prior to the last error; and the probability that any particular trial will be the trial of last error.

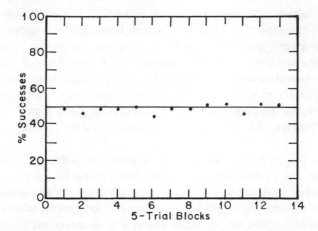

Fig. 5.   Concept experiment: percentage of successes prior to the last error
(from Bower and Trabasso).

Now there are in fact *two* distinct all-or-none generalizations that can be formulated in terms of these two empirical quantities. The first, already mentioned, is the generalization that the probability of making a *correct response* is constant as long as the subject holds the wrong hypothesis about the concept (i.e., up to the trial of his last error). The second, quite different, is the generalization that the probability of switching to the *correct hypothesis* about the concept does not change over trials (i.e., that the probability is constant that each trial will be the trial of last error).

To test the first (correct response) all-or-none generalization, we have one datum from each subject for each trial prior to his last error — a considerable body of data to judge the approximation of the error rate to a constant. To test the second (correct hypothesis) all-or-none generalization, we have only one datum from each subject — the trial on which he made his last error. Hence, trial-to-trial changes in the probability of switching to the right concept are confounded with differences in that probability among subjects. If, for any single subject, this probability increases with trials, the increase is counterbalanced by the fact that the subjects with lowest average probability will tend to learn last. Thus (as Bower and Trabasso are careful to point out) the data to test the second generalization directly are scanty and inadequate.

## 7. THE PARSIMONY OF THEORIES

The Bower-Trabasso stochastic model is an explanation of the observed constancy of the error rate. But it is a very bland model, making rather minimal assumptions about the process that is going on. We can pursue the goal of explanation a step further by constructing a more detailed model of the cognitive processes used by subjects in concept attainment, then using this detailed model to subject the theory to further tests. (As Gregg and I have shown in our previous paper on this topic (Gregg and Simon, 1967a), Bower and Trabasso do, in fact, employ such a process model, but only informally.)

There are two important differences between the summary stochastic model and the more detailed process model. The process model, but not the stochastic model, spells out how the experimenter selects (on a random basis) the successive instances, how the subject responds, and how he selects a new concept when his current one is found wrong. The stochastic model, but not the detailed model, contains two free parameters, one specifying the probability that the subject's response will be (fortuitously) correct when he does not hold the correct concept; the other specifying the probability that he will select the correct concept as his new one when his current concept is found wrong.

The stochastic model and process model can be formalized by stating them in a computer programming language (Gregg and Simon, 1967a). When this is done, it is found that the stochastic model requires 15 statements – i.e., simple computer instructions – for its formulation, the detailed process model 27. Against this parsimony of the stochastic model must be balanced the fact that that model contains two free numerical parameters, the process model none. Which model is the simpler?

If we apply Popper's criteria of simplicity – the simpler theory being the one that is more highly falsifiable – then the question has a definite answer. The detailed process model is simpler than the stochastic model (see Gregg and Simon, 1967a, pp. 271–272). For, by a straightforward aggregation of variables, the stochastic model, with particular values for the free parameters, can be derived deductively from the process model. Hence, the process model is a special case of the stochastic model. (The process model predicts an error rate of about 0.5 per trial prior to the trial of last error. It also predicts the probability that the last error will occur on a particular trial, but this probability depends on the structure of the stimuli – the number of attributes they possess, and the number of values of each attribute.)

The additional detail incorporated in the process model's assumptions also provides additional opportunities for subjecting the model to empirical test. The hypotheses held by the subject as to the correct concept do not appear explicitly in the stochastic model; hence data relating to these hypotheses (obtained, say, by asking the subject on each trial what concept he holds, as was done by Feldman (1964), or obtained by indirect procedures developed by Levine (1966)) cannot be used to test that model, but can be used to test the process model.

If parsimony refers to the brevity with which a theory can be described, then the stochastic model is the more parsimonious (fifteen statements against twenty-seven). But lack of parsimony, so defined, must not be confused with degrees of freedom. We have seen in this case that the less parsimonious theory is the simpler (by Popper's (1961) criterion), and by far the more falsifiable.

Testing the detailed process theory raises all the problems mentioned earlier with respect to extreme hypotheses. If the error rate on guessing trials deviates from 0.5 should the theory be rejected? How much of a deviation should be tolerated? In how many cases can a subject report he is holding a concept different from that predicted by the theory before we reject the latter? I have given my reasons earlier for thinking that these questions are judgmental, and for concluding that the theory of statistical tests offers no help in answering them. A judgmental answer is that the theory should be rejected only if it turns out to be 'radically' wrong. Otherwise, deviations should lead to a search for variables to account for them, and for the 'ideal' limiting case in which they would disappear.

Justice Holmes once said: 'Logic is not the life of the law'. I would paraphrase his aphorism by saying: 'Statistics is not the life of science'. No existing statistical theory explains what scientists do (or should do) to retroduce, develop, test, and modify scientific theories.

## 8. STATISTICAL FIT AND EXPLANATORY SUCCESS

Just as statistically significant deviations of data from a generalization should not always, or usually, lead us to abandon the generalization, so we should not be unduly impressed by excellent statistical fits of data to theory. More important than whether the data fit is why they fit — i.e., what components in the theory are critical to the goodness of fit. To answer this question, we must analyse the internal structure of the theory.

For example, under the conditions where all-or-none learning can be expected to take place, the learning trials can generally be divided into two parts: an initial sequence prior to learning, during which the subject can only guess at the correct answer; a terminal sequence, during which the subject knows the correct concept, and makes no new mistakes. Let us suppose that the boundary between these two segments can be detected (as it can in the concept-learning experiments by the trial on which the last error is made).

Under these conditions, no important conclusions can be drawn about psychological characteristics of the subjects by examining the statistical structure of their responses prior to learning. For the statistics of these responses are simply reflections of the experimenter's randomization of the sequence of stimuli. In one experiment, Estes (1959), for example, employed three different conditions differing only with respect to the number of alternative resonses (2, 4 and 8, respectively) available to the subject (see Simon, 1962). He found that the relative number of errors per trial made in these three conditions could be represented by the formula, $A(N-1)/N$, where $A$ is a constant and $N$ is the number of alternative responses.

The data on relative numbers of errors fit this formula with great accuracy — a clearcut case of success for an extreme hypothesis of the kind we have been commending in this paper. However, the hypothesis that was being tested was not a generalization about psychology, but a well-known generalization about the laws of probability: that in drawing balls at random from an urn containing white and black balls in the ratio of 1 to $(N - 1)$, on the average $(N - 1)/N$ of the balls drawn will be black. This is true regardless of whether the subjects themselves, prior to learning, thought they were simply guessing or thought they were responding in selective, patterned ways to the stimuli. By randomizing the sequence of stimuli presented, the experimenter guaranteed the applicability of the laws of probability to the subject's errors, independently of the systematic or 'random' character of the subject's behavior.

As I have pointed out elsewhere, a number of other excellent fits of simple generalizations to data can be attributed to the random presentation of stimuli, rather than to characteristics of the subjects (Simon, 1957; Simon, 1962; Gregg and Simon, 1967a). This does not imply that it is useless to extract the underlying regularities from the data; but we must be careful to provide the regularities with a correct explanation. To do so, we must examine the internal structure of the theories that lead to the successful generalization.

## 9. DISCOVERY AS PATTERN INDUCTION

Throughout this paper, considerable stress has been placed on the close interaction between hypotheses and data in the building and testing of theories. In most formal theories of induction, particularly those that belong to the genus 'hypothetico-deductive' or 'H-D', hypotheses spring full-blown from the head of Zeus, then are tested with data that exist timelessly and quite independently of the hypotheses.[8] Theories as otherwise divergent as Popper's and Carnap's share this common framework.

It was one of Norwood Hanson's important contributions to challenge this separation of hypothesis from data, and to demonstrate that in the history of science the retroduction of generalizations and explanations from data has been one of the central and crucial processes. In making his point, Hanson was careful not to revert to naive Baconian doctrines of induction. To look at a series of size-rank distributions, approximately log-linear with slopes of minus one; then to conclude that *all* such distributions share these properties, is Baconian. To look at the raw data, and conclude that they can be described adequately by the log-linear function with slope of minus one is not Baconian. It is the latter form of derivation of generalizations from data with which Hanson was primarily concerned, and to which he (following Peirce) applied the name 'retroduction'.

One of my principal theses here has been that hypotheses retroduced in this way are usually highly plausible, and not highly improbable, as Popper (1961) would insist. We have already resolved part of the apparent paradox. The 'improbability' to which Popper refers is improbability of the very special state of nature described by the empirical generalization, not improbability of the generalization itself. But it remains to understand how the scientist can ever be lucky enough to discover the very special generalizations that describe these a priori improbable (but actual) states of nature.

Fortunately, considerable light has been cast on this question by progress in the past decade in our understanding of the theory of human problem solving (Simon, 1966). If the scientist had to proceed by searching randomly through the (infinite) space of possible hypotheses, comparing each one with the data until he found one that matched, his task would be hopeless and endless. This he does not need to do. Instead, he extracts information from the data themselves (or the data 'cleaned up' to remove some of the noise), and uses this information to construct the hypothesis directly, with a modest amount of search.

Let us consider a concrete example (Banet, 1966). Suppose we are presented with the sequences: $\frac{9}{5}, \frac{4}{3}, \frac{25}{21}, \frac{9}{8}, \ldots$. What simple generalization can we discover to fit this sequence? We note that all the numerators are squares, that the first and third denominators are four less than their numerators, the second and fourth denominators are one less. We notice that the sequence appears to be monotone decreasing, and to approach a limit — perhaps unity. Nine is $3^2$, 25 is $5^2$. Suppose we number the terms 3, 4, 5, 6. The corresponding squares are 9, 16, 25, 36. Let's multiply numerator and denominator of the second and fourth terms by four, getting: $\frac{9}{5}, \frac{16}{12}, \frac{25}{21}, \frac{36}{32}, \ldots$. Now the empirical generalization is obvious: the general term of the sequence is $n^2/(n^2 - 4)$. Physicists will recognize this as the well known Balmer series of the hydrogen spectrum, and what we have done is to reconstruct hypothetically part of Balmer's retroduction. (He probably followed a somewhat different path, and we have only considered the last half of his problem of getting from data to generalization, but this partial and somewhat unhistorical example will serve to illustrate our central point. For the actual history, see Banet's (1966) interesting paper.)

However great a feat it was for Balmer to extract his formula from the data, the process he used was certainly not one of generating random hypotheses, then testing them. It is better described as a process of searching for the pattern in the data. It can be shown, for a considerable class of patterns that are of practical importance, in science, in music, and in intelligence tests, that the range of relations the searcher must be prepared to detect is quite small. It may be that these are the sole relations from which the simplicity of nature is built; it may be they are the only relations we are equipped to detect in nature. In either event, most of the patterns that have proved important for science are based, at bottom, on these few simple relations that humans are able to detect.

## 10. CONCLUSIONS

In this paper, I have examined several aspects of the problem of testing theories, and particularly those important theories that take the form of extreme hypotheses. In part, my argument has been aimed at a negative goal – to show that when we look at realistic examples from natural and social science, statistical theory is not of much help in telling us how theories are retroduced or tested.

As an alternative to standard probabilistic and statistical accounts of these matters, I have proposed that we take into account a whole sequence of events:

(1) The enterprise generally begins with empirical data, rather than with a hypothesis out of the blue.

(2) 'Striking' features of the data (e.g., that they are linear on a log scale with slope of minus one) provide for a simple generalization that summarizes them – approximately.

(3) We seek for limiting conditions that will improve the approximation by manipulating variables that appear to affect its goodness.

(4) We construct simple mechanisms to explain the simple generalizations – showing that the latter can be deduced from the former.

(5) The explanatory theories generally make predictions that go beyond the simple generalizations in a number of respects, and hence suggest new empirical observations and experiments that allow them to be tested further.

'Testing' theories, as that process is generally conceived, is only one of the minor preoccupations of science. The very process that generates a theory (and particularly a simple generalization) goes a long way toward promising it some measure of validity. For these reasons, histories of science written in terms of the processes that discover patterns in nature would seem closer to the mark than histories that emphasize the search for data to test hypotheses created out of whole cloth.

NOTES

*This work was supported in part by Public Health Service Research Grant MH-07722 from the National Institutes of Mental Health.

I should like to dedicate this essay to the memory of Norwood Russell Hanson, in acknowledgment of my debt to his *Patterns of Discovery*. His work did much to reestablish the notion that the philosophy of science must be as fully concerned with origins of scientific theories as with their testing – indeed that the two are inextricably interwoven. His reconstruction of Kepler's retroduction of the laws of planetary motion will long serve as a model of inquiry into the history and philosophy of science.

[1] For a brief, but adequate statement of the reasons why "literally to test such hypotheses ... is preposterous", see Savage (1954) pp. 254–256. Since such tests are often reported in the literature, it is perhaps worth quoting Savage (1954) p. 254 at slightly greater length: "The unacceptability of extreme null hypotheses is perfectly well known; it is closely related to the oftenheard maxim that science disproves, but never proves, hypotheses. The role of extreme hypotheses in science and other statistical activities seems to be important but obscure. In particular, though I, like everyone who practices statistics, have often 'tested' extreme hypotheses, I cannot give a very satisfactory analysis of the process, nor say clearly how it is related to testing as defined in this chapter and other theoretical discussions".

[2] Hanson (1961) pp. 85–88.

[3] Especially Chapter VII.

[4] The most serious attempts at formalization are those undertaken by Jeffreys and Wrinch (1921), and Goodman (1958). I must note in passing that in his discussion of the former authors Popper (1961) does not do justice to their technical proposal for introducing prior probabilities based on simplicity.

[5] Postman (1963), Underwood (1964).

[6] As a matter of history, I might mention that in 1957, prior to Rock's (1957) publication of his experiment, a theory of rote learning, designed especially to explain data that were in the literature prior to World War II (the serial position curve, the constancy of learning time per item, some of E. Gibson's experiments on stimulus similarity) had been developed by E. Feigenbaum and the author. This theory, EPAM, was sufficiently strong to predict the conditions under which one-trial learning would occur. It was not widely known among psychologists at that time, however, and had little immediate influence on the controversy. (But see Gregg, Chenzoff and Laughery (1963), also, Gregg and Simon (1967b).)

[7] Bower and Trabasso (1964); Gregg and Simon (1967a).

[8] For a criticism of this view, see Simon (1955). In that paper I was concerned specifically with the relative dating of theory and data, and while I still subscribe to the general position set forth there – that this dating is relevant to the corroboration of hypotheses by data – I would want to modify some of my specific conclusions about the form of the relevance, as various paragraphs in the present paper will show.

REFERENCES

Banet, L., 'Evolution of the Balmer Series', *Am. J. Phys.* **34**, 496–503 (1966).
Bower, G. H. and T. R. Trabasso, 'Concept Identification', in: *Studies in Mathematical Psychology*, ed. by R. C. Atkinson (Stanford: Stanford University Press, 1964) pp. 32–94.

Estes, W. K., 'Growth and Functions of Mathematical Models for Learning', in: *Current Trends in Psychological Theory* (Pittsburgh: University of Pittsburgh Press, 1959) pp. 134–151.

Feldman, J., 'Simulation of Behavior in the Binary Choice Experiment, in: *Computers and Thought*, eds. E. A. Feigenbaum and J. Feldman (New York: McGraw-Hill, 1964) pp. 329–346.

Goodman, N., 'The Test of Simplicity', *Science* 176, 1064–1069 (1958).

Gregg, L. W. and H. A. Simon, 'Process Models and Stochastic Theories of Simple Concept Formation', *J. Math. Psych.* 4, 246–276 (1967a).

Gregg, L. W. and H. A. Simon, 'An Information Processing Explanation of One-Trial and Incremental Learning', *J. Verbal Learning and Verbal Behavior* 6, 780–787 (1967b).

Gregg, L. W., A. P. Chenzoff, and K. Laughery, 'The Effect of Rate of Presentation, Substitution and Mode of Response in Paired-Associate Learning', *Am. J. Psych.* 76, 110–115 (1963).

Hanson, N. R., *Patterns of Discovery* (Cambridge: The University Press, 1961).

Jeffreys, H. and D. Wrinch, 'On Certain Fundamental Principles of Scientific Inquiry', *Phil. Magazine* 42, 369–390 (1921).

Levine, M., 'Hypothesis Behavior by Humans During Discrimination Learning', *J. Exper. Psych.* 71, 331–338 (1921).

Popper, K. R., *The Logic of Scientific Discovery* (New York: Science Editions, 1961).

Postman, L., 'One-Trial Learning', in: *Verbal Behavior and Learning*, ed. by C. F. Cofer and B. S. Musgrave (New York: McGraw-Hill, 1963) pp. 295–321.

Rock, I., 'The Role of Repetition in Associative Learning', *Am. J. Psych.* 70, 186–193 (1957).

Savage, L. J., *The Foundations of Statistics* (New York: Wiley, 1954).

Simon, H. A., 'Prediction and Hindsight as Confirmatory Evidence', *Phil. Sci.* 22, 227–230 (1955) (reprinted as Chapter 1.3 of this volume).

Simon, H. A., 'On a Class of Skew Distribution Functions', *Biometrika* 42, 425–440 (1955); reprinted in: *Models of Man* (New York: Wiley, 1957) pp. 145–164.

Simon, H. A., 'Amounts of Fixation and Discovery in Maze Learning Behavior', *Psychometrika* 22, 261–268 (1957).

Simon, H. A., 'A Note on Mathematical Models for Learning', *Psychometrika* 27, 417–418 (1962).

Simon, H. A., 'Scientific Discovery and the Psychology of Problem Solving', in: *Mind and Cosmos*, ed. by R. Colodny (Pittsburgh: University of Pittsburgh Press, 1966) pp. 22–40 (reprinted as Chapter 5.2 of this volume).

Underwood, B. J. and G. Keppel, 'One-Trial Learning', *J. Verbal Learning and Verbal Behavior* 3, 385–396 (1964).

# CAUSES AND POSSIBLE WORLDS

The questions dealt with in this section were first brought to my attention when I was a student at the University of Chicago. Political science courses raised the difficult problem of defining terms like 'influence,' 'power,' and 'authority,' and of devising procedures for measuring these quantities. In his statistics courses, Henry Schultz introduced the problem of selecting the appropriate regression line for determining the relation between two variables by the method of least squares. It was some years before I recognized that the two problems are essentially identical: that both demand the identification of a causal ordering among two or more variables.

The papers reprinted here do not have anything further to say about the definition of power. That is discussed in my essay, 'Notes on the Observation and Measurement of Political Power', published in the *Journal of Politics* **15**, 500–516 (1953), and reprinted as Chapter 4 in *Models of Man* (New York: Wiley, 1957).

The regression problem is this: Suppose we have a set of observations of two variables, $x$ and $y$, and wish to estimate by least squares the straight-line equation that connects them. We obtain one answer if we take $y$ as the dependent variable, and $x$ as the independent variable (the regression of $y$ on $x$), and another answer if we reverse their roles (the regression of $x$ on $y$). Similarly, suppose that we are given a series of observations of the price of a commodity and of the quantity sold of the same commodity. Economic theory tells us that price and quantity are connected by two relations – a supply equation and a demand equation. If we use the observational data and standard statistical techniques to estimate the relation between price and quantity, is the equation thus determined to be identified as the supply equation or the demand equation?

## 1. THE PROBLEM OF ASYMMETRY

After putting these problems aside for some years, I returned in about 1950 to the task of defining political power, only to find myself as unable as ever to arrive at a satisfactory result. The difficulty appeared to reside in a very specific technical point: influence, power, and authority are all intended as *asymmetrical* relations. When we say that $A$ has power over $B$, we do not mean to imply that $B$ has power over $A$. The mathematical counterpart to this asymmetrical relation appears to be the distinction between independent and dependent variable — the independent variable determines the dependent, and not the converse. But in algebra, the distinction between independent and dependent variable is purely conventional — we can usually rewrite our equations without altering their content in such a way as to reverse their roles. Thus, if $y = ax$, it is equally true that $x = by$, where $b = 1/a$. Neither way of writing the equation is preferred to the other.[1]

When the question was stated in this form — as a problem of giving operational meaning to the asymmetry of the relation between independent and dependent variable — it became clear that it was identical with the general problem of defining a *causal relation* between two variables. That is to say, for the assertion, '$A$ has power over $B$' we can substitute the assertion, '$A$'s behavior causes $B$'s behavior.' If we can define the causal relation, we can define influence, power, or authority, and *vice versa*. The four essays in this section embody my solution to the problem of defining a causal relation and giving operational meaning to the asymmetry of that relation. When I had arrived at the solution, I realized that it was intimately related to the second problem — the identification of statistical parameters — and I was able to demonstrate a direct connection between my results and the advances that had just then been made toward the solution of the statistical identification problem by Tjalling Koopmans and his associates at the Cowles Commission for Research in Economics.

Chapter 2.1 defines causal relations among variables and equations in an ordinary linear algebraic system; Chapter 2.2 does exactly the same thing, but for a Boolean algebra or, equivalently, for the propositional calculus of logic. On the surface the correspondence between the two definitions is not entirely obvious, but the following remarks may help to make the relation clear.

If $x$ and $y$ are variables in a system of algebraic equations, then to say that $y$ is a cause of $x$ is to say that there is a certain order in which the equations must be solved — specifically, that we must first solve for $y$ and insert its value in another equation which we then solve for $x$. Correspondingly, to say that $p$ causes $q$ is to say that we have a set of propositions (Boolean equations) such that we first determine the truth or falsity of $p$ from some subset of these, and then use the truth value of $p$ to determine the truth value of $q$.

Chapter 2.3 applies the causal definition of Chapter 2.1 to the problem of spurious correlation. This paper, having caught the attention of sociologists, especially Prof. H. M. Blalock, Jr.,[2] has played a very large role in the diffusion of the econometric theory of identification and simultaneous equation estimation to sociology and political science, where notions of causal ordering and the closely allied notion of path coefficients are now widely used in the treatment of statistical data.

## 2. THE COUNTERFACTUAL CONDITIONAL

In Chapter 2.2, it is suggested in a note (note 15) that my explication of the causal relation would provide a basis for a treatment of the counterfactual conditional. For more than a decade, philosophers responded to this proposal with complete silence. Chapter 2.4, written collaboratively with Nicholas Rescher, states the claim more explicitly and fully.

This interpretation of the counterfactual conditional can readily be put in model-theoretic terms. A set of equations determines a class of models — the models that satisfy the equations, that is to say, the 'possible worlds'. If the model is complete, it defines a causal ordering of both the variables that appear in the equations and the equations themselves. A counterfactual conditional describes an 'impossible world' — a class of models that do not satisfy the system of equations. However, when one or more equations is removed from the system, these models satisfy the remainder. But which equation's elimination is implied by the counterfactual conditional? Rescher and I argue that the appropriate equation to eliminate is one that is high in the hierarchy of causes. Thus, 'if the wheat crop had been smaller last year, the price would have been higher', supposes suspension of the causal laws that determine the wheat crop (e.g., laws governing the amount of rainfall), while retaining the laws connecting the size of the crop with its price. Reference to Chapter 2.4 will show that the latter laws are lower in the causal hierarchy than the former.

This explication of the counterfactual still does not deal unambiguously with certain of the examples frequently cited in the literature of the problem as 'hard cases' (e.g., 'If Caesar had been a compatriot of Copernicus, he would have spoken Polish'). But the ambiguity in these cases does not lie with the treatment of the counterfactual. Rather it stems from the fact that interpretation of the counterfactual always requires a context — an implied model — and no such model is unambiguously implied by these anomalous sentences.

## 3. OPERATIONAL MEANING OF MECHANISM

The identification problem raises an issue, treated briefly in paragraph 7.1 of Chapter 2.1, and in Section 5 of Chapter 2.4, that deserves a bit of emphasis.

In empirical sciences, a great deal of importance attaches to the *operational definition of variables*, a term introduced by Percy W. Bridgman. An operational definition of a variable is a specification of the way in which the variable is to be measured. The analysis of the causal relation shows that it is equally essential to provide operational definitions for each of the *equations.*

The meaning of the phrase 'operational definition of an equation' becomes clearer if we substitute 'mechanism' for 'equation.' To provide an operational definition for a mechanism is to specify a method for determining whether the mechanism is operative or inoperative (other than by measuring the variables that the mechanism is supposed to connect).

In the natural sciences it is often the case that when there is a direct causal connection between two variables, the mechanism underlying the connection is tangible or visible or both. (Prior to the discovery — it would almost be more accurate to say 'invention' — of the phenomena of electricity and magnetism, gravity was perhaps the only important exception.) In a pulley or lever, a rope or bar connects the applied force to the load, and cutting the rope or breaking the bar provides a graphic demonstration of the role of the mechanism in the phenomenon. In physiology, likewise, the disruption of mechanisms by surgery has been, and remains, one of the basic means of investigation.

What corresponds, in the social sciences, to the postulate of 'no action at a distance'? I think the direct analogue is 'no influence without communication.' Thus, one of the principal means for producing group phenomena in the laboratory is to manipulate the communication net, either by placing limits on communication or by inserting the experimenter (e.g., through the use of 'stooges') into the net. Of course 'communication' cannot be taken quite literally as 'verbal communication', but the principle remains an important, and probably indispensable, tool for the identification of influence mechanisms.

We will return to the topic of mechanism again in Section 6 of this book. We will see, especially in Chapter 6.5 and 6.7, that the identification of mechanism plays an important role in the axiomatization of physical theories.

### NOTES

[1] Parenthetically, the asymmetry of the causal relation has been the main stumbling block for attempts to build a causal modal logic with special inference rules. Any rule of counterposition will reverse the causal ordering of terms, and if all such rules are omitted, the inference rules of the logic will be too weak for the desired applications. See the comment on Burks' modal logic of causality in Chapter 2.2, note 3.
[2] *Causal Inferences in Nonexperimental Research* (Chapel Hill: University of North Carolina Press, 1964).

# CAUSAL ORDERING AND IDENTIFIABILITY† *

## 1. INTRODUCTION

In careful discussions of scientific methodology, particularly those carried on within a positivist or operationalist framework, it is now customary to avoid any use of the notion of causation and to speak instead of 'functional relations' and 'interdependence' among variables. This avoidance is derived, no doubt, from the role that the concept of causality has played in the history of philosophy since Aristotle, and particularly from the objectionable ontological and epistemological overtones that have attached themselves to the causal concept over the course of that history.

Empiricism has accepted Hume's critique that necessary connections among events cannot be perceived (and hence can have no empirical basis). Observation reveals only recurring associations. The proposition that it is possible to discover associations among events that are, in fact, invariable ceases to be a provable statement about the natural world and becomes instead a working rule to guide the activity of the scientist. He says, 'I will seek for relationships among events that seem always to hold in fact, and when it occurs that they do not hold, I will search for additional conditions and a broader model that will (until new exceptions are discovered) restore my power of prediction.' The only 'necessary' relationships among variables are the relationships of logical necessity that hold in the scientist's model of the world, and there is no guarantee that this model will continue to describe the world that is perceived.

Even this narrower notion of causality — that causal orderings are simply properties of the scientist's model, properties that are subject to change as the model is altered to fit new observations — has been subjected to criticism on two scores. First of all, the viewpoint is becoming more and more prevalent that the appropriate scientific model of the world is not a deterministic model but a probabilistic one. In quantum mechanics and thermodynamics,

† [Hood and Koopmans (eds.), *Studies in Econometric Methods*, New York: John Wiley & Sons, 1953, pp. 49–74].

and in many social science models, expressions in terms of probabilities have taken the place of completely deterministic differential equations in the relationships connecting the variables. However, if we adopt this viewpoint, we can replace the causal ordering of the variables in the deterministc model by the assumption that the realized values of certain variables at one point or period in time determine the probability distribution of certain variables at later points or periods.

The second criticism is in one sense more modest; in another, more sweeping. It has already been alluded to above. It is simply that 'causation' says nothing more than 'functional relationship' or 'interdependence,' and that, since 'causation' has become encrusted with the barnacles of nonoperationalist philosophy, it is best to abandon this term for the others.

In view of the generally unsavory epistemological status of the notion of causality, it is somewhat surprising to find the term in rather common use in scientific writing (when the scientist is writing about his science, not about its methodology). Moreover, it is not easy to explain this usage as metaphorical, or even as a carry-over of outmoded language habits. For, in ordinary speech and writing the causal relationship is conceived to be an asymmetrical one – an ordering – while 'functional relationship' and 'interdependence' are generally conceived as entirely symmetrical. When we say that $A$ causes $B$, we do not say that $B$ causes $A$; but when we say that $A$ and $B$ are functionally related (or interdependent), we can equally well say that $B$ and $A$ are functionally related (or interdependent). Even when we say that $A$ is the independent variable in an equation, while $B$ is the dependent variable, it is often our feeling that we are merely stating a convention of notation and that, by rewriting our equation, we could with equal propriety reverse the roles of $A$ and $B$.

The question, then, of whether we wish to retain the word 'cause' in the vocabulary of science may be narrowed down to the question of whether there is any meaning in the assertion that the relationship between two variables in a model is sometimes asymmetrical rather than symmetrical. If the answer to this question is in the negative, there would seem to be good reason for abandoning 'cause' in favor of its synonyms. If the answer is affirmative, the term 'cause', carefully scrubbed free of any undesirable philosophical adhesions, can perform a useful function and should be retained.

It is the aim of this chapter to show how the question just raised can be answered in the affirmative and to provide a clear and rigorous basis for determining when a causal ordering can be said to hold between two variables or groups of variables in a model. Two preliminary remarks may help to clarify the approach that will be taken.

First, the concepts to be defined all refer to a model – a system of equations – and not to the 'real' world the model purports to describe. Hence both Hume's critique and the determinism-indeterminism controversy are irrelevant to the question of whether these concepts are admissible in scientific discourse. The most orthodox of empiricists and antideterminists can use the term 'cause', as we shall define it, with a clear conscience.

Second, it might be supposed that cause could be defined as functional relationship in conjunction with sequence in time. That is, we might say that if $A$ and $B$ are functionally related and if $A$ precedes $B$ in time, then $A$ causes $B$. There is no logical obstacle to this procedure. Nevertheless, we shall not adopt it. We shall argue that time sequence does, indeed, sometimes provide a basis for asymmetry between $A$ and $B$, but that the asymmetry is the important thing, not the sequence. By putting asymmetry, without necessarily implying a time sequence, at the basis of our definition we shall admit causal orderings where no time sequence appears (and sometimes exclude them even where there is a time sequence). By so doing we shall find ourselves in closer accord with actual usage, and with a better understanding of the meaning of the concept than if we had adopted the other, and easier, course. We shall discover that causation (as we shall define it) does not imply time sequence, nor does time sequence imply causation.

We conclude these introductory comments with two examples of relationships that 'common sense' would regard as causal. First, the classical work of the biologists Henderson, Cannon, and others on homeostasis is replete with references to asymmetrical relationships among the variables. On thirst, Cannon (1939, pp. 62–66) states: 'Thirst is a sensation referred to the inner surface of the mouth and throat, especially to the root of the tongue and the back part of the palate .... When water is lacking in the body the salivary glands are unfavorably affected ... [They] are therefore unable to secrete, the mouth and pharynx become dry and thus the sensation of thirst arises.'

The causal chain clearly implied by this statement is

> *deficiency of water in body tissues→reduction in salivation→dryness of tongue and palate→stimulation of nervous system (sensation of thirst).*

To this Cannon adds elsewhere:

→*activity of drinking→restoration of water content of tissues.*

It is difficult to think or write of these functional relationships as symmetrical, or as asymmetrical but running in the opposite direction. For example, if there is normal salivation but the saliva is prevented from reaching the tongue and palate, thirst is produced, but this neither reduces salivation nor produces a deficiency of water in the body tissues.

Similarly, in economics we speak of relations like

*poor growing weather→small wheat crops→increase in price of wheat*

and we reject the notion that by changing the price of wheat we can affect the weather. The weather is an 'exogenous' variable, the price of wheat an 'endogenous' variable.

## 2. SELF-CONTAINED STRUCTURES

The task we have set ourselves is to show that, given a system of equations and a set of variables appearing in these equations, we can introduce an asymmetrical relationship among individual equations and variables (or subsets of equations and variables) that corresponds to our common-sense notion of a causal ordering. Let us designate the relationship by an arrow, →. Then we shall want to construct our definition in such a manner that $A{\rightarrow}B$ if and only if $A$ is a direct cause (in ordinary usage of the term) of $B$.

In the following discussion we shall seek mathematical simplicity by limiting ourselves to systems of linear algebraic equations without random disturbances. Later we shall indicate how the concepts can readily be extended to nonlinear systems, but a discussion of stochastic systems is beyond the scope of this chapter.

DEFINITION 2.1: *A* linear structure *is a system of linear nonhomogeneous equations* (cf. Marschak, 1950, p. 8) *that possesses the following special properties:*

(a) *That in any subset of k equations taken from the linear structure at least k different variables appear with nonzero coefficients in one or more of the equations of the subset.*

(b) *That in any subset of k equations in which $m \geqslant k$ variables appear with nonzero coefficients, if the values of any $(m - k)$ variables are chosen arbitrarily, then the equations can be solved for unique values of the remaining k variables.*

In particular, a linear structure is an independent and consistent set of linear nonhomogeneous equations, independence and consistency being guaranteed by properties (a) and (b).[1]

DEFINITION 2.2: *A linear structure is* self-contained *if it has exactly as many equations as variables* (cf. Marschak, 1950, p. 7).

Because of (b), a self-contained linear structure possesses a unique solution — there is precisely one set of values of the variables that satisfies the equations.

A linear structure can be represented by the matrix of the coefficients (augmented to include the constant terms) of the equations of the structure. We have already required that the system be nonhomogeneous (that not all the constant terms be zero) and that a sufficient number of variables appear with nonzero coefficients in one or more of the equations in any subset of the structure.

DEFINITION 2.3: *A linear model is the class of all linear structures that can be obtained from a given structure by the substitution of new nonzero coefficients for the nonzero coefficients of the original structure [without, of course, violating (a) or (b)].*[2]

With these terms defined we can undertake to introduce the notion of a causal ordering of the variables, and a corresponding precedence ordering of the equations, of a self-contained linear structure. We shall then see at once that all the linear structures belonging to the same linear model possess the same causal ordering. Hence, we shall see that the causal ordering is determined as soon as we know which variables appear with nonzero coefficients in which equations.

## 3. CAUSAL ORDERING

3.1. Consider any subset $A$ of the equations of a linear structure (alternatively, a subset of the rows of the augmented coefficient matrix) and the corresponding subset $\alpha$ of the variables that appear with a nonzero coefficient in at least one of the equations of $A$. Let $N_A$ be the number of equations in $A$, and $n_\alpha$ the number of variables in $\alpha$. By (a), $n_\alpha \geqslant N_A$. If we extend Definition 2.2 to subsets of equations in a linear structure, then we may say:

DEFINITION 3.1: *A subset $A$ of a linear structure is* self-contained *if and only if $n_\alpha = N_A$.*

DEFINITION 3.2: *If $n_\alpha > N_A$, we shall say that $A$ is* sectional [Marschak, 1950, p. 7].

Now suppose that $A$ and $B$ are two subsets of equations of the same linear structure. We prove the theorem:

THEOREM 3.1: *Let $A$ be self-contained and $B$ be self-contained. Then their intersection $C$ (the set of equations belonging to both $A$ and $B$) is self-contained.*

Designate by $\alpha$ the set of variables that appear in $A$, by $\beta$ the set in $B$, and by $\gamma$ the set in $C$; let $A \cap B$ designate the intersection of the sets $A$ and $B$, and $A \cup B$ their sum (i.e., the set of elements belonging either to $A$ or to $B$). Then the theorem states that if $n_\alpha = N_A$, $n_\beta = N_B$, and $C = A \cap B$, then $n_\gamma = N_C$.

PROOF: Designate by $N_S$ the number of equations in $(A \cup B)$, and by $n_\sigma$ the number of variables in $(\alpha \cup \beta)$. Then we have

$$(3.1) \qquad N_A + N_B - N_C = N_S.$$

Designate by $n_{(\alpha \cap \beta)}$ the number of variables belonging to both $\alpha$ and $\beta$. Then, similarly, we have for the sets of variables

$$(3.2) \qquad n_\alpha + n_\beta - n_{(\alpha \cap \beta)} = n_\sigma.$$

But by hypothesis we have $N_A = n_\alpha$ and $N_B = n_\beta$, while, by (a), $N_S \leqslant n_\sigma$. Substituting these relations in (3.1) we get

$$(3.3) \qquad n_\alpha + n_\beta - N_C = N_S \leqslant n_\sigma.$$

Finally, $\gamma$ is included in $(\alpha \cap \beta)$ since if a variable is in $\gamma$ it must appear in $C$, and hence in both $A$ and $B$. Therefore, $n_{(\alpha \cap \beta)} \geqslant n_\gamma$. Employing this relationship together with (3.2), we get

(3.4) $\qquad n_\sigma \leqslant n_\alpha + n_\beta - n_\gamma,$

whence, combining (3.3) and (3.4) and eliminating identical terms from both sides of the resulting inequality, we obtain

(3.5) $\qquad N_C \geqslant n_\gamma.$

But since, by (a), $n_\gamma \geqslant N_C$ (3.5) implies

(3.6) $\qquad n_\gamma = N_C,$

which proves the theorem.

DEFINITION 3.3: *We call those self-contained subsets of a linear structure that do not themselves contain self-contained (proper) subsets the* minimal self-contained subsets of the structure.

From Theorem 3.1 there follows immediately

THEOREM 3.2: *The minimal self-contained subsets $A_i$ of the equations of a linear structure, and likewise the subsets of variables that appear in these minimal subsets of equations, are disjunct.*

That the subsets of equations are disjunct is obvious from Theorem 3.1. That the subsets of *variables* appearing in the several minimal self-contained subsets of equations are also disjunct follows from the observation that, if this were not so, the sums of minimal subsets with common variables would contain fewer variables than equations, contrary to (a). That is, let $A$ and $B$ be minimal self-contained subsets and let $C = A \cup B$. Then, since $A$ and $B$ are disjunct, $N_C = N_A + N_B$, while $n_\gamma = n_\alpha + n_\beta - n_{(\alpha \cap \beta)}$. But $n_\alpha = N_A$, $n_\beta = N_B$. Hence $n_{(\alpha \cap \beta)} > 0$ implies $n_\gamma < N_C$, which contradicts (a).

3.2. We can now decompose a self-contained linear structure $A$ containing variables $\alpha$ into two parts: a part $A'$, which is the sum of all the minimal self-contained subsets, $A' = A_1 \cup A_2 \cup \ldots \cup A_k$ (containing variables $\alpha' = \alpha_1 \cup \alpha_2 \cup \ldots \cup \alpha_k$); and a remainder, $B$. Since the $A_i$ are disjunct, $N_{A'} = \Sigma N_{A_i}$. Similarly, $n_{\alpha'} = \Sigma n_{\alpha_i} = \Sigma N_{A_i}$. Hence $N_{A'} = n_{\alpha'}$, i.e., the number of variables appearing in $A'$ is equal to the number of equations in $A'$. Further, if $B$ is not null ('empty'), we must have $n_\beta > N_B$; otherwise $B$ would be self-contained, contrary to its definition. Hence, at least one of the variables of $\alpha'$ must belong to $\beta$.

It is convenient to distinguish three cases:

I. $A'$ consists of a single self-contained set, which coincides with the entire structure; i.e., the structure $A$ contains no self-contained proper subset. In this case $B$ is null, and we may say that the structure is completely *integrated*.

II. $A'$ consists of one or more proper subsets of the structure and $B$ is not null. In this case we may say that the structure is *causally ordered*.

III. $A'$ consists of more than one proper subset of the structure and $B$ is null. In this case we may say that the structure is *unintegrated*.

In all three cases we shall call the minimal self-contained subsets belonging to $A'$ the (minimal) *complete subsets of zero order*.

DEFINITION 3.4: *If in Case II we solve the equations of $A'$ for the unique values of the variables in $\alpha'$, and substitute these values in the equations of $B$ [by (b) this is always possible], the linear structure we obtain is the* derived structure of first order, *a self-contained structure of $N_B$ equations in* $n_{(\beta - \beta \cap \alpha')} = N_B$ *unknowns. We can now find the minimal self-contained subsets of the first derived structure, $B' = B_1 \cup B_2 \cup \ldots \cup B_m$ (complete subsets of first order), and proceed as before, obtaining Case I, II, or III. If Case II holds, we repeat the process with the* derived structure of second order, *and so forth. Since the number of equations in the original structure was finite, we must finally reach a derived structure that falls under Case I or Case III.*

DEFINITION 3.5: *The minimal self-contained subsets of the derived structure of k-th order will be called the* complete subsets of $k$th order.

3.3. By the process just described we have arrived at a complete ordering of disjunct subsets of the equations of $A$, so that $A = A' \cup B' \cup \ldots \cup N$, where $N$, the derived structure of highest order, is either unintegrated or completely integrated. Each of the minimal complete subsets, of whatever order, reached in the process may be interpreted in either of two ways. The subset, taken by itself, may be regarded (as above) as a self-contained structure with as many variables as equations, the remaining variables having been eliminated by substitution after solution of the equations of the lower-order structures. Alternatively, it may be viewed as a *complete* subset, in which case the variables in question are not eliminated by substitution but are regarded as *exogenous variables*, the remaining variables (equal in number to the equations of the subset) being regarded as *endogenous variables*. (It will be clear that these terms are used in a sense relative to the complete subset of equations in question.)[3]

Adopting the latter interpretation of subsets in the derived structures, it is clear that each complete subset of first order must contain at least one variable in $\alpha'$, for if it did not, the subset would be a complete subset of zero order. Similarly, each complete subset of $k$th order must contain at least one variable that appears in a complete subset of $(k-1)$th order and that does not appear in any complete subset of order less than $(k-1)$.

Since the concepts of endogenous and exogenous variables will play an important role in the following discussion, it will be useful to have for these terms a definition more formal than that just given.

DEFINITION 3.6: *If D is a complete subset of order k, and if a variable $x_i$ appears in D but in no complete subset of order lower than k, then $x_i$ is* endogenous *in the subset D. If $x_i$ appears in D but also in some complete subset of order lower than k, then $x_i$ is* exogenous *in the subset D.*

From our previous discussion (in particular, the paragraph following Theorem 3.2) it can be seen that each variable in a self-contained linear structure appears as an endogenous variable in one and only one complete subset of the structure, that it appears in no complete subset of order lower than the one in which it is endogenous, and that it appears in complete subsets of higher order (if at all) as an exogenous variable. Therefore, there exists a one-to-one correspondence between the complete subsets of equations and the subsets of variables occurring as endogenous variables in these equations.

We can now employ the distinction between exogenous and endogenous variables to define a causal ordering of the sets of variables endogenous to the corresponding complete subsets of equations.

DEFINITION 3.7: *Let $\beta$ designate the set of variables endogenous to a complete subset B, and let $\gamma$ designate the set endogenous to a complete subset C. Then the variables of $\gamma$ are directly causally dependent on the variables of $\beta$ ($\beta \to \gamma$) if at least one member of $\beta$ appears as an exogenous variable in C. We can say also that the subset of equations B has direct precedence over the subset C.*

We have now partitioned the equations of a self-contained structure into disjunct subsets (the minimal complete subsets of various orders); we have similarly partitioned into disjunct subsets the variables of the structure (the sets of endogenous variables corresponding to the complete subsets of equations); and we have partially ordered these minimal subsets of equations and corresponding sets of variables by means of the (isomorphic) relations of direct precedence and direct causal dependence, respectively.

## 4. ANALYSIS OF EXAMPLES

4.1. Our first example is the simple one mentioned in the introduction to this chapter:

> *poor growing weather→small wheat crops→increase in price of wheat.*

We may translate this into the form of a self-contained linear structure as follows: Let $x_1$ be an index measuring the favorableness of weather for growing wheat; $x_2$, the size of the wheat crop; and $x_3$, the price of wheat. We suppose the weather to depend only on a parameter; the wheat crop, upon the weather (we ignore a possible dependence of supply on price); and the price of wheat, on the wheat crop; and we suppose all relations to be linear. The resulting equations are

$$(4.1) \qquad a_{11}x_1 \qquad\qquad\qquad = a_{10},$$

$$(4.2) \qquad a_{21}x_1 + a_{22}x_2 \qquad\quad = a_{20},$$

$$(4.3) \qquad\qquad\quad a_{32}x_2 + a_{33}x_3 = a_{30}.$$

Equation (4.1) contains only one variable and hence is a minimal complete subset of zero order, with $x_1$ as the endogenous variable. There are no other such subsets. Solving (4.1) for $x_1$ and substituting this value in (4.2) and (4.3), we get the derived structure of first order,

$$(4.2a) \qquad a_{22}x_2 \qquad\qquad = a_{20} - a_{21}(a_{10}/a_{11}),$$

$$(4.3a) \qquad a_{32}x_2 + a_{33}x_3 = a_{30}.$$

We see that Equation (4.2a) is a minimal complete subset of first order, with $x_2$ as its endogenous variable. Solving (4.2a) for $x_2$ and eliminating $x_2$ from the third equation, we are left with a single equation as the minimal complete subset of second order. Applying Definition 3.7, we may write:

$$(4.1) \to (4.2) \to (4.3)$$

[read: "(4.1) has direct precedence over (4.2), and (4.2) over (4.3)"] , and

$$x_1 \rightarrow x_2 \rightarrow x_3$$

[read: "$x_1$ is the direct cause of $x_2$, and $x_2$ of $x_3$"] .

4.2. A less trivial example, which also shows that our definitions correspond with common-sense notions of causality, is the structure whose coefficients are estimated by Girshick and Haavelmo in Hood and Koopmans (1953) Chapter V, pp. 107—110. In writing their system we omit the random terms and employ a different notation for the coefficients:

$$(4.4) \quad a_{11}y_1 + a_{12}y_2 + a_{13}y_3 \qquad\qquad + a_{18}z_8$$
$$+ a_{19}z_9 = a_{10},$$

$$(4.5) \quad a_{21}y_1 + a_{22}y_2 \qquad + a_{24}y_4 \qquad\qquad + a_{28}z_8$$
$$= a_{20},$$

$$(4.6) \qquad\qquad + a_{33}y_3 \qquad\qquad + a_{37}z_7$$
$$+ a_{39}z_9 = a_{30},$$

$$(4.7) \qquad\qquad a_{44}y_4 + a_{45}y_5 + a_{46}z_6 \qquad + a_{48}z_8$$
$$= a_{40},$$

$$(4.8) \qquad a_{52}y_2 \qquad\qquad + a_{55}y_5 \qquad + a_{58}z_8$$
$$= a_{50},$$

$$(4.9) \qquad\qquad\qquad a_{66}z_6$$
$$= a_{60},$$

$$(4.10) \qquad\qquad\qquad a_{77}z_7$$
$$= a_{70},$$

$$(4.11) \qquad\qquad\qquad a_{88}z_8$$
$$= a_{80},$$

$$(4.12) \qquad\qquad\qquad a_{99}z_9 = a_{90}.$$

Analysis of this structure, which the reader may wish to carry out as an exercise, shows that there are four single-equation subsets of zero order: Equations (4.9), (4.10), (4.11), (4.12), and one subset of first order: Equation (4.6). The four remaining equations form a single subset of second order in the endogenous variables $y_1, y_2, y_4$, and $y_5$. In terms of equations,

the precedence relations are

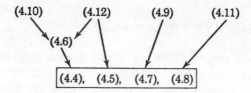

Interpreting this result in terms of the corresponding sets of variables, we find that Girshick and Haavelmo are asserting:

1. That food consumption ($y_1$), retail food prices ($y_2$), food production ($y_4$), and food prices received by farmers ($y_5$) are interdependent (members of the same minimal complete subset of second order) and directly causally dependent upon disposable income ($y_3$), last years's food prices received by farmers ($z_6$), time ($z_8$), and last year's disposable income ($z_9$).

2. That disposable income ($y_3$) is directly causally dependent upon net investment ($z_7$) and last year's disposable income ($z_9$).

4.3. We present, without interpretation, a final example:

$$(4.13) \quad \alpha_{11}x_1 + \alpha_{12}x_2 + \alpha_{13}x_3 \qquad\qquad + \alpha_{16}x_6 \qquad\qquad = \alpha_{10},$$

$$(4.14) \qquad\qquad\qquad\qquad \alpha_{24}x_4 + \alpha_{25}x_5 \qquad\qquad = \alpha_{20},$$

$$(4.15) \qquad\qquad \alpha_{32}x_2 \qquad\qquad\qquad\qquad\qquad = \alpha_{30},$$

$$(4.16) \qquad\qquad\qquad \alpha_{43}x_3 \qquad\qquad\qquad\qquad = \alpha_{40},$$

$$(4.17) \quad \alpha_{51}x_1 + \alpha_{52}x_2 + \alpha_{53}x_3 + \alpha_{54}x_4 \qquad\qquad = \alpha_{50},$$

$$(4.18) \qquad\qquad\qquad\qquad\qquad\qquad \alpha_{66}x_6 + \alpha_{67}x_7 = \alpha_{60},$$

$$(4.19) \quad \alpha_{71}x_1 \qquad\qquad\qquad\qquad\qquad\qquad = \alpha_{70}.$$

It can be shown that there are three complete subsets of zero order: Equation (4.15) and variable $x_2$, Equation (4.16) and variable $x_3$, and Equation (4.19) and variable $x_1$. There are two complete subsets of first order: Equation (4.13) and $x_6$, and Equation (4.17) and $x_4$. Finally, there are two complete subsets of second order: Equation (4.14) and $x_5$, and Equation (4.18) and $x_7$. In this case each complete subset consists of one equation in one endogenous variable, and we can represent the precedence and causal partitioning alternatively as follows:

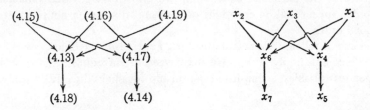

Reordering our equations to correspond with the order of the corresponding variables, the partitioning can also be represented as in Table I. In Table I, nonzero coefficients in the matrix are designated by ×, zero coefficients by 0. The coefficients of the constant term are not displayed.

TABLE I

|        | $x_1$ | $x_2$ | $x_3$ | $x_4$ | $x_6$ | $\cdot x_5$ | $x_7$ |
|--------|-------|-------|-------|-------|-------|-------|-------|
| (4.19) | ×     | 0     | 0     | 0     | 0     | 0     | 0     |
| (4.15) | 0     | ×     | 0     | 0     | 0     | 0     | 0     |
| (4.16) | 0     | 0     | ×     | 0     | 0     | 0     | 0     |
| (4.17) | ×     | ×     | ×     | ×     | 0     | 0     | 0     |
| (4.13) | ×     | ×     | ×     | 0     | ×     | 0     | 0     |
| (4.14) | 0     | 0     | 0     | ×     | 0     | ×     | 0     |
| (4.18) | 0     | 0     | 0     | 0     | ×     | 0     | ×     |

4.4. We see from this last representation that ordering the equations and variables according to their precedence and causal relations places the matrix in a canonical form that in a certain sense is as nearly triangular as the structural equations permit. This suggests that calculation of the causal relations in a structure may have some value in indicating the optimum arrangement of equations and variables in fixing the sequence of computation of their solutions. It would be easy to construct an electrical computing device which, even for very large structures, would rapidly locate the complete subsets from this matrix representation.

The blocks of zeros above and to the right of the main diagonal in the canonical form of the matrix show clearly also that our concept of causal ordering is essentially identical with the concept of unilateral coupling, employed in connection with dynamical systems.[4]

4.5. The blocks of zeros in the lower left-hand corner are really accidental properties of the particular partitioning we are studying — that variables of zero order appear only in equations of zero and first order, not in equations of second order.

The causal relation we have defined is a nontransitive relation — $\alpha \rightarrow \beta$ and $\beta \rightarrow \gamma$ does not imply $\alpha \rightarrow \gamma$. We may wish to introduce, among sets of endogenous variables, a transitive relationship meaning 'directly or indirectly caused.'

DEFINITION 4.1: $\alpha \supset \gamma$ *(read: "$\alpha$ is a cause of $\gamma$") if there exist $\beta_1$, $\beta_2, \ldots, \beta_k$ such that $\alpha \rightarrow \beta_1 \rightarrow \beta_2 \rightarrow \ldots \rightarrow \beta_k \rightarrow \gamma$. We may also speak of a relationship of* precedence *holding between the corresponding subsets of equations; for instance, $A \supset C$.*

## 5. CAUSALITY IN SYSTEMS NOT SELF-CONTAINED

5.1. We now proceed to show that it is essential that we assume a self-contained structure in order to introduce the notion of causal ordering.

Consider the structure used as an example in Section 4.3. Suppose that we omit equations (4.15) and (4.19) and replace them with

(5.1)         $\alpha_{85} x_5 \qquad = \alpha_{80}$,

(5.2)                 $\alpha_{99} x_7 = \alpha_{90}$.

We then obtain the following causal structure:

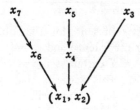

where $(x_1, x_2)$ represents the complete subset of second order comprising the variables $x_1$ and $x_2$. We see that we have not only reversed the direction of causation between $x_5$ and $x_7$, on the one hand, and $x_1$ and $x_2$ on the other, but have also changed the relation of $x_3$ to the remainder of the structure. Hence we cannot speak of an 'internal' causal structure among the variables of a sectional (not self-contained) structure apart from the particular self-contained structure in which it is imbedded. In our new case the canonical form of matrix is as Table II shows.

TABLE II

| | $x_3$ | $x_5$ | $x_7$ | $x_4$ | $x_6$ | $x_1$ | $x_2$ |
|---|---|---|---|---|---|---|---|
| (4.16) | X | 0 | 0 | 0 | 0 | 0 | 0 |
| (5.1) | 0 | X | 0 | 0 | 0 | 0 | 0 |
| (5.2) | 0 | 0 | X | 0 | 0 | 0 | 0 |
| (4.14) | 0 | X | 0 | X | 0 | 0 | 0 |
| (4.18) | 0 | 0 | X | 0 | X | 0 | 0 |
| (4.13) | X | 0 | 0 | 0 | X | X | X |
| (4.17) | X | 0 | 0 | X | 0 | X | X |

Of the five equations common to both structures, only Equation (4.16) has retained the same order. Moreover, the complete subsets of equations are associated with subsets of variables different from those before.

5.2. In general, we can complete a sectional structure by adding an appropriate number of additional equations, and in general we can do this in a number of different ways. Each of the resulting self-contained structures is likely to have different causal relationships among its variables. One way to complete a sectional structure is to specify which variables are exogenous and to add a sufficient number of equations in which these exogenous variables alone occur (Marschak, 1950, p. 8).

## 6. OPERATIONAL SIGNIFICANCE OF CAUSAL ORDERING

6.1. An important objection to our definition of causal ordering remains to be examined — the objection that it is essentially artificial, since the same set of observations could be represented by different structures with different causal orderings of the variables. Consider the following three sets of two equations each:

(6.1)  
(6.2)  
$$\begin{cases} a_{11}y_1 + a_{12}y_2 = a_{10}, \\ a_{21}y_1 + a_{22}y_2 = a_{20}; \end{cases}$$

(6.3)  
(6.4)  
$$\begin{cases} b_{11}y_1 = b_{10}, \\ a_{21}y_1 + a_{22}y_2 = a_{20}, \end{cases}$$

with $b_{11} = a_{11} - (a_{12}/a_{22})a_{21}, b_{10} = a_{10} - (a_{12}/a_{22})a_{20};$

(6.5)  
(6.6)  
$$\begin{cases} b_{11}y_1 = b_{10}, \\ a_{22}y_2 = c_{20}, \end{cases}$$

with $c_{20} = a_{20} - (a_{21}/b_{11})b_{10}.$

All three sets of equations are satisfied by precisely the same set of values of $y_1$ and $y_2$, namely,

$$(6.7) \qquad y_1 = b_{10}/b_{11}, \qquad y_2 = c_{20}/a_{22}.$$

Yet the causal ordering in the three sets is different. Equations (6.1) and (6.2) comprise a single minimal complete set of zero order. Equation (6.3) is a complete set of zero order, while (6.4) is a complete set of first order to which (6.3) is directly precedent. Equations (6.5) and (6.6) each constitute a complete set of zero order. The first structure is completely integrated, the second causally ordered, and the third unintegrated. If the three sets are to be regarded as operationally equivalent, because each can be obtained from either of the others by algebraic manipulation without altering the solution, then causal ordering has no operational meaning.

Closer inspection of the three sets of equations, (6.1)–(6.6), suggests a possible basis for distinguishing them even though they have an identical solution. Consider the first pair of equations. Suppose that Equation (6.1) were altered (say, by a change in the constant term or one of the other coefficients). Then the values of both $y_1$ and $y_2$ would, in general, be altered. The same would be true if (6.2) were altered.

Consider next the second pair of equations. Suppose that Equation (6.3) were altered. Again, both $y_1$ and $y_2$ would be changed in value. On the other hand, if (6.4) were altered, only $y_2$ would be affected and $y_1$ would remain unchanged.

Finally, consider the third pair of equations. Suppose that Equation (6.5) were altered. This would change the value of $y_1$ but not of $y_2$. However, if (6.6) were altered, this would change the value of $y_2$ but not of $y_1$.

The principle illustrated by the example above can easily be generalized.

THEOREM 6.1: *Let $A$ be a self-contained linear structure, let $A_1$ be a complete subset of order $k$ in $A$, and let $A'$ be a self-contained linear structure that is identical with $A$ except for a single equation belonging to $A_1$. (We assume that the set of variables appearing in $A_1$ is unaltered.) Consider the (unique) solutions of $A$ and $A'$, respectively. Then (a) the values of all variables in $A$ that are neither endogenous variables of $A_1$ nor causally dependent, directly or indirectly, on the endogenous variables of $A_1$ are identical with the values of the corresponding variables in $A'$; and (b) the values of all variables in $A$ that are endogenous in $A_1$ or are causally dependent on the endogenous variables of $A_1$ are (in general) different from the values of the corresponding variables in $A'$.*

*PROOF:* We can solve the equations of a linear structure for values of the variables appearing in a particular complete subset $A_2$ by (1) solving successively the complete subsets (starting with those of zero order) that have precedence over $A_2$, and finally (2) substituting in $A_2$ the values of all the exogenous variables appearing in $A_2$ and solving the equations of $A_2$ for the endogenous variables. Hence, altering an equation belonging to one of these complete subsets will, in general, alter the values of the variables in $A_2$; but altering an equation in a complete subset that does not have precedence over $A_2$ cannot alter the values of the variables in $A_2$.

6.2. Let us apply this notion to the example used in Section 4.1. The structure represented by Equations (4.1)–(4.3) might be altered by changing any one of the three equations, each of which constitutes a complete subset.

I. If (4.1) is altered (e.g., rainfall is increased by sowing carbon dioxide crystals in clouds), this will also affect the wheat crop and the price of wheat.

II. If (4.2) is altered (e.g., a drought-resistant variety of wheat is introduced), this will affect the wheat crop and the price of wheat but not the weather.

III. If (4.3) is altered (e.g., a population increase shifts upward the demand schedule for wheat), the price of wheat will change but not the size of the wheat crop or the weather.

The causal relationships have operational meaning, then, to the extent that particular alterations or 'interventions' in the structure can be associated with specific complete subsets of equations. We can picture the situation, perhaps somewhat metaphorically, as follows. We suppose a group of persons whom we shall call 'experimenters'. If we like, we may consider 'nature' to be a member of the group. The experimenters, severally or separately, are able to choose the nonzero elements of the coefficient matrix of a linear structure, but they may not replace zero elements by nonzero elements or vice versa (i.e., they are restricted to a specified linear model). We may say that they *control directly* the values of the nonzero coefficients. Once the matrix is specified, the values of the $n$ variables in the $n$ linear equations of the structure are uniquely determined. Hence, the experimenters *control indirectly* the values of these variables. The causal ordering specifies which variables will be affected by intervention at a particular point (a particular complete subset) of the structure.

We see that, in addition to a language describing the linear model, we require, in order to discuss causality, a second language (a 'metalanguage') describing the relationship between the 'experimenters' and the model. The terms 'direct control' and 'indirect control' are in this metalanguage. Thus, in our metalanguage we have an asymmetrical relationship ($>$) – behavior of experimenters $>$ equation coefficients $>$ values of variables – that must be introduced in order to establish the asymmetrical causal relationship ($\rightarrow$).

In one sense we have moved our problem from the language of the original model to the metalanguage. In order to establish a causal ordering we must have a priori knowledge of the limits imposed on the 'experimenters' – in this case knowledge that certain coefficients of the matrix are zeros. If the causal ordering is to have operational meaning it is necessary that, within these limits, the 'experimenters' be able to alter at least some equation in each complete subset in some way.

## 7. CAUSAL ORDERING AND IDENTIFIABILITY

The concept of identifiability has been introduced in Hood and Koopmans (1953), Chapter II. In the present chapter no hint has been given thus far as to the relationship between identifiability and causal ordering. In fact, however, there appears to be a very close relationship between the two concepts, and it is the task of the present section to describe it.[5]

7.1. In Section 6 we sought an operational basis for the concept of causal ordering, a basis that would make of the ordering something more than an arbitrary property of a particular (and arbitrary) way of writing the equations governing certain empirical variables. We found that we could provide the ordering with an operational basis if we could associate with each equation of a structure a specific power of intervention, or 'direct control'. That is, any such intervention would alter the structure but leave the model (and hence the causal ordering) invariant. Hence, causal ordering is a property of models that is invariant with respect to interventions within the model, and structural equations are equations that correspond to specified possibilities of intervention.

The usual notion of operationalism requires us to associate with each *variable* of an empirical system a method (set of operations) for measuring it. The extended notion introduced in Section 6 requires us to associate with each *equation* a procedure (set of operations) for altering its constant term or coefficients. It is by virtue of such procedures that we can distinguish between 'structural' and 'nonstructural' sets of equations describing the same set of observations.

But it is precisely this same notion of intervention, and this same distinction between structural and nonstructural equations, that lies at the root of the identifiability concept.[6] As long as structure remains unaltered, identifiability is not required in order to estimate the parameters that are needed for prediction. When a recognizable change in structure occurs, however, identifiability of at least some of the parameters of the structural equations is necessary if correct predictions are to be made in the new structure. From these epistemological considerations we conclude that the conditions under which the causal ordering of a structure is operationally meaningful are generally the same as the conditions under which structural equations can be distinguished from nonstructural equations, and the same as the conditions under which the question of identifiability of the equations is meaningful.

7.2. Parallel with the epistemological relationship just described, we should expect to find a mathematical relationship between the two concepts. In this we are not disappointed.

Identifiability of a linear structure is obtained when certain a priori constraints are placed on the model. For complete identifiability of a structure these restraints must preclude the existence in the model of a different equivalent structure, that is (in linear models), a different set of equations whose members are linear combinations of the original equations.[7].

The simplest basis for identifiability is obtained if we can specify a priori that certain coefficients appearing in the model must be zero. But if the $j$th coefficient in the $i$th equation is zero, then the $j$th variable does not appear in the $i$th equation. Hence, these specifications may be regarded as determining which variables appear in which equations. In a self-contained structure specification of which variables appear with nonzero coefficients in which equations determines the causal ordering. (In the present section we shall restrict ourselves to a priori specifications of the kind just described.)

7.3. The argument just set forth may be restated in a more formal way, which will perhaps clarify further the operational status of the terms 'causal ordering' and 'identifiability.' An important guiding principle in the relationship between mathematical models and empirical data is that a property of a mathematical model cannot be regarded as reflecting a property of the empirical world the model purports to describe unless this property is invariant under permissible (operationally nonsignificant) transformations of the equations specified by the model.

For example, in Newtonian mechanics it is meaningless to ask whether a body is at rest or in uniform motion in a straight line, for by a trivial transformation of the reference system the motion of the body can be transformed from the first state to the second.[8] It is meaningful however, to ask whether the body is accelerated or unaccelerated since this property is invariant under transformation from one physically admissible reference system to another.

In the classical theory of systems of linear equations we are interested in properties of a system that are invariant under certain groups of transformations of the coefficients of its matrix. In particular, we may be interested in the solutions of any given system (the sets of values of the variables satisfying the system). These are invariant under elementary row transformations of the matrix.

DEFINITION 7.1: *Elementary row transformations of a matrix are those which (1) interchange rows of the matrix (i.e. reorder the equations), (2) add to a given row multiples of another row or rows, (3) multiply a row by a nonzero scalar. These all amount to premultiplication of the coefficient matrix by a nonsingular matrix.[9] The group of transformations thus generated we will call the R-transformations.*

DEFINITION 7.2: *Any two coefficient matrices that are obtainable from one another by R-transformations we will call R-equivalent.*

Concentration of interest on those properties (e.g., solutions) that are invariant under the group of $R$-transformations has led to the replacement of the notion of causality by the notion of mutual dependence. For, given a (consistent and independent) set of $k$ linear equations in $n$ ($n \geqslant k$) variables, then, in general, each variable belonging to any subset (Bôcher, 1907, p. 46) of $k$ variables can be expressed as a function of the remaining $(n - k)$.

We have seen that the causal ordering in a linear structure is not invariant under the group of $R$-transformations (cf. Sections 6.1, 6.2). Hence, to give invariant meaning to this causal ordering we must restrict ourselves to a more limited group of transformations than the $R$-transformations.

DEFINITION 7.3: *We say that two coefficient matrices are structurally equivalent (S-equivalent) if the second can be obtained from the first by premultiplication by a nonsingular diagonal matrix (i.e. .by row transformations of the third type only). The group of transformations thus admitted we shall call the group of S-transformations.*

It is clear that if only the $S$-transformations are admitted (multiplication of each equation by a constant), the positions of the zero and nonzero coefficients cannot be affected. That is, the causal ordering of a linear structure and the identifiability of its several equations are invariant under the group of $S$-transformations but not under the wider group of $R$-transformations.

Now the operational significance of distinguishing between these two groups of transformations has already been suggested in Sections 6.2 and 7.1. If with each equation of a structure we associate a specific power of intervention, then, under $S$-transformations, this one-to-one correspondence between equations and interventions will not be disturbed — each equation will retain its identity. But, under $R$-transformations of types (1) or (2), the equations will be scrambled and combined. Suppose that the $j$th and $k$th equations belong to different complete subsets. If the $j$th equation is interchanged with the $k$th, the interventions will have to be correspondingly reordered; while if the $j$th equation is replaced by a sum of multiples of the $j$th and $k$th, the $k$th power of intervention will now not be associated with a single equation but with both the $j$th and the $k$th.

The definition of identifiability implies that a linear structure is completely identifiable if and only if the a priori restrictions on the model (e.g., the zeros of the coefficient matrix) are such as to permit only $S$-transformations upon the matrix. If the identifiable structure is self-contained, there will then be a unique causal ordering associated with it, and this ordering will be invariant under any transformations permitted by the a priori restrictions.[10]

## 8. IDENTIFIABILITY IN COMPLETE SUBSETS

The relationship, just explored, between causal ordering and identifiability casts some light upon the conditions under which the coefficients of a structure can be determined from data in the case of nonstochastic models. First, some preliminary explanations are necessary.

8.1. We suppose that we have a large number of observations of the simultaneous values of $n$ variables entering in a linear model. Each observation may be regarded as a point in an $n$-dimensional space whose coordinates are the values of the $n$ variables. We suppose, further, that the model specifies $k$ equations ($k < n$) which are assumed to govern the behavior of the variables; any single observation must satisfy the $k$ equations. Under what conditions will the observations be sufficient to determine the unknown coefficients of all $k$ equations, that is, the unknown structure within the model?

The answer to this question can be obtained from geometrical considerations. If each observation is to satisfy all the equations, all observations must lie in a hyperplane of not more than $(n - k)$ dimensions. This hyperplane must be the intersection of the $k(n - 1)$-dimensional hyperplanes representing the $k$ equations. (For example, if there are three variables and two equations, each equation will be represented by a plane, and all observations will lie on the straight line that is the intersection of the two planes.)

Now if the observations do not lie in a hyperplane of *fewer* than $(n - k)$ dimensions, the criteria for identifiability of equations that have been derived for linear stochastic models[11] are also sufficient to assure unique determination of the coefficients of these equations in the present nonstochastic case. For a model satisfying these criteria restricts transformations of the equations to the group of $S$-transformations (which do not affect the location of the planes represented by the equations), and hence only one set of $k$ admissible hyperplanes can intersect in the $(n - k)$-dimensional hyperplane defined by the observations. That is to say, any other set of $k(n - 1)$-dimensional hyperplanes intersecting in the same $(n - k)$-dimensional hyperplane must consist of linear combinations of the original set, and this possibility is ruled out by that a priori restrictions, specified by the model, that produce identifiability.

However, if the observations are 'degenerate' [i.e., lie in a hyperplane of fewer than $(n - 1)$ dimensions], it may be impossible to determine all the coefficients of the structure. Hence, to insure the possibility of determining these coefficients we must require that the variables not be subject to any equations in addition to those of the structure.[12]

8.2. We shall now see how a knowledge of the causal ordering of a set of variables can be used to help determine whether the coefficients of a linear structure governing these variables can be determined. In the discussion of criteria for identifiability of a structural equation by a linear model, given in Chapter II of Hood and Koopmans (1953) and in Section 4.4 of Chapter VI, a necessary order condition and a necessary and sufficient rank condition for identifiability are derived. For simplicity, in the following discussion we shall consider only the order condition. The exposition would be considerably complicated, and the results not materially altered, if the rank condition were included as well. In the following theorem we restate the order condition, which, in view of the discussion of Section 8.1, applies also to the present nonstochastic case.

THEOREM 8.1: *In a linear model with a priori restrictions in the form of exclusions of variables from equations, a necessary condition for the identifiability of the k-th equation of a structure A consisting of m equations in n variables is that at least (m − 1) of the variables in A be excluded from the k-th equation.*

It follows immediately that, if $A$ is a self-contained structure, the only equations belonging to it that are identifiable are those containing a single variable (i.e., the equations that consitute complete subsets of zero order). Hence, the prospects of determining the coefficients of a self-contained structure (unless it is made up entirely of one-variable equations) are nil as long as all observations are restricted by the entire system of equations. In fact, in a nonstochastic structure, repeated observations could in this case only produce the same set of values for all variables that was obtained in the first observation. This suggests that we shall need to intervene (see Section 6.2) to 'relax' certain of the relationships in order to obtain observations adequate for determining the coefficients of the remaining equations.

In a self-contained structure $A$ consider an identifiable complete subset $S$ of $k$ equations in $n$ variables. [By Theorem 8.1, no equation of $S$ contains more than $(n − k + 1)$ variables.] If we can produce a set of observations of the variables that satisfies these $k$ equations, and no others independent of these, then we can determine the coefficients of $S$. Now let us add to $S$ any number of additional equations of $A$ which either (1) belong to complete subsets of the same or higher order than $S$, or (2) do not contain any of the variables of $S$. Designate by $S'$, this structure (which includes $S$). Then the equations of $S$ also satisfy the order condition of identifiability in this new system. For the number of variables in $S'$ must exceed the number of variables in $S$ by at least the number of equations added [by (a)]. None of these new variables appear in the equations of $S$. Therefore, the equations of $S$ still satisfy the condition of Theorem 8.1 and hence, as far as the order condition is concerned, are still identifiable in $S'$. We have proved

THEOREM 8.2: *If each equation of a complete subset S of a linear structure A is identifiable in that subset, it also satisfies the order condition of identifiability in the larger set S' that is formed by adding to S any equations of A which either (1) belong to complete subsets of the same or higher order than S or (2) do not contain any of the variables of S.*

By virtue of this theorem we see that in order to permit the determination of the coefficients of an identifiable complete subset of equations we need to relax, at most, the equations that are precedent to this subset. This theorem makes clear the point, referred to in note 7, that identifiability has reference to complete subsets of equations.[13] As a matter of fact, the condition of Theorem 8.2, while sufficient for the preservation of the order condition, is not necessary. Without pursuing the matter in detail, we may illustrate the situation with an example. Consider a complete subset $S$ of $k$ equations in $k$ endogenous and $m$ exogenous variables. Suppose the $m$ exogenous variables to be endogenous to a complete subset $T$ (of lower order of precedence) of $m$ equations in $m + p$ $(p \geqslant m)$ variables. Then it is easy to see that, if an equation of $S$ is identifiable in $S$, it is identifiable in the system consisting of $S$ and $T$ together. To guarantee that the order condition of identifiability will be satisfied when we add new equations to an identifiable complete subset we need merely make sure that we add as many new variables as equations.

8.3. The rationale of the identifiability concept with reference to a complete subset $A_k$ of a self-contained structure $A$ would appear to be the following. We suppose the equations of $A_k$ of order $k$ to be identifiable in $A_k$, and we wish to determine their coefficients. All the variables of $A$ of order less than $k$ that appear in $A_k$ are exogenous variables relative to $A_k$. We now suppose that these variables can be arbitrarily varied (by relaxing the structural equations of order less than $k$) to produce a set of observations of the highest dimensionality consistent with the relations of $A_k$. This set of observations, together with the condition that the equations of $A_k$ be identifiable, permits us to determine the coefficients.

It is to be noted that we have here again implicitly introduced the notion of an experimenter who, by his direct control over the parameters of the equations in $A$ of order less than $k$ (or by selection of observations provided by 'nature'), can bring about independent variations in the variables that are exogenous to $A_k$. If this procedure is operationally meaningful, the experimenter, confronted with a self-contained structure $A$, can partition the structure into its complete subsets and, isolating each of these from the whole, proceed to determine its parameters. This seems to correspond exactly to the procedure of a physiologist who (in the example used in the introduction) prevents an animal's saliva from reaching the palate and in this way explores the thirst mechanism.

In the stochastic case nature may provide some of the necessary variability of exogenous variables that escape experimental control. In fact, the discussion of identifiability of complete structures in the stochastic case is meaningful only if sufficient independent variation of 'exogenous' variables is provided by nature.[14]

## 9. CAUSALITY IN NONLINEAR SYSTEMS

Thus far we have considered only the case of linear, nonstochastic structures. In this chapter the problem of causal ordering in the stochastic case will not be considered, but a few comments may be made on the nonlinear case.

We consider a system of functional relations of the form

$$(9.1) \qquad \phi_i(x_1, \ldots, x_n) = 0 \qquad (i = 1, \ldots, n).$$

We assume further that the system has, at most, a denumerably infinite set of solutions. Now we can again decompose the system into complete subsets of equations of various orders, such that each subset contains as many variables not appearing in subsets of lower order as it contains equations. If appropriate conditions are imposed on our system, this decomposition will again be unique.

In our linear structure we assumed that an experimenter could directly control the parameters appearing in the equations. In the present case we assume that an experimenter can relax or modify any equation or set of equations in the system. In this way we have the same general relationship as in the linear case between the problem of defining the causal ordering and the problem of identification.

## 10. CONCLUSION

In this chapter we have defined a concept of causality that corresponds to the intuitive use of that term in scientific discussion. Causality is an asymmetrical relation among certain variables, or subsets of variables, in a self-contained structure. There is no necessary connection between the asymmetry of this relation and asymmetry in time, although an analysis of the causal structure of dynamical systems in econometrics and physics will show that lagged relations can generally be interpreted as causal relations.

In models specifying which variables are excluded from which equations, the concept of causality has been shown to be intimately connected with the concept of identifiability, although the conditions under which a self-contained structure possesses a nontrivial causal structure are somewhat weaker than the conditions under which it is completely identifiable.

A study of the operational meaning of the causal ordering (or of the concept of 'structural' equations) appears to require a metalanguage that permits discussion of the relation between the structure and an experimenter who has direct control over some of the parameters of the structure. As the brief discussion of the nonlinear case implies, the distinction between parameters and variables can be disregarded if the former are regarded as exogenous variables (determined by a larger system) with respect to the latter. In this case the experimenter must be regarded as being able to relax or alter particular equations in this larger system.

## NOTES

*I am indebted to Tjalling C. Koopmans ror his valuable suggestions and comments on earlier drafts of this chapter, particularly with regard to the discussion of the relation between causal ordering and identifiability. A distinction between endogenous and exogenous variables similar to the concept of causal ordering here developed was made by Orcutt (1952). For a discussion of the incorporation of the notion of causality in a system of formal logic, see Simon (1952).

[1] It should be noted that Conditions (a) and (b), incorporated in Definition 2.1, are absent from the definitions of linear structure employed in other chapters of Hood and Koopmans (1953). This slight difference in definition simplifies the exposition and should cause the reader little difficulty. The relevant theorems on independence and consistency will be found in Bôcher (1907, pp. 43—49). Condition (a) can be omitted if we exclude from consideration certain exceptional sets of values of the coefficients of the equation system; in this case we can develop properties of the system, parallel to those described in the present chapter, which hold 'almost everywhere' (see Koopmans, Rubin, and Leipnik, (1950, p. 82) in the space of these coefficients.

[2] Again this definition, for purposes of simplification, is somewhat narrower than in other chapters of Hood and Koopmans (1953).

[3] This usage of 'complete,' 'exogenous,' and 'endogenous' is consistent with Marschak's definition of those terms (Marschak, 1950, pp. 7—8).

[4] As a matter of fact, the writer originally approached his problem from the standpoint of unilateral coupling (cf. Goodwin, 1947, pp. 183—184).

[5] In addition to the logical connection, to be discussed in the text, between causal ordering and identifiability, it may be of interest to point to a number of historical connections. Pioneering work on identifiability was done by Ragnar Frisch (1934), who explored the problem discussed in Section 8.1 below. Other authors in econometrics began to use the concept of causality in their writings without explicit definition; for example, Haavelmo (1944, especially p. 22) and Wold (1949). An explicit causal ordering for a special class of cases was introduced by Tinbergen (1940).

[6] See Marschak (1950, pp. 8—18), Hurwicz (1950b, pp. 266—273), Chapter I of Hood and Koopmans (1953) and Section 8 of Chapter II.

[7] The definition of identifiability from which this statement is derived (see Chapter II, Section 3, and Koopmans, Rubin, and Leipnik (1950, Definition 2.1.5.3)) refers to stochastic models. We shall see in Section 8 that the statement remains valid for an equivalent identifiability concept formulated for nonstochastic models (Marschak, 1950, Section 1.3). In either case, the concept of identifiability always refers to a complete structure, whose equations may be a complete subset (Definition 3.5) of a (stated or

unstated) structure consisting of a larger number of equations. The implications of this fact have not received sufficient emphasis in the literature on identifiability, and will be elaborated in Section 8.

[8] This is the classical problem of 'absolute' versus 'relative' motion. The notion of invariance under transformation as a necessary condition for a 'real' property of a physical system has provided a leading motivation for the development of relativistic mechanics and other branches of modern physics. For the identification problems that arise in classical mechanics, see Simon (1947).

[9] Albert (1941, pp. 24, 43).

[10] On the other hand, the causal ordering may be defined even if the structure is not completely identifiable. Since the causal ordering depends only on which subsets of variables appear in which complete subsets of equations, it will also be invariant over the group of $R$-transformations upon the equations of any complete subset.

[11] Chapter II, Section 4; Chapter VI, Section 4.4 and Appendix A of Hood and Koopmans (1953).

[12] This requirement is a sufficient, but not a necessary, condition for determinacy. If the a priori restrictions are more than the minimum required for identifiability, determinacy may be present even if the variables are subject to additional, unknown restrictions. The problem under discussion here is the question of 'confluence,' first studied intensively by Frisch (1934).

[13] In the stochastic case discussed in Hood and Koopmans (1953), Chapter II, Section 3, and in Koopmans, Rubin, and Leipnik (1950, Definition 2.1.3.2) this is reflected in the stipulation that structures are regarded as equivalent only if they give rise to identical distributions of the observations for all values of the 'exogenous' variables, i.e., exogenous with reference to the subset considered (Definition 3.6 above).

[14] See note 12 above and also Hood and Koopmans (1953), Chapter II, Footnotes 7 and 13. from which it will be clear that 'exogenous' as used in the sentence to which this note is appended corresponds to 'predetermined' in the context of Chapters II and VI.

## REFERENCES

Albert, A. A., *Introduction to Algebraic Theories* (Chicago: University of Chicago Press, 1941) 137 pp.

Bôcher, Maxime, *Introduction to Higher Algebra* (New York: The Macmillan Co., 1907).

Cannon, Walter B., *The Wisdom of the Body* (New York: W. W. Norton & Co., 1939, revised ed.) 333 pp.

Frisch, Ragnar, *Statistical Confluence Analysis by Means of Complete Regression Systems* (Oslo: Universitetets Økonomiske Institutt, 1934) 192 pp.

Girshick, M. A. and Trygve Haavelmo, 'Statistical Analysis of the Demand for Food: Examples of Simultaneous Estimation of Structural Equations', Chapter V in *Studies in Econometric Method*, Cowles Commission Monograph 14, Wm. C. Hood and T. C. Koopmans (eds.) (New York: John Wiley & Sons, Inc., 1953) pp. 92–111.

Goodwin, Richard M., 'Dynamical Coupling with Especial Reference to Markets Having Production Lags', *Econometrica* 15, 181–204 (July, 1974).

Haavelmo, Trygve, 'The Probability Approach in Econometrics', *Econometrica* 12, Supplement (July, 1944) 118 pp. (reprinted as Cowles Commission Paper, New Series, No. 4).

Hood, Wm. C. and T. C. Koopmans (eds.), *Studies in Econometric Method*, Cowles Commission Monograph 14 (New York: John Wiley & Sons, Inc., 1953).

Hurwicz, Leonid, 'Prediction and Least Squares,' Chapter VI in *Statistical Inference in*

*Dynamic Economic Models*, Cowles Commission Monograph 10, T. C. Koopmans (ed.), (New York: John Wiley & Sons, Inc., 1950) pp. 266–300.

Koopmans, T. C., H. Rubin, and R. B. Leipnik, 'Measuring the Equation Systems of Dynamic Economics', Chapter II in *Statistical Inference in Dynamic Economic Models*, Cowles Commission Monograph 10, T. C. Koopmans (ed.), (New York: John Wiley & Sons, Inc., 1950) pp. 53–237.

Marschak, J., 'Statistical Inference in Economics: An Introduction', Chapter I in *Statistical Inference in Dynamic Economic Models*, Cowles Commission Monograph 10, T. C. Koopmans (ed.), (New York: John Wiley & Sons, Inc., 1950) pp. 1–50.

Orcutt, Guy H., 'Toward Partial Redirection of Econometrics', *Review of Economics and Statistics* 34, (August, 1952).

Simon, Herbert A. 'The Axioms of Newtonian Mechanics', *Philosophical Magazine* 37, 888–905 (December, 1947) (reprinted as Chapter 6.1 of this volume.)

——, 'On the Definition of the Causal Relation', *Journal of Philosophy* 49, (July 31, 1952) (reprinted as Chapter 2.1 of this volume.)

Tinbergen, Jan, 'Econometric Business Cycle Research', *Review of Economic Studies* 7, 73–90 (1939–40).

Wold, Herman O. A., 'Statistical Estimation of Economic Relationships', *Econometrica* 17, 1–22 (1949).

# ON THE DEFINITION OF THE CAUSAL RELATION†*

In a recent paper in *Mind*[1] Prof. Arthur W. Burks has made an interesting proposal for the construction of a logic of causal propositions. Such a logic is greatly needed, for however completely the word 'cause' has been eliminated from epistemology, it is still very much a part of the working vocabulary of most empirical scientists. Prof. Burks begins, wisely, by avoiding the Humean controversy, and asks instead whether it is possible to give a clear and consistent explication within a system of logic of the term 'cause' as it is used in common speech. While I am wholly in accord with Prof. Burks' suggestion that such an explication is possible and useful, my own investigations into the question have led me to a definitional proposal that is somewhat different from his.

## 1. INTRODUCTION

We shall take as our problem, then, the introduction into a system of logic of a relation between sentences that is equivalent, or as nearly equivalent as is feasible, to the relation of 'causation' as that relation is used in scientific writing. A number of points regarding the undertaking should be made clear at the outset:

(a) Our undertaking is logical rather than ontological. That is, we wish to be able to assert: 'The sentence $A$ stands in a causal relation to the sentence $B$ (in a specified system of sentences)'; and not: 'That which is denoted by sentence $A$ causes that which is denoted by sentence $B$.' Hence, the causal relation that we shall introduce is in the metalanguage and not in the object language.

(b) We shall require that the causal relation be an asymmetrical one – that '$A$ causes $B$' be incompatible with '$B$ causes $A$'. Our requirement will be even somewhat stronger. We shall so define the relation that '$A$ causes $B$' is incompatible with 'not-$B$ causes not-$A$.'[2] The reason for the requirement is, again, that we wish to keep as close as possible to ordinary usage. Ordinary usage does not sanction: 'If the rain causes Jones to wear his raincoat, then Jones' not wearing his raincoat causes it not to rain.'[3]

† [*The Journal of Philosophy* 49, 517–528 (1952)].

(c) We shall avoid the usual assumption that the asymmetry of cause and effect has something to do with sequence in time. From the proposition that 'A causes B' it will not be possible to draw any inference as to the time sequence of the events denoted by A and B, respectively. The reason is that in many instances where the scientist speaks of cause (e.g., 'force causes acceleration') no time sequence is involved.[4]

(d) Initially, we shall restrict our definition to models of experimental systems — that is, systems in which an experimenter can alter the values of certain variables, or the truth-values of certain propositions. I think it can be verified that in scientific literature the word 'cause' most often occurs in connection with some explicit or implicit notion of an experimenter's intervention in a system. The word is used frequently in experimental physiology, seldom in astronomy. After the definition has been developed fully, this point will be discussed further.

## 2. CONSTRUCTION OF THE DEFINITION

Our construction of a logic of causality will be limited initially to the calculus of propositions, and, indeed, to systems involving a finite number of atomic sentences. This restriction will permit us to deal with the problem in its barest essentials, and even so we shall not find it lacking in complications.[5] We begin with a set of $n$ atomic sentences, $a_1, \ldots, a_n$, which are assumed to be empirical and logically independent. We define as a *state-description* a molecular sentence (a) that is the conjunction of atomic sentences and their negations, and (b) in which each atomic sentence or its negation (but not both) appears once (e.g., $a_1.-a_2; \ldots a_{n-1}.-a_n.$).[6] A state-description designates a *state*. In saying that the sentences are empirically testable we mean that we can determine empirically which state-description is true; and in saying they are logically independent we mean that no state-description is self-contradictory.

We define as an *empirical law* a molecular sentence formed from one or more of the $n$ atomic sentences. We describe a state-description, $S_i$, as *realizable* (i.e., the corresponding state is empirically possible) relative to a set of laws, $P_1, \ldots, P_k$, if $P_1.P_2 \ldots P_k.S_i$ is not self-contradictory.[7]

A set of empirical laws is *complete* for a set of atomic sentences if only a single unique state-description is realizable relative to this set of laws — i.e., if $P_1 \ldots P_k.S_i$ is self-contradictory except for a single state-description $S_j$. The empirical laws form a *minimal complete set* for the atomic sentences if no proper subset of the laws is complete for that set of sentences.

Example: Let $a$ be the atomic sentence stating that a lighted match is observed in a room at time $t$; $b$ the atomic sentence stating that an explosion is observed to occur in the room at time $t$. Then the state-descriptions are: $a.b, -a.b, a.-b$, and $-a.-b$. Let $A$ be the empirical law defined by: $A \equiv a$; let $B$ be the empirical law defined by: $B \equiv .-avb$. Then $a.b$ and $a.-b$ are realizable relative to $A$; $a.b, -a.b$, and $-a.-b$ are realizable relative to $B$; while only $a.b$ is realizable relative to the set comprised of $A$ and $B$. Hence, this latter set is a complete set, and indeed a minimal complete set, for the atomic sentences $a$ and $b$.

The state-descriptions that are realizable relative to a set of laws characterize the set extensionally. Hence, if we substitute for a set of laws another set that is extensionally equivalent, the set of state-descriptions that is realizable will remain invariant. For example, define: $A' \equiv b$ and $B' \equiv .a \equiv b$. Then only $a.b$ is realizable relative to the set comprised of $A'$ and $B'$, and $A'.B'$ is equivalent to $A.B$.

However, it does not follow that, if we have two sets of laws that are extensionally equivalent, we can set up a one-one correspondence between the *individual* laws comprising the two sets, such that the members of each pair are extensionally equivalent. In the previous example, $A'$ is equivalent to neither $A$ nor $B$; nor is $B'$ equivalent to $A$ or $B$. We may express this by saying that if two sets of laws are extensionally equivalent, yet the sets need not be isomorphic.

Now we propose to define causality in terms of this notion of isomorphism. Given a set of atomic sentences, and a minimal complete set of laws for them, we wish to specify what causal relations among the sentences are implied by these laws. To accomplish this we will need one more definition.

We will say that a set of empirical laws *determines* an atomic sentence, $a_k$, if only state-descriptions in which $a_k$ appears or only state-descriptions in which $-a_k$ appears are realizable relative to this set of laws. Then a complete set of laws for a set of $n$ sentences determines, simultaneously, all $n$ sentences.

For a complete set of laws, $P_1, \ldots, P_k$, form the smallest subset, $R_1$, that determines $a_1$, the smallest subset, $R_2$, that determines $a_2$, and so on. Then we will say that $a_j$ has causal precedence over $a_i$ if the set $R_j$ is properly included in the set $R_i$. We will say that $a_j$ and $a_i$ are mutually dependent if $R_j$ and $R_i$ are identical; we will say that $a_j$ and $a_i$ are independent if $R_j$ and $R_i$ are disjunct.

Taking again the propositions $a$ and $b$, and the laws $A$ and $B$ as example, we find that $(A)$ is the smallest set that determines $a$ and $(A, B)$ is the smallest set that determines $b$. Since $(A)$ is included in $(A, B)$ it follows that $a$ has causal precedence over $b$ — we can say (elliptically) that 'the lighted match causes the explosion.' On the other hand, taking the extensionally equivalent laws $A'$ and $B'$, we find that, relative to these, $b$ is determined by $(A')$ and $a$ by $(A', B')$. Hence, $b$ has causal precedence over $a$ relative to the set of laws $(A', B')$.

This completes the first formal definition of the causal relation. We see that it is a relation in the metalanguage that induces a partial ordering among the members of a set of atomic sentences. Moreover, this ordering is defined relatively to a minimal complete set of molecular sentences (laws) that determines a single state-description of the atomic sentences as realizable. Finally, the ordering may be altered if for the original set of laws we substitute a different, but extensionally equivalent set.

### 3. SOME EXAMPLES OF CAUSAL RELATIONS

The meaning of the proposed definition may be clearer if illustrated by two more examples:

(I) Let $a$ be: 'It is raining.' Let $b$ be: 'John is wearing his raincoat.' Let $A \equiv a$, and $B \equiv . a \equiv b$. Then $(A, B)$ is a minimal complete set of laws for $(a, b)$. Again $a$ is determined by $(A)$, and $b$ by $(A, B)$; hence, by definition, $a$ causes $b$ — 'Rain cause John to wear his raincoat.' Suppose now that we have $-A$ instead of $A$. Now $(-A, B)$ is a minimal complete set of laws for $(a, b)$. In this case we can still say that 'rain causes John to wear his raincoat', but we can express the new situation more felicitously by the counterfactual conditional: 'If it had rained, John would have worn his raincoat.'

We see from this example that the causal relation rests, not upon the truth or falsehood of $a$ or $b$, but upon (i) the assumed 'lawful' connection between them expressed by $B$, and (ii) the 'independent' determination of $a$ expressed by $A$ or $-A$.[8] Perhaps the best way of expressing the relation is by saying: "The state of the weather is the cause of John's attire."

(II) Consider next a slightly more complicated example. Let $a$ be: 'There is more than the usual rainfall this year'; $b$: 'The wheat crop is large this year'; $c$: 'The price of wheat is low this year.' Takes as laws: $A \equiv a$; $B \equiv . a \equiv b$; and $C \equiv . b \equiv c$. Then we can say: 'The large rainfall caused a large wheat crop, and this caused the price of wheat to be low.' $A$ may be regarded as extensionally equivalent to the whole concatenation of initial conditions and laws that determines the weather; $B$ to the botanical laws governing the growth of wheat; and $C$ to the demand function determining the price at which a wheat crop can be sold. In this case, again, $A$ can be replaced by $-A$ without disturbing the causal ordering. Likewise, $B$ can be replaced by $-B$ (the causal ordering would be the same with a variety of wheat that was drought-resistant but damaged by excessive moisture); and $C$ can be replaced by $-C$ (the causal ordering would be the same if there were a positive rather than a negative demand relation between quantity and price).

## 4. THE PROBLEM OF INVARIANCE

Before we can regard this explication of the causal relation as satisfactory, several questions must be answered. These concern the notion of 'lawful connection', and the related notion that one or more of our atomic sentences (in our examples, sentence $a$) can be determined 'independently' of the others. We do not propose to deal with the problem of confirmation of laws, but only with problems of their *meaning*.[9]

From the formal standpoint, the questions just raised may be regarded as questions of uniqueness and invariance. There are, in fact, two such questions: (i) whether the smallest subsets determining the atomic sentences are unique; and (ii) whether all extensionally equivalent complete sets of laws yield the same causal ordering of the atomic sentences.[10] We have already obtained a negative answer to the second question, but before pursuing it further we wish to deal briefly with the first.

(a) It is easy to find an example of non-uniqueness of the smallest subset determining an atomic sentence. Consider a system comprised of three atomic sentences, $a$, $b$, and $c$, and two laws, $A \equiv a.b$, and $B \equiv b.c$. The set of laws $(A, B)$ is a minimal complete set for the sentences $(a, b, c)$; but both $(A)$ and $(B)$ are smallest sets determining $b$.

To assure uniqueness of the causal ordering with respect to a set of empirical laws, we must insist that if there are two subsets, $S_i$ and $S_i'$, determining the same atomic sentence, $a_i$, then one of the subsets must be included in the other. A minimal complete set of empirical laws satisfying this requirement for all the atomic sentences will be called *consistent*.

(b) Reverting to the match-explosion example, we have seen that we arrive at 'the lighted match causes the explosion' or 'the explosion causes the lighted match' depending on whether we take $(A, B)$ or $(A', B')$ as the complete set of empirical laws. The first choice corresponds to everyday language, the second certainly does not.

To see what is involved, let us reverse the question. What do we wish to convey when we say: 'The lighted match caused the explosion' in addition to what we wish to convey by: 'A lighted match was observed, and an explosion was observed'? It will be argued here that what we wish to convey by the first is precisely: '$A \cdot B$', while what we wish to convey by the second is '$a \cdot b$'. But since the two statements are extensionally equivalent, what is meant by the distinction?

One possible meaning is that in the first case we wish to indicate the realization of the state $a \cdot b$ is a selection of a particular state out of the whole set of states ($a.b$, $-a.b$, and $-a. \; -b$) that are realizable relative to $B$. In the second case we wish merely to denote realization of the state $a \cdot b$ without reference to a wider set of states. This is perhaps true, but certainly vague. In particular, the notion of the 'selection' of a state from some set of 'realizable' states might be suspected of harboring objectionable metaphysics. In a deterministic world, only one state is realizable — that which is the fact. The natural laws are not relaxed from time to time to permit this act of selection.[11] As Mach says: "The universe is not *twice* given, with an earth at rest and an earth in motion; but only *once*, with its *relative* motions, alone determinate. It is, accordingly, not permitted us to say how things would be if the earth did not rotate."[12]

To deal with this apparent paradox, we shall have to complicate, slightly, the system of definitions outlined in Section 2. This we proceed to do next.

## 5. ELABORATION OF THE DEFINITION

For the present purpose, we require an object language with a finite number of one-place predicates, $a_1(\;), \ldots, a_n(\;)$, in one-one relation with our original set of atomic sentences. We need an individual variable, $t$, which may be interpreted as the *time*, or more generally, the 'location' of events. Then our new atomic sentences (*observation-sentences*) will be of the form: $a_i(t)$ — the sentence $a_i$ of our original language holds at 'time' or 'location' $t$. We now introduce a second set of predicates, $A_1(\;), \ldots A_k(\;)$, also admitting the $t$'s as their arguments, which we will refer to as *condition-sentences* or, more briefly, *conditions*. That is, $A_1(t_1)$ means that the first condition holds at time $t_1$. The $A$'s, like the $a$'s, are assumed to be empirical sentences, and the entire set of $A$'s and $a$'s, taken jointly, to be logically independent. in this language, a state-description for time $t$ is constituted by a conjunction of atomic sentences in which each $A_i(t)$ or its negation (but not both), and each $a_i(t)$ or its negation (but not both) appear. We introduce the additional concept of a *conditional state-description:* a conjunction of atomic sentences in which each $a_i(t)$ or its negation (but not both) appears. The language is supposed to contain also a universal quantifier, so that we can construct sentences of the form: $(t) (\ldots)$.

We now define as an *empirical law* a quantified sentence of the form:

$$(t) \cdot A_i(t) \supset f_i(a_1(t), \ldots, a_n(t)),$$

where $f_i(\ldots)$ is a molecular sentence formed of the $a$'s. We also define a conditional state-description as realizable relative to a set of laws if the conjunction $f_1 \ldots f_k$, of the $f$'s appearing in the set of laws, does not imply the falsity of the conditional state-description. It is important to note that in the present language, a sentence of the form $(t) A_i(t) \supset f_i$ is an empirical sentence, while in the original language, sentences of the form $A \equiv f(a, b)$ were definitional, and hence tautologous.

We will say that a set of conditions (and a corresponding set of laws) *determines* an atomic sentence, $a_j$, if (i) we have an empirical law for each condition in the set, and (ii) in the set of states for which all these conditions are $T$, $a_j$ is either always $T$ or always $F$. We define a complete set of laws as one that determines a unique conditional state-description — i.e., determines all the $a$'s. Given a complete set of laws, we will say that $a_j$ has causal precedence over $a_i$ if the minimal set of laws determining the former is a proper subset of the minimal set of laws determining the latter. (For uniqueness, we must again impose a consistency requirement on the set of laws.)

In our present formulation, there is no difficulty in speaking of the realizability of states. For if the $A$'s are not invariant with respect to time, but if at any given time we have a sufficient number of $A$'s holding to provide a complete system of laws, then at each $t$, a particular conditional state will be $T$, but at different times different conditional states will be $T$. We can guarantee that the proper number of conditions will be $T$ at any time by the following device: corresponding to each condition, $A_k$, we will postulate a whole family of 'related' conditions, $A_k, B_k, C_k, \ldots$ such that one and only one is $T$ at any given $t$.[13] Now we construct a set of laws by selecting a law corresponding to one (and only one) condition in *each* such family. We require that every such set be consistent and complete.

Our system may seem rather special in that it does not admit any laws that relate atomic sentences for two different points in time. This is easily remedied. It is not necessary that a sentence of the form $a(t)$ denote an event *occurring* at time $t$, but only that it denote an event *referred* to time $t$. Thus, the sentence $a(t)$ might mean that a particular body had a particular position two seconds before $t$. In this way all the laws of dynamics that are invariant with respect to translations of the origin of time can be accommodated.

### 6. THE PROBLEM OF INVARIANCE RE-EXAMINED

In our first language we were confronted with the problem that the causal ordering was, in general, non-unique because we could always find a number of minimal complete sets of laws extensionally equivalent to any given minimal complete set but inducing different causal orderings among the atomic sentences. But in our second language, two minimal complete sets of laws determining the same *conditional* state will not, in general, be extensionally equivalent.

To illustrate this, let us elaborate the match-explosion example. As $A_1(t)$ we take the sentence: 'A match is struck at time $t$, it is dry, there is oxygen present, etc. As $A_2(t)$, we take: 'A space is filled at time $t$ with an explosive mixture of gases.' Here 'explosive' must be supposed to be defined by the chemical composition of the gases. As $a_1(t)$ we take: 'A lighted match is in the space an instant after $t$'; and as $a_2(t)$: 'An explosion occurs in the space an instant after $t$.' We postulate empirical laws corresponding to the two conditions:

$$A_1(t) \supset a_1(t); A_2(t) \supset a_1(t) \equiv a_2(t).$$

The two conditions, together with the two observation-sentences, define $2^4 = 16$ logically possible states. Only the nine states listed in the truth-table. (Table I) are realizable relative to the laws. (If both conditions are $T$, then

TABLE I

| $A_1(t)$ | $A_2(t)$ | $a_1(t)$ | $a_2(t)$ |
|----------|----------|----------|----------|
| $T$ | $T$ | $T$ | $T$ |
| $T$ | $F$ | $T$ | $T$ |
| $T$ | $F$ | $T$ | $F$ |
| $F$ | $T$ | $T$ | $T$ |
| $F$ | $T$ | $F$ | $F$ |
| $F$ | $F$ | $T$ | $T$ |
| $F$ | $F$ | $T$ | $F$ |
| $F$ | $F$ | $F$ | $T$ |
| $F$ | $F$ | $F$ | $F$ |

TABLE II

| $A_1(t)$ | $A_2(t)$ | $a_1(t)$ | $a_2(t)$ |
|---|---|---|---|
| T | T | T  T | T |
| T | F | T  T | T |
| T | F | F  F | F |
| F | T | T  T | T |
| F | T | F  T | T |
| F | F | T  T | T |
| F | F | T  F | F |
| F | F | F | T |
| F | F | F | F |

only the conditional state $a_1 . a_2$ is realizable; if the first condition is $T$, the second $F$, two states are realizable; if the first condition is $F$, the second $T$, two states are realizable; and if both conditions are $F$, four states are realizable.)

Now consider an alternative set of laws:

$$A_1(t) \supset . a_1(t) \equiv a_2(t); A_2(t) \supset a_2(t).$$

Can we distinguish empirically between the new set of laws and the original set? Again, if both conditions are $T$, then only the conditional state $a_1. a_2$ is realizable. But if one or both of the conditions is $F$, the states that are realizable are not the same as before. This is exhibited by a truth-table (Table II) that shows which states are realizable if the new laws are empirically valid.

If, for example, we can find a $t$ such that $A_1. -A_2. a_1. -a_2$, then we know that the second set of laws is not valid. It is possible, of course, that the first set of laws is not valid either, but the point remains that the two sets of laws are not extensionally equivalent.

We see that the empirical testability of laws (and the empirical significance of causal ordering) is intimately connected with the contingent character of laws, and with the fact that the conditions that constitute antecedents of laws are not $T$ at all times.[14] Herein lies the rationale of experimentation — it is a procedure for systematically varying the conditions that hold, and hence for producing observations of situations in which not all the conditions in a complete set of laws hold simultaneously. The observations permit an empirical choice to be made between two complete sets of laws that determine the same state.

The experiments may, of course, be performed by nature. Reverting to the match-explosion example, nature may provide at various time and places examples of all the nine conditional states that are empirically realizable relative to the original laws, and no others. While this does not prove the validity of these laws, it serves to rule out many alternative explanations for the observation that at some $t$ we have $A_1.A_2.a_1.a_2$.

## 7. OPERATIONAL SIGNIFICANCE OF THE DEFINITION

Have we succeeded in providing a satisfactory explication of the causal relation? The question is not one that can be answered definitively. The test is whether a relation of the kind we have defined holds in those cases where scientists speak of one observable as 'causing' another. In the examples that have been given in this paper, the explication appears to be consistent with ordinary usage. Moreover, it appears to avoid at least one of the fundamental objections (the reversal of the ordering through negation) that can be raised against earlier definitions. The reader will presumably wish to test the definition further with examples of his own.

One point deserves further examination. The determination of the causal ordering depends in a fundamental way upon the distinction made in the previous section between conditions and observation-sentences. From an empirical standpoint, both observation-sentences and conditions are atomic sentences whose truth or falsehood depends on empirical evidence. We have not given any basis for classifying a particular atomic sentence as one or the other. If the classification is purely conventional, then the causal ordering is equally conventional. I have not arrived at an entirely satisfactory answer to this question of classification, but can make two suggestions that may provide a basis for further exploration.

(a) In experimental situations, certain atomic sentences may denote behaviors of the experimenter. If we call these sentences 'conditions', then the remaining sentences may be regarded as 'observation-sentences' that are indirectly, but not directly, determined by the behavior of the experimenter. While this procedure appears to agree very well with the use of 'cause' in experimental situations, it rules out statements like 'rain causes trees to grow in the Amazon basin'. If we accept this limitation, then we admit that any extension of causal language to non-experimental situations is metaphor and anthropomorphism.

(b) In non-experimental situations, all we are given at the outset is the fact that of all the logically possible states, only some subset has been empirically realized. Let us make the further assumption that we are justified in regarding the realized states as the only ones that are realizable. (More precisely: let us formulate laws with respect to which only those states that have been realized are realizable.)

In order to distinguish between conditions and observation-sentences, we must find some asymmetry among the different columns of the truth-table describing the realizable states. That is, columns belonging to atomic sentences that we wish to classify as conditions must be distinguishable, on the basis of intrinsic criteria, from columns belonging to observation-sentences.

I propose the following criterion:

Given $n$ atomic sentences, and given a truth-table displaying the states that are realizable, select any subset of $k$ atomic sentences, designating the members of this subset by $A_1, \ldots, A_k$, and the remaining atomic sentences by $a_1, \ldots, a_m (m = n - k)$. Define a conditional state of the $a$'s as before. Consider the subset $S(B)$, of conditional states that are realizable when a particular subset, $B$, of the $A$'s are $T$ (and the remainder $F$). The set of $A$'s will be called an admissible set of conditions if the sets $S(B)$ satisfy the following requirements: (1) $S(O)$ has $2^{n-k}$ members (i.e., all conditional states are realizable when all the conditions are F); (2) $S(B)$ has $2^{n-k-g}$ members when $B$ has $g$ members; (3) $S(B_1 \vee B_2) = S(B_2) \cdot S(B_1)$, where $B_1$ and $B_2$ are any two subsets of conditions. The last two requirements mean that the conditional states that are realizable when both a set of conditions. $B_1$, holds and a second set of conditions, $B_2$, holds, are those which are realizable both when $B_1$ alone holds and when $B_2$ alone holds — the laws are in this sense 'additive'

Now an examination of the first truth-table for the match-explosion example shows that the sentences $A_1$ and $A_2$ constitute a set of admissible conditions, and, indeed, the *unique* set. It is not, unfortunately, the case that every such truth-table will possess a set of admissible conditions, or if such a set exists, that it will be unique. Perhaps some modification of the requirements would remedy these defects, or perhaps the causal ordering should be regarded as defined only in those instances where these rather restrictive requirements are satisfied.

## NOTES

*Profs. Arthur Burks, Herbert Feigl, Emile Grunberg, Tjalling Koopmans, and Manley Thompson have been most helpful in commenting on earlier drafts of this paper.

[1] Arthur W. Burks, The Logic of Causal Propositions,' *Mind* **60**, 363–382 (1951).

[2] This is one fundamental departure of the present proposal from that of Professor Burks, whose causal relation is asymmetrical, but only in the sense that the implication relation is asymmetrical. Thus, in his system, from '*A* cause *B*' it follows that 'not-*B* causes not-*A*. (*Op. cit.*, p. 369.)

[3] Insofar as it is possible, I shall employ Professor Burks' examples to permit easy comparison between his definition and mine.

[4] Time sequence is integrally involved in Mill's theory of causation. His canons of induction only permit the inference of invariant relation, and to this must be added a time sequence in order to distinguish between cause and effect. It may well be empirically true that, in most or all cases where '*A* causes *B*' is true, *A* precedes *B* in time; but we do not wish to incorporate this requirement in our definition.

[5] In another paper, the author has shown how the same kind of causal relation can be introduced in ordinary algebraic systems of simultaneous equations. See 'Causal Ordering and Identifiability', Chapter 3 in T. Koopmans (ed.), *Econometric Methods* (Cowles Commission Monograph 14), (reprinted as Chapter 2.1 in this volume). A similar definition has been arrived at independently by Prof. Guy Orcutt of Harvard University. See his abstract, 'The Influence of Causation,' *Econometrica* **19**, 60 (January, 1951). A definition along the same lines, but developed less formally, was proposed by Lewis A. Dexter, 'Causal Imputation and Purposes of Investigation,' *Philosophy of Science,* **6**, 404–410 (1939).

[6] Cf. Rudolf Carnap, *Introduction to Semantics* (Cambridge: Harvard University Press, 1942), p. 105.

[7] Cf. Carnap, *op. cit.*, pp. 95–97.

[8] This explains why, in distinction to other explications of the causal realtion (e.g., that of Burks, *op. cit.* p. 369), ours does not permit the inference of '–*b* causes –*a*' from '*a* causes *b*'. Definitions of cause that interpret that relation as somehow analogous to the relation of implication can hardly be expected to avoid this difficulty.

[9] The importance of settling the question of meaning prior to the question of confirmation has been pointed out by Elizabeth Lane Beardsley, ' "Non-Accidental" and Counterfactual Sentences', *Journal of Philosophy* **46**, 573–591 (September 1, 1949).

[10] The second question, *re* properties invariant over the group of extensionally equivalent laws, is discussed by Carnap, *Logical Foundations of Probability* (Chicago: University of Chicago Press, 1950), pp. 146–147.

[11] Hence, it is not a satisfactory answer to limit causal notions to experimental situations, since the behavior of the experimenter is presumably also governed by law.

[12] Ernst Mach, *The Science of Mechanics* (La Salle, Ill.: Open Court, 1941), p. 284.

[13] This notion is analogous to Carnap's 'family of related properties' (*Logical Foundations of Probability*, pp. 76–77).

[14] From this it may be seen that if our explication of the causal relation is acceptable, it provides a basis for a treatment of the counterfactual conditional. Cf. Nelson Goodman, 'The Problem of Counterfactual Conditionals', *Journal of Philosophy*, **44**, 113–128 (1947).

# SPURIOUS CORRELATION: A CAUSAL INTERPRETATION† *

Even in the first course in statistics, the slogan "Correlation is no proof of causation!" is imprinted firmly in the mind of the aspiring statistician or social scientist. It is possible that he leaves the course (and many subsequent courses) with no very clear ideas as to what *is* proved by correlation, but he never ceases to be on guard against 'spurious' correlation, that master of imposture who is always representing himself as 'true' correlation.

The very distinction between 'true' and 'spurious' correlation appears to imply that while correlation in general may be no proof of causation, 'true' correlation does constitute such proof. If this is what is intended by the adjective 'true', are there any operational means for distinguishing between true correlations, which do imply causation, and spurious correlations, which do not?

A generation or more ago, the concept of spurious correlation was examined by a number of statisticians, and in particular by G.U. Yule [8]. More recently important contributions to our understanding of the phenomenon have been made by Hans Zeisel [9] and by Patricia L. Kendall and Paul F. Lazarsfeld [1]. Essentially, all these treatments deal with the three variable case – the clarification of the relation between two variables by the introduction of a third. Generalizations to *n* variables are indicated but not examined in detail.

Meanwhile, the main stream of statistical research has been diverted into somewhat different (but closely related) directions by Frisch's work on confluence analysis and the subsequent exploration of the 'identification problem' and of 'structural relations' at the hands of Haavelmo, Hurwicz, Koopmans, Marschak, and many others.[1] This work has been carried on at a level of great generality. It has now reached a point where it can be used to illuminate the concept of spurious correlation in the three-variable case. The bridge from the identification problem to the problem of spurious correlation is built by constructing a precise and operationally meaningful definition of

† [*Journal of the American Statistical Association* 49, 467–479 (1954)].

causality – or, more specifically, of causal ordering among variables in a model.[2]

## 1. STATEMENT OF THE PROBLEM

How do we ordinarily make causal inferences from data on correlations? We begin with a set of observations of a pair of variables, $x$ and $y$. We compute the coefficient of correlation, $r_{xy}$, between the variables and whenever this coefficient is significantly different from zero we wish to know what we can conclude as to the causal relation between the two variables. If we are suspicious that the observed correlation may derive from 'spurious' causes, we introduce a third variable, $z$, that, we conjecture, may account for this observed correlation. We next compute the partial correlation, $r_{xy.z}$, between $x$ and $y$ with $z$ 'held constant,' and compare this with the zero order correlation, $r_{xy}$. If $r_{xy.z}$ is close to zero, while $r_{xy}$ is not, we conclude that either: (a) $z$ is an intervening variable – the causal effect of $x$ on $y$ (or vice versa) operates through $z$; or (b) the correlation between $x$ and $y$ results from the joint causal effect of $z$ on both those variables, and hence this correlation is spurious. It will be noted that in case (a) we do not know whether the causal arrow should run from $x$ to $y$ or from $y$ to $x$ (via $z$ in both cases); and in any event, the correlations do not tell us whether we have case (a) or case (b).

The problem may be clarified by a pair of specific examples adapted from Zeisel.[3]

I. The data consist of measurements of three variables in a number of groups of people: $x$ is the percentage of members of the group that is married, $y$ is the average number of pounds of candy consumed per month per member, $z$ is the average age of members of the group. A high (negative) correlation, $r_{xy}$, was observed between marital status and amount of candy consumed. But there was also a high (negative) correlation, $r_{yz}$, between candy consumption and age; and a high (positive) correlation, $r_{xz}$, between marital status and age. However, when age was held constant, the correlation $r_{xy.z}$, between marital status and candy consumption was nearly zero. By our previous analysis, either age is an intervening variable between marital status and candy consumption; or the correlation between marital status and candy consumption is spurious, being a joint effect caused by the variation in age. 'Common sense' – the nature of which we will want to examine below in detail – tells us that the latter explanation is the correct one.

II. The data consist again of measurements of three variables in a number of groups of people: $x$ is the percentage of female employees who are married, $y$ is the average number of absences per week per employee, $z$ is the average number of hours of housework performed per week per employee.[4] A high (positive) correlation, $r_{xy}$, was observed between marriage and absenteeism. However, when the amount of housework, $z$ was held constant, the correlation $r_{xv.z}$ was virtually zero. In this case, by applying again some common sense notions about the direction of causation, we reach the conclusion that $z$ is an intervening variable between $x$ and $y$: that is, that marriage results in a higher average amount of housework performed, and this, in turn, in more absenteeism.

Now what is bothersome about these two examples is that the same statistical evidence, so far as the coefficients of correlation are concerned, has been used to reach entirely different conclusions in the two cases. In the first case we concluded that the correlation between $x$ and $y$ was spurious; in the second case that there was a true causal relationship, mediated by the intervening variable $z$. Clearly, it was not the statistical evidence, but the 'common sense' assumptions added afterwards, that permitted us to draw these distinct conclusions.

## 2. CAUSAL RELATIONS

In investigating spurious correlation we are interested in learning whether the relation between two variables persists or disappears when we introduce a third variable. Throughout this paper (as in all ordinary correlation analyses) we will assume that the relations in question are linear, and without loss of generality, that the variables are measured from their respective means.

Now suppose we have a system of three variables whose behavior is determined by some set of linear mechanisms. In general we will need three mechanisms, each represented by an equation — three equations to determine the three variables. One such set of mechanisms would be that in which each of the variables *directly influenced* the other two. That is, in one equation $x$ would appear as the dependent variable, $y$ and $z$ as independent variables; in the second equation $y$ would appear as the dependent variable, $x$ and $z$ as the independent variables; in the third equation, $z$ as dependent variable, $x$ and $y$ as independent variables.[5]

The equations would look like this:

$$(2.1) \qquad x + a_{12}y + a_{13}z = u_1,$$

$$(I)\,(2.2) \qquad a_{21}x + \quad y + a_{23}z = u_2,$$

$$(2.3) \qquad a_{31}x + a_{32}y + \quad z = u_3,$$

where the $u$'s are 'error' terms that measure the net effects of all other variables (those not introduced explicitly) upon the system. We refer to $A = \|a_{ij}\|$ as the *coefficient matrix* of the system.

Next, let us suppose that not all the variables directly influence all the others — that some independent variables are absent from some of the equations. This is equivalent to saying that some of the elements of the coefficient matrix are zero. By way of specific example, let us assume that $a_{31} = a_{32} = a_{21} = 0$. Then the equation system (I) reduces to:

$$(2.4) \qquad x + a_{12}y + a_{13}z = u_1,$$

$$(II) \ (2.5) \qquad\qquad y + a_{23}z = u_2,$$

$$(2.6) \qquad\qquad\qquad z = u_3.$$

By examining the equations (II), we see that a change in $u_3$ will change the value of $z$ directly, and the values of $x$ and $y$ indirectly; a change in $u_2$ will change $y$ directly and $x$ indirectly, but will leave $z$ unchanged; a change in $u_1$ will change only $x$. Then we may say that $y$ *is causally dependent on $z$* in (II), and that $x$ is causally dependent on $y$ and $z$.

If $x$ and $y$ were correlated, we would say that the correlation was genuine in the case of the system (II), for $a_{12} \neq 0$. Suppose, instead, that the system were (III):

$$(2.7) \qquad x + a_{13}z = u_1,$$

$$(III) \ (2.8) \qquad y + a_{23}z = u_2,$$

$$(2.9) \qquad\qquad z = u_3.$$

In this case we would regard the correlation between $x$ and $y$ as spurious, because it is due solely to the influence of $z$ on the variables $x$ and $y$. Systems (II) and (III) are, of course, not the only possible cases, and we shall need to consider others later.

## 3. THE *A PRIORI* ASSUMPTIONS

We shall show that the decision that a partial correlation is or is not spurious (does not or does indicate a causal ordering) can in general only be reached if *a priori* assumptions are made that certain *other* causal relations do *not* hold among the variables. This is the meaning of the 'common sense' assumptions mentioned earlier. Let us make this more precise.

Apart from any statistical evidence, we are prepared to assert in the first example of Section 1 that the age of a person does *not* depend upon either his candy consumption or his marital status. Hence $z$ cannot be causally dependent upon either $x$ or $y$. This is a genuine empirical assumption, since the variable 'chronological age' really stands, in these equations, as a surrogate for physiological and sociological age. Nevertheless, it is an assumption that we are quite prepared to make on evidence apart from the statistics presented. Similarly, in the second example of Section 1, we are prepared to assert (on grounds of other empirical knowledge) that marital status is not causally dependent upon either amount of housework or absenteeism.[6]

The need for such *a priori* assumption follows from considerations of elementary algebra. We have seen that whether a correlation is genuine or spurious depends on which of the coefficients, $a_{ij}$, of $A$ are zero, and which are non-zero. But these coefficients are not observable nor are the 'error' terms, $u_1$, $u_2$ and $u_3$. What we observe is a sample of values of $x$, $y$, and $z$.

Hence, from the standpoint of the problem of statistical estimation, we must regard the $3n$ sample values of $x$, $y$, and $z$ as numbers given by observation, and the $3n$ error terms, $u_i$, together with the six coefficients, $a_{ij}$, as variables to be estimated. But then we have $(3n + 6)$ variables ($3n$ $u$'s and six $a$'s) and only $3n$ equations (three for each sample point). Speaking roughly in 'equation-counting' terms, we need six more equations, and we depend on the *a priori* assumptions to provide these additional relations.

The *a priori* assumptions we commonly employ are of two kinds:

(1) *A priori* assumptions that certain variables are not directly dependent on certain others. Sometimes such assumptions come from knowledge of the time sequence of events. That is, we make the general assumption about the world that if $y$ precedes $x$ in time, then $a_{21} = 0 - x$ does not directly influence $y$.

(2) *A priori* assumptions that the errors are uncorrelated — i.e., that 'all other' variables influencing $x$ are uncorrelated with 'all other' variables influencing $y$, and so on. Writing $E\,(u_i u_j)$ for the expected value of $u_i u_j$, this give us the three additional equations:

$$E(u_1 u_2) = 0; \qquad E(u_1 u_3) = 0; \qquad E(u_2 u_3) = 0.$$

Again it must be emphasized that these assumptions are 'a priori' only in the sense that they are not derived from the statistical data from which the correlations among $x$, $y$, and $z$ are computed. The assumptions are clearly empirical.

As a matter of fact, it is precisely because we are unwilling to make the analogous empirical assumptions in the two-variable case (the correlation between $x$ and $y$ alone) that the problem of spurious correlation arises at all. For consider the two-variable system:

(IV) $\quad$ (3.1) $\qquad x + b_{12}y = v_1$

$\qquad$ (3.2) $\qquad\qquad\quad y = v_2$

We suppose that $y$ precedes $x$ in time, so that we are willing to set $b_{21} = 0$ by an assumption of type (1). Then, if we make the type (2) assumption that $E(v_1 v_2) = 0$, we can immediately obtain a unique estimate of $b_{12}$. For multiplying the two equations, and taking expected values, we get:

(3.3) $\qquad E(xy) + b_{12}E(y^2) = E(v_1 v_2) = 0.$

Whence

(3.4) $\qquad b_{12} = -\dfrac{E(xy)}{E(y^2)} = -\dfrac{\sigma_y}{\sigma_x} r_{xy}.$

It follows immediately that (sampling questions aside) $b_{12}$ will be zero or non-zero as $r_{12}$ is zero or non-zero. *Hence correlation is proof of causation in the two-variable case if we are willing to make the assumptions of time precedence and non-correlation of the error terms.*

If we suspect the correlation to be spurious, we look for a common component, $z$, of $v_1$ and $v_2$ which might account for their correlation:

(3.5a) $\qquad v_1 \equiv u_1 - a_{13}z,$

(3.5b) $\qquad v_2 \equiv u_2 - a_{23}z.$

Substitution of these relations in (IV) brings us back immediately to systems like (II). This substitution replaces the unobservable $v$'s by unobservable $u$'s. Hence, we are not relieved of the necessity of postulating independence of the errors. We are more willing to make these assumptions in the three-variable case because we have explicitly removed from the error term the component $z$ which we suspect is the source, if any, of the correlation of the $v$'s.

Stated otherwise, introduction of the third variable, $z$, to test the genuineness or spuriousness of the correlation between $x$ and $y$, is a method for determining whether in fact the $v$'s of the original two variable system were uncorrelated. But the test can be carried out only on the assumption that the unobservable error terms of the three variable system are uncorrelated. If we suspect this to be false, we must further enlarge the system by introduction of a fourth variable and so on, until we obtain a system we are willing to regard as 'complete' in this sense.

Summarizing our analysis we conclude that:

(1) Our task is to determine which of the six off-diagonal matrix coefficients in a system like (I) are zero.

(2) But we are confronted with a system containing a total of nine variables (six coefficients and three unobservable errors), and only three equations.

(3) Hence we must obtain six more relations by making certain *a priori* assumptions.

(a) Three of these relations may be obtained, from considerations of time precedence of variables or analogous evidence, in the form of direct assumptions that three of the $a_{ij}$ are zero.

(b) Three more relations may be obtained by assuming the errors to be uncorrelated.

## 4. SPURIOUS CORRELATION

Before proceeding with the algebra, it may be helpful to look a little more closely at the matrix of coefficients in systems like (I), (II), and (III), disregarding the numerical values of the coefficients, but considering only whether they are non-vanishing $(X)$, or vanishing $(0)$. An example of such a matrix would be

$$\begin{Vmatrix} X & 0 & 0 \\ X & X & X \\ 0 & 0 & X \end{Vmatrix}$$

In this case $x$ and $z$ both influence $y$, but not each other, and $y$ influences neither $x$ nor $z$. Moreover, a change in $u_2 - u_1$ and $u_3$ being constant – will change $y$, but not $x$ or $z$; a change in $u_1$ will change $x$ and $y$, but not $z$; a change in $u_3$ will change $z$ and $y$, but not $x$. Hence the causal ordering may be depicted thus:

In this case the correlation between $x$ and $y$ is 'true,' and not spurious.

Since there are six off-diagonal elements in the matrix, there are $2^6 = 64$ possible configurations of $X$'s and 0's. The *a priori* assumptions (1), however, require 0's in three specified cells, and hence for each such set of assumptions there are only $2^3 = 8$ possible distinct configurations. If (to make a definite assumption) $x$ does not depend on $y$, then there are three possible orderings of the variables $(z, x.y; x.z, y; x.y, z)$, and consequently $3 \cdot 8 = 24$ possible configurations, but these 24 configurations are not all distinct. For example, the one depicted above is consistent with either the ordering $(z, x\ y)$ or the ordering $(x\ z, y)$.

Still assuming that $x$ does not depend on $y$, we will be interested, in particular, in the following configurations:

$$\begin{Vmatrix} X & 0 & 0 \\ X & X & X \\ 0 & 0 & X \end{Vmatrix} \quad \begin{Vmatrix} X & 0 & X \\ X & X & 0 \\ 0 & 0 & X \end{Vmatrix} \quad \begin{Vmatrix} X & 0 & 0 \\ X & X & 0 \\ X & 0 & X \end{Vmatrix}$$

$$\qquad (\alpha) \qquad\qquad (\beta) \qquad\qquad (\gamma)$$

$$\begin{Vmatrix} X & 0 & X \\ 0 & X & X \\ 0 & 0 & X \end{Vmatrix} \quad \begin{Vmatrix} X & 0 & 0 \\ 0 & X & X \\ X & 0 & X \end{Vmatrix}$$

$$\qquad (\delta) \qquad\qquad (\epsilon)$$

In Case $\alpha$, either $x$ may precede $z$; or $z, x$. In Cases $\beta$ and $\delta$, $z$ precedes $x$; in Cases $\gamma$ and $\epsilon$, $x$ precedes $z$. The causal orderings that may be inferred are:

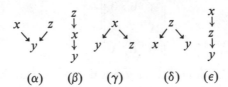

$$(\alpha) \quad (\beta) \quad (\gamma) \qquad (\delta) \quad (\epsilon)$$

The two cases we were confronted with in our earlier examples of Section 1 were $\delta$ and $\epsilon$, respectively. Hence, $\delta$ is the case of spurious correlation due to $z$; $\epsilon$ the case of true correlation with $z$ as an intervening variable.

We come now to the question of which of the matrices that are consistent with the assumed time precedence is the correct one. Suppose for definiteness, that $z$ precedes $x$, and $x$ precedes $y$. Then $a_{12} = a_{31} = a_{32} = 0$; and the system (I) reduces to:

(4.1)         $x \quad + a_{13}z = u_1,$

(4.2)         $a_{21}x + y + a_{23}z = u_2,$

(4.3)                      $z = u_3.$

Next, we assume the errors to be uncorrelated:

(4.4)         $E(u_1u_2) = E(u_1u_3) = E(u_2u_3) = 0.$

Multiplying Equations (4.1)–(4.3) by pairs, and taking expected values we get:

(4.5)         $a_{21}E(x^2) + E(xy) + a_{23}E(xz) + a_{13}[a_{21}E(xz) + E(yz) + a_{23}E(z^2)]$
$$= E(u_1u_2) - 0,$$

(4.6)                      $E(xz) + a_{13}E(z^2) = E(u_1u_3) = 0,$

(4.7)         $a_{21}E(xz) + E(yz) + a_{23}E(z^2) = E(u_2u_3) = 0.$

Because of (4.7), the terms in the bracket of (4.5) vanish, giving:

(4.8)         $a_{21}E(x^2) + E(xy) + a_{23}E(xz) \equiv 0.$

Solving for $E(xz)$, $E(yz)$ and $E(xy)$ we find:

(4.9)         $E(xz) = -a_{13}E(z^2),$

(4.10)        $E(yz) = (a_{13}a_{21} - a_{23})E(z^2).$

(4.11)        $E(xy) = a_{13}a_{23}E(z^2) - a_{21}E(x^2).$

Case $\alpha$: Now in the matrix of case $\alpha$, above, we have $a_{13} = 0$. Hence:

(4.12a)       $E(xz) = 0;$    (4.12b)    $E(yz) = -a_{23}E(z^2),$

(4.12c)       $E(xy) = -a_{21}E(x^2).$

Case $\beta$: In this case, $a_{23} = 0$, hence,

(4.13a)       $E(xz) = -a_{13}E(z^2);$    (4.13b)    $E(yz) = a_{13}a_{21}E(z^2);$

(4.13c)       $E(xy) = -a_{21}E(x^2);$

from which it also follows that:

(4.14)        $E(xy) = E(x^2)\dfrac{E(yz)}{E(xz)}.$

Case $\delta$: In this case, $a_{21} = 0$. Hence,

(4.14a)    $E(xz) = -a_{13}E(z^2)$;    (4.15b)    $E(yz) = -a_{23}E(z^2)$;

(4.15c)    $E(xy) = a_{13}a_{23}E(z^2)$;

and we deduce also that:

(4.16)    $E(xy) = \dfrac{E(xz)E(yz)}{E(z^2)}$

We have now proved that $a_{13} = 0$ implies (4.12a); that $a_{23} = 0$ implies (4.14); and that $a_{21} = 0$ implies (4.16). We shall show that the converse also holds.

To prove that (4.12a) implies $a_{13} = 0$ we need only set the left-hand side of (4.9) equal to zero.

To prove that (4.14) implies that $a_{23} = 0$ we substitute in (4.14) the values of the cross-products from (4.9)–(4.11). After some simplification, we obtain:

(4.17)    $a_{23}[E(x^2) - a_{13}{}^2 E(z^2)] = 0$.

Now since, from (4.1)

(4.18)    $E(x^2) - E(u_1{}^2) + 2a_{13}E(zu_1) = a_{13}{}^2 E(z^2)$,

and since, by multiplying (4.3) by $u_1$, we can show that $E(zu_1) = 0$, the second factor of (4.17) can vanish only in case $E(u_1{}^2) = 0$. Excluding this degenerate case, we conclude that $a_{23} = 0$.

To prove that (4.16) implies that $a_{21} = 0$, we proceed in a similar manner, obtaining:

(4.19)    $a_{21}[E(x^2) - a_{13}{}^2 E(z^2)] = 0$,

from which we can conclude that $a_{21} = 0$.

We can summarize the results as follows:

(1) If $E(xz) = 0$, $E(yz) \neq 0$, $E(xy) \neq 0$, we have Case $\alpha$

(2) If none of the cross-products is zero, and

$$E(xy) = E(x^2)\frac{E(yz)}{E(xz)},$$

we have Case $\beta$.

(3) If none of the cross-products is zero, and

$$E(xy) = \frac{E(xz)E(yz)}{E(z^2)},$$

we have Case $\delta$.

We can combine these conditions to find the conditions that two or more of the coefficients $a_{13}, a_{23}, a_{21}$ vanish:

(4) If $a_{13} = a_{23} = 0$, we find that:

$$E(xz) = 0, E(yz) = 0. \text{ Call this Case } (\alpha\beta).$$

(5) If $a_{13} = a_{21} = 0$, we find that:

$$E(xz) = 0, E(xy) = 0. \text{ Call this Case } (\alpha\delta).$$

(6) If $a_{23} = a_{21} = 0$, we find that:

$$E(yz) = 0, E(xy) = 0. \text{ Call this Case } (\beta\delta).$$

(7) If $a_{13} = a_{23} = a_{21} = 0$, then

$$E(xz) = E(yz) = E(xy) = 0. \text{ Call this Case } (\alpha\beta\delta).$$

(8) If none of the conditions (1)–(7) are satisfied, then all three coefficients $a_{13}, a_{23}, a_{21}$ are non-zero. Thus, by observing which of the conditions (1) through (8) are satisfied by the expected values of the cross products, we can determine what the causal ordering is of the variables.[7]

We can see also, from this analysis, why the vanishing of the partial correlation of $x$ and $y$ is evidence for the spuriousness of the zero-order correlation between $x$ and $y$. For the numerator of the partial correlation coefficient $r_{xy.z}$, we have:

$$(4.20) \qquad N(r_{xy.z}) = \frac{E(xy)}{\sqrt{E(x^2)E(y^2)}} - \frac{E(xz)E(yz)}{E(z^2)\sqrt{E(x^2)E(y^2)}}$$

We see that the condition for Case $\delta$ is precisely that $r_{xy.z}$ vanish while none of the coefficients, $r_{xy}, r_{xz}, r_{yz}$ vanish. From this we conclude that the first illustrative example of Section 1 falls in Case $\delta$, as previously asserted. A similar analysis shows that the second illustrative example of Section 1 falls in Case $\epsilon$.

In summary, our procedure for interpreting, by introduction of an additional variable $z$, the correlation between $x$ and $y$ consists in making the six *a priori* assumptions described earlier; estimating the expected values,

$E(xy)$, $E(xz)$, and $E(yz)$; and determining from their values which of the eight enumerated cases holds. Each case corresponds to a specified arrangement of zero and non-zero elements in the coefficient matrix and hence to a definite causal ordering of the variables.

## 5. THE CASE OF EXPERIMENTATION

In Sections (3)–(4) we have treated $u_1$, $u_2$ and $u_3$ as random variables. The causal ordering among $x$ .$y$, and $z$ can also be determined without *a priori* assumptions in the case where $u_1$, $u_2$, and $u_3$ are controlled by an experimenter. For simplicity of illustration we assume there is time precedence among the variables. Then the matrix is triangular, so that $a_{ij} \neq 0$ implies $a_{ji} = 0$; and $a_{ij} \neq 0$, $a_{jk} \neq 0$ implies $a_{ki} = 0$.

Under the given assumptions at least three of the off-diagonal $a$'s in (I) must vanish, and the equations and variables can be reordered so that all the non-vanishing coefficients lie on or below the diagonal. If (with this ordering) $u_2$ or $u_3$ are varied, at least the variable determined by the first equation will remain constant (since it depends only on $u_1$). Similarly, if $u_3$ is varied, the variables determined by the first and second equations will remain constant.

In this way we discover which variables are determined by which equations. Further, if varying $u_i$ causes a particular variable other than the $i$th to change in value, this variable must be causally dependent on the $i$th.

Suppose, for example, that variation in $u_1$ brings about a change in $x$ and $y$, variation in $u_2$ a change in $y$, and variation in $u_3$ a change in $x$, $y$, and $z$. Then we know that $y$ is causally dependent upon $x$ and $z$, and $x$ upon $z$. But this is precisely the Case $\beta$ treated previously under the assumption that the $u$'s were stochastic variables.

## 6. CONCLUSION

In this paper I have tried to clarify the logical processes and assumptions that are involved in the usual procedures for testing whether a correlation between two variables is true or spurious. These procedures begin by imbedding the relation between the two variables in a larger three-variable system that is assumed to be self-contained, except for stochastic disturbances or parameters controlled by an experimenter.

Since the coefficients in the three-variable system will not in general be identifiable, and since the determination of the causal ordering implies identifiability, the test for spuriousness of the correlation requires additional assumptions to be made. These assumptions are usually of two kinds. The first, ordinarily made explicit, are assumptions that certain variables do *not* have a causal influence on certain others. These assumptions reduce the number of degrees of freedom of the system of coefficients by implying that three specific coefficients are zero.

The second type of assumption, more often implicit than explicit, is that the random disturbances associated with the three-variable system are uncorrelated. This assumption gives us a sufficient number of additional restrictions to secure the identifiability of the remaining coefficients, and hence to determine the causal ordering of the variables.

## NOTES

*I am indebted to Richard M. Cyert, Paul F. Lazarsfeld, Roy Radner, and T. C. Koopmans for valuable comments on earlier drafts on this paper.
[1] See Koopmans [2] for a survey and references to the literature.
[2] Simon [6] and ]7]. See also Orcutt [4] and [5]. I should like, without elaborating it here, to insert the *caveat* that the concept of causal ordering employed in this paper does not in any way solve the 'problem of Hume' nor contradict his assertion that all we can ever observe are covariations. If we employ an ontological definition of cause – one based on the notion of the 'necessary' connection of events – then correlation cannot, of course, prove causation. But neither can anything else prove causation, and hence we can have no basis for distinguishing 'true' from 'spurious' correlation. If we wish to retain the latter distinction (and working scientists have not shown that they are able to get along without it), and if at the same time we wish to remain empiricists, then the term 'cause' must be defined in a way that does not entail objectionable ontological consequences. That is the course we shall pursue here.
[3] Zeisel [9]. pp. 192–95. Reference to the original source will show that in this and the following example we have changed the variables from attributes to continuous variables for purposes of exposition.
[4] Zeisel [9], pp. 191–92.
[5] The question of how we distinguish between 'dependent' and 'independent' variables is discussed in Simon [7], and will receive further attention in this paper.
[6] Since these are empirical assumptions it is conceivable that they are wrong, and indeed, we can imagine mechanisms that would reverse the causal ordering in the second example. What is argued here is that these assumptions, right or wrong are implicit in the determination of whether the correlation is true or spurious.
[7] Of course, the expected values are not, strictly speaking, observables except in a probability sense. However, we do not wish to go into sampling questions here, and simply assume that we have good estimates of the expected values.

## REFERENCES

[1] Kendall, Patricia L. and Lazarsfeld, Paul F., 'Problems of Survey Analysis', in Merton and Lazarsfeld (eds.), *Continuities in Social Research*, (New York: The Free Press, 1950) pp. 133–96.

[2] Koopmans, Tjalling C., 'Identification Problems in Economic Model Construction', *Econometrica* 17, 125–44 (April 1949) reprinted as Chapter II in *Studies in Econometric Methods,* Cowles Commission Monograph 14, Wm. C. Hood and T. C. Koopmans (eds.) (New York: John Wiley Sons, Inc., 1953).

[3] Koopmans, Tjalling C., 'When Is an Equation System Complete for Statistical Purposes?' Chapter 17 in *Statistical Inference in Dynamic Economic Models,* Cowles Commission Monograph 10, T. C. Koopmans, (ed.) (New York: John Wiley Sons, Inc., 1950).

[4] Orcutt, Guy H., 'Toward Partial Redirection of Econometrics', *The Review of Economics and Statistics* 34, 195–213 (1952).

(5) Orcutt, Guy H., 'Actions, Consequences, and Causal Relations', *The Review of Economics and Statistics* 34, 305–14 (1952).

[6] Simon, Herbert A., 'On the Definition of the Causal Relation', *The Journal of Philosophy* 49, 517–28 (1952). (reprinted as Chapter 2.2 in this volume).

[7] Simon, Herbert A., 'Causal Ordering and Identifiability', Chapter III in *Studies in Econometric Methods,* Cowles Commission Monograph 14 Wm. C. Hood and T. C. Koopmans (eds.) (New York: John Wiley Sons, Inc., 1953). (reprinted as Chapter 2.1 in this volume).

[8] Yule, G. Udny, *An Introduction to the Theory of Statistics,* (London: Charles Griffin and Co., 10th ed., 1932), Chapters 4, 12. (Equivalent chapters will be found in all subsequent editions of Yule and Yule and Kendall, through the 14th.)

[9] Zeisel, Hans, *Say It With Figures* (New York: Harper and Brothers, 1947).

## CAUSE AND COUNTERFACTUAL†

### (with Nicholas Rescher)

### 1. INTRODUCTION

The problem of the causal counterfactual conditional continues to loom large despite determined efforts to put it to rest. It is the thesis of this paper that the judicious combination of a formulation of the concept of a causal ordering, already available, with a notion of modal categories, also available, provide the clearest means for treating the causal counterfactual conditional.

### 2. CAUSE[1]

The causal relation is often described as a relation between events or conditions; e.g.:

The rain caused the wheat to grow.

This mode of expression commonly leads to the misconception that the asymmetry of the causal relation (i.e., the fact that cause and effect cannot be commuted) has something to do with the non-symmetry of implication — that the above statement has something to do with:

If it rains, the wheat grows.

The fatal difficulty in this view is that implication contraposes, so that we are tempted to continue:

If the wheat does not grow, it does not rain, and thence:

The wheat's not growing causes it not to rain.

Attempts to introduce a modal relation meaning 'implies causally' (e.g. Burks's, Angell's)[2] have uniformly foundered on this rock of contraposition. The lack of congruence between causality and implication is forceably indicated by the fact that (1) 'If $X$ then $Y$' is compatible with 'If $Y$ then $X$.' whereas '$X$ causes $Y$' is incompatible with '$Y$ causes $X$', and (2) 'If $X$ then $Y$' entails 'If not-$Y$ then not-$X$ whereas '$X$ causes $Y$' not merely fails to entail 'not-$Y$ causes not-$X$' but is actually incompatible with it. We establish as a

† [*Philosophy of Science* 33, 323–340 (1966)].

regulative guidepost the principle:

*Principle 1*: The asymmetry of the causal relation is unrelated to the asymmetry of any mode of implication that contraposes.

If we are not bound to relate causality to implication, then we may reconsider, at the outset, what is being related by causal statements. It is usually suggested that the wheat's growing is related to the rain. Let us propose as an alternative that it is rather the size of the wheat crop that is causally related to the weather. That is to say, the following three statements are all part of a single causal relation:

> The absence of rain prevents the wheat's growing.
> With moderate rain, the wheat crop is good.
> With heavy rain, there is a large wheat crop.

or generalizing:

> The amount of wheat is a function of the amount of rain.

We draw a second pragmatic conclusion from the example:

*Principle 2:* A causal relation is not a relation between values of variables, but a function of one variable (the cause) on to another (the effect).

Regarding causality as functional relation eliminates the unwanted asymmetry produced by contraposition, for contraposition does not interchange an independent with a dependent variable. On the other hand, it is not immediately obvious that the asymmetry of functional relation provides a suitable interpretation of the wanted asymmetry between cause and effect; for many, if not most, of the functions that enter in causal discussions possess inverses; and by inverting them, we can interchange a dependent with an independent variable. Thus if $\phi$ possesses an inverse, $\phi^{-1}$, then, from

$$y = \phi(x)$$

we obtain

$$x = \phi^{-1}(y).$$

Therefore the distinction between independent and dependent variables does not explicate, by itself, the asymmetry between cause and effect. Surely we wish to invest the latter distinction with more significance than is accorded by the arbitrary choice of which variable to measure on the abscissa, and which on the ordinate.

## 3. COMPLETE STRUCTURES

We turn now to the positive task of showing that, given a system of equations – functional relations – and a set of variables appearing in these equations, we can introduce an asymmetric relation among individual equations and variables which corresponds to our commonsense notion of a causal ordering. (When we have occasion to write out functional relations explicitly, we shall generally write them in the canonical form $f_i(x_1, x_2, \ldots) = 0$, where $f_i$ is a name for the function, and the $x$'s are the variables that appear in it.)

DEFINITION 1: A *structure* is a set of $m$ functions involving $n$ variables $(n \geqslant m)$, such that:

(a) In any subset of $k$ functions of the structure, at least $k$ different variables appear.

(b) In any subset of $k$ functions in which $r(r \geqslant k)$ variables appear, if the values of any $(r - k)$ variables are chosen arbitrarily, then the values of the remaining $k$ variables are determined uniquely. (Finding these unique values is a matter of solving the equations for them.)

For illustration, we will sometimes consider *linear structures* – i.e., structures in which the functions are linear and non-homogeneous. A linear structure is a set of independent and consistent linear non-homogeneous equations.

DEFINITION 2: A structure is *self-contained* if it has exactly as many functions as variables.

A self-contained structure can be solved for a unique set of values of its variables.

A structure can be represented simply by a matrix of 1's and 0's, the various columns of the matrix being associated with the variables of the structure, and the rows with the functions. Then a 1 in the $j$th column of the $i$th row means the $j$th variable appears in the $i$th function, while a zero in that position means that the $j$th variable does not appear in the $i$th function.

Consider the following structure matrix:

|        | $x_1$ | $x_2$ | $x_3$ | $x_4$ | $x_5$ | $x_6$ | $x_7$ |
|--------|-------|-------|-------|-------|-------|-------|-------|
| $f_1$  | 1     | 0     | 0     | 0     | 0     | 0     | 0     |
| $f_2$  | 0     | 1     | 0     | 0     | 0     | 0     | 0     |
| $f_3$  | 0     | 0     | 1     | 0     | 0     | 0     | 0     |
| $f_4$  | 1     | 1     | 1     | 1     | 1     | 0     | 0     |
| $f_5$  | 1     | 0     | 1     | 1     | 1     | 0     | 0     |
| $f_6$  | 0     | 0     | 0     | 1     | 0     | 1     | 0     |
| $f_7$  | 0     | 0     | 0     | 0     | 1     | 0     | 1     |

By Definition 2, this matrix represents a self-contained structure. Since $f_1$, $f_2$, and $f_3$ each contain only one variable ($x_1$, $x_2$, and $x_3$, respectively) each is also a self-contained structure (and obviously a *minimal* self-contained structure), and each can be solved, by Definition 1, for the value of its variable.

If we now substitute these values of $x_1$, $x_2$, and $x_3$ in $f_4$ though $f_7$, we obtain a new *derived structure of first order* with the following matrix (which is simply the lower right-hand 4 x 4 component of the original structure):

|         | $x_4$ | $x_5$ | $x_6$ | $x_7$ |
|---------|-------|-------|-------|-------|
| $f'_4$  | 1     | 1     | 0     | 0     |
| $f'_5$  | 1     | 1     | 0     | 0     |
| $f'_6$  | 1     | 0     | 1     | 0     |
| $f'_7$  | 0     | 1     | 0     | 1     |

In this derived structure the set consisting of $f'_4$ and $f'_5$ is a minimal self-contained structure, which can be solved for the values of $x_4$ and $x_5$. Substituting these values in $f'_6$ and $f'_7$, we obtain the *derived structure of second order*:

|         | $x_6$ | $x_7$ |
|---------|-------|-------|
| $f''_6$ | 1     | 0     |
| $f''_7$ | 0     | 1     |

This structure consists of the two minimal self-contained structures, $f''_6$ and $f''_7$, which can be solved for $x_6$ and $x_7$, respectively.

We see that there was a certain asymmetry in the equations and variables of our original structure, such that subsets of equations could be solved for certain variables without solving for others, by not vice versa. We may depict this ordering:

$$f_1 \searrow$$
$$f_2 \to \begin{cases} {}^{\backprime}f_4 \to f_6 \\ f_5 \to f_7 \end{cases}$$
$$f_3 \nearrow$$

or, alternatively, in terms of variables:

$$x_1 \searrow$$
$$x_2 \to \begin{cases} x_4 \to x_6 \\ x_5 \to x_7 \end{cases}$$
$$x_3 \nearrow$$

It is clear that variables belonging to derived structures of higher order are *dependent* on variables belonging only to the lower-order structures, while the latter variables are *exogenous* to the structures determining the former. We shall interpret the ordering as a causal ordering, so that a variable at the head of an arrow is *directly caused* by the variable or variables at the origin of the arrow. Thus $x_4$ and $x_5$ are directly caused by $x_1$ (and jointly by $x_2$ and $x_3$ also), $x_6$ by $x_4$ and $x_7$ by $x_5$.

By recursion, we can then define the transitive relation, *caused*, so that $x_7$, for example, is caused by $x_1$ (jointly with $x_2$ and $x_3$, and via $x_5$).

Let us see to what extent these definitions lead to results that conform to English usage. Consider our example:

The rain causes the wheat to grow.

Add the following statements, which we wish to interpret as simultaneously valid:

Fertilizer causes large wheat yields.
A large wheat crop causes the wheat price to fall.
An increase in population causes the wheat price to rise.

We define the following variables: $R$ is the rainfall in the given year; $W$, the size of the wheat crop; $F$, the amount of fertilizer used; $P$, the price of wheat; $N$, the size of the population. We next represent our first two causal sentences by the following functional relation:

$$f_1(R, W, F) = 0,$$

Then we represent the last two causal sentences by another functional relation:

$$f_2(W, P, N) = 0.$$

The two functions together do not define a self-contained structure, since they contain five variables. Let us suppose the structure completed by adding three additional functional relations describing (a) a theory of the weather, (b) a theory of how fertilizer applications are decided upon, and (c) a theory of population growth. The function (a) should contain $R$ but none of the other four variables in our system, (b) should contain, of these variables, only $F$, and (c) should contain only $N$:

$$\text{(a) } f_3(R) = 0, \text{ (b) } F_4(F) = 0, \text{ (c) } f_5(N) = 0.$$

We now have a complete structure, with matrix:

|       | R | W | F | P | N |
|-------|---|---|---|---|---|
| $f_1$ | 1 | 1 | 1 | 0 | 0 |
| $f_2$ | 0 | 1 | 0 | 1 | 1 |
| $f_3$ | 1 | 0 | 0 | 0 | 0 |
| $f_4$ | 0 | 0 | 1 | 0 | 0 |
| $f_5$ | 0 | 0 | 0 | 0 | 1 |

It is easily seen that this structure determines the causal ordering:

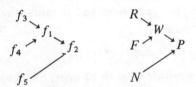

Reading off the relations in the diagram, we find: The amount of rain ($R$) and the amount of fertilizer ($F$) are the causal determinants of the size of the wheat crop ($W$), while the size of the wheat crop ($W$) and the population ($N$) are the causal determinants of the price of wheat ($P$).

Thus the formalization translates accurately the causal assertions in the original English-language sentences. We are not now asserting that these causal statements are empirically correct (nor have we explained what might be meant by such an assertion); we are merely showing that the formalization captures the common meaning of 'cause'.

Note that $f_1$ and $f_2$, by themselves, are entirely symmetrical in the variables they contain. It is only when they are imbedded in a complete structure, containing $f_3$, $f_4$, and $f_5$, that asymmetry appears. We do not need to designate which is the dependent variable in each of these relations taken singly. Hence the formalization does not rest on the essentially arbitrary distinction between independent and dependent variables.

On the other hand, it is essential that the structure we consider be complete, and if we complete a structure in a different way, we will generally find that we have altered the causal ordering. In the previous example, suppose we replace $f_5(N) = 0$ by $f_6(P) = 0$ ('the wheat price is fixed by the government', say). The reader can easily verify that the causal ordering in this modified structure is:

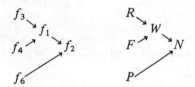

This system now asserts that the population is determined by the price of wheat and the size of the wheat crop (that is, the population will reach the size that will just consume the wheat crop at the given price). Now, by common sense, we might suppose that given any particular amount of wheat, the price would be higher the larger the population. From this assumption and the new causal ordering we reach the curious conclusion that, by raising the price of wheat, the government can increase the population (and without increasing the amount of wheat raised!).

For this and other reasons, we would intuitively regard the original structure as the empirically valid one, and the modified one as invalid. Again we postpone the discussion of what is meant by 'valid' here and observe simply that different causal orderings obtain when a partial structure is completed in different ways.

### 4. INVARIANCE

Suppose that we have a complete structure of $n$ functions and $n$ variables. In general, we can replace any one of the functions of the structure by a linear combination of it with one or more of the others, without altering the values of the variables satisfying the entire set of functions. Thus, if we have a complete structure in three variables consisting of $f_1 = 0$, $f_2 = 0$, $f_3 = 0$, the structure consisting of $f_1 = 0$, $f_2 = k$, $f_1 + k_2 f_2 + k_3 f_3 = 0$, $f_3 = 0$ ($k_1$, $k_2$, $k_3$

are non-zero constants) will also (in general) be complete, and will have the same solution as the original structure. However, the two structures will not generally have the same ordering. For example, suppose the matrix of the first structure was:

$$
\begin{array}{c c c c}
      & x_1 & x_2 & x_3 \\
f_1 & 1 & 0 & 0 \\
f_2 & 0 & 1 & 0 \\
f_3 & 1 & 1 & 1
\end{array}
$$

The ordering would be

$$
\begin{array}{c}
x_1 \searrow \\
\quad\quad x_3 \\
x_2 \nearrow
\end{array}
$$

But the second structure would have (in general) the matrix:

$$
\begin{array}{c c c c}
      & x_1 & x_2 & x_3 \\
f_1 & 1 & 0 & 0 \\
f'_2 & 1 & 1 & 1 \\
f_3 & 1 & 1 & 1
\end{array}
$$

with an ordering:

$$
x_1 \to \begin{cases} x_2 \\ x_3 \end{cases}
$$

It might be thought that the effect of replacing individual functions by linear combinations of several would always be to introduce new variables in the modified function, as in the above example. But this is not so, for the linear combination may turn out to be an identity in one (or more) of the variables, which then can be cancelled out. Take $k_1 = -1$, $k_2 = -1$, and $k_3 = 1$ in the last example, and suppose $f_1 = x_1$, $f_2 = x_2$ and $f_3 = x_1 + x_2 + ax_3$. Then $f'_2 = k_1 f_1 + k_2 f_2 + k_3 f_3 = ax_3$, yielding the ordering:

$$
\begin{array}{c}
f_1 \searrow \\
\quad\quad f_3 \quad \text{or} \\
f_2 \nearrow
\end{array}
\qquad
\begin{array}{c}
x_1 \searrow \\
\quad\quad x_2 \\
x_3 \nearrow
\end{array}
$$

In algebra, operations of replacing rows (columns, respectively) in a matrix by linear combinations of rows (columns, respectively) are called *elementary row* (column, respectively) *operations*. The application of elementary row operations to a system of equations does not change the set of solutions to the equations. Indeed, a standard technique for solving simultaneous linear equations is to apply elementary row operations to obtain a diagonal matrix — with one variable in each equation.

But if solutions to equations are invariant under elementary row operations, the causal orderings of variables in complete structures are not — as our example has shown. If causal ordering is to have more than conventional or notational significance, we must have some basis for singling out from among a whole class of matrices that are equivalent under the group of row transformations the particular matrix that represents the empirically valid causal ordering. We turn now to this problem.

Perhaps we can get a clue to the answer by considering the analogy of the elementary *column* operations, which are not admissible algebraic operations. Each column of the matrix of a structure corresponds to a variable. A column operation would replace some single variable of the system by a linear combination of variables. In the earlier example, it might replace . . . 'price of wheat' by twice the price of wheat minus four times the population.' This operation is inadmissible because it destroys the identity of the variables in terms of which the problem is stated — variables that presumably correspond to empirical observations on the system. Hence, among all matrices equivalent under elementary column transformations, that one alone is uniquely admissible which puts columns and variables in one-to-one correspondence.

Now let us return to row transformations, and assign a label to each function, the label to denote the *mechanism* (a term here introduced informally) which that particular function represents. In the wheat example, $f_1$ represents the biochemical mechanism involved in the growth of wheat, $f_2$ represents the economic mechanism relating to wheat buying, $f_3$ is the meteorological mechanism that determines the weather, $f_4$ is the producers' decision mechanism with respect to fertilizer, and $f_5$ is the mechanism of population growth.

An elementary row transformation would replace one of these mechanisms with a linear combination of several of them. For example, replacing $f_3$ by a combination of $f_1$ and $f_3$ would introduce a composite biological-meterological mechanism pertaining to wheat growth and the weather. Hence, among all matrices equivalent under elementary row transformations, that one alone is uniquely admissible that puts rows and mechanisms in one-to-one correspondence.

It is intuitively clear how we identify the variables of the system (and distinguish them from linear combinations of variables). Our intuitions seem less clear about identifying mechanisms. Unless we regard this identification as intuitively obvious, we have simply substituted a new problem for the original one. The new problem — how to identify mechanisms — may well, however, turn out to be more tractable than the old one.

## 5. IDENTIFIABILITY OF MECHANISMS

First, we shall show that no amount of observation of the values of the variables in a complete structure can identify the mechanisms — can distinguish a particular matrix from all those equivalent to it under elementary row transformations. The proof is immediate. Suppose we have a set of $k$ consistent equations in $n$ variables ($n \geqslant k$), and suppose that $(\bar{x}_1, \bar{x}_2, \ldots, \bar{x}_n$ is an empirically observed set of values for the $n$ variables that satisfies the equations. Then these observed values will also satisfy any set of equations equivalent to the original set under elementary row transformations — all such sets of equations having the same solutions. Thus no number of simultaneous observations of rainfall, fertilizer, wheat crop, wheat price, and population will verify the causal ordering in our example.

Notice that the causal ordering depends on which variables *do not* appear in which mechanisms. Thus, in the wheat example, to introduce the mechanism $f_3(R) = 0$ is equivalent to asserting that a meteorological theory can be constructed that predicts rainfall independently of fertilizer practices, wheat crop, price of wheat, or size of population. With respect to this set of variables, weather is an unmoved mover — an exogenous variable. Similarly, in this structure, population and fertilizer are asserted to be exogenous variables. These assumptions are crucial to the causal ordering.

Cosmology might provide one basis for such assumptions. It might be assumed, for example, that the behaviour of any system involving very large quantities of energy (e.g., the atmosphere), is practically autonomous of the behaviour of variables involving very much less energy (e.g., wheat growing). We may call this principle the Postulate of Prepotence.

Or, it might be assumed that most variables in the world are not directly connected with most other variables, and that such connections as exist involve a very small number of different kinds of mechanisms. Then, one would include a particular variable in a subsystem only if one could select a mechanism from the list of admitted mechanisms through which that variable could possibly act on that subsystem. We might call this assumption the Postulate of Independence, or, more vividly, the Empty World Postulate.

To see that these cosmological assumptions really correspond to the way we reason about causality, consider the objections that might be raised against the proposed causal ordering of the wheat example. First, it might be argued that the wheat crop influences the weather, since the acreage planted to wheat affects the rate of evaporation of ground moisture. Notice the objection conforms to the Empty World Postulate, since it does not simply urge that anything may influence anything else, but proposes a specific mechanism of a kind known to be efficacious in other situations. If the proposal to include the wheat crop as a variable affecting the¹ weather were rejected, the Postulate of Prepotence could provide a plausible basis for the rejection.

A similar discourse could examine the plausibility of assuming that the amount of fertilizer applied is independent of the price of wheat, or the population of the size of the wheat crop. To carry out this discussion in detail would call for the static structure considered so far to be expanded into a dynamic model. (We shall postpone questions of dynamics to a later point.)

Having offered the Postulate of Prepotence and the Empty World Postulate as possible sources for the identifying assumptions underlying a causal ordering, we leave this foray into cosmology to consider other possible bases for identification.

## 6. INTERVENTION

In many, though not all, contexts where causal language is used, the structure under examination can be altered by intervention. The specific possibilities for intervention then become bases for causal attribution. 'Intervention', as the term is used here, has nothing to do with change through time, hence we can illustrate its significance with a wholly static example.

Consider the physical situation depited in Figure 1. A quantity of gas is confined in a chamber by a moveable piston (having unit area of cross-section) on which rests a weight. Assuming the Gas Laws hold in this situation, we have, in equilibrium:

(1)        $PV = kT,$

where $P$ is pressure per unit area (equal to $W$, the weight resting on the piston), $V$ is the volume of the chamber, $T$ is the absolute temperature of the confined gas, and $k$ is a constant that depends on the amount of gas confined. We assume that, under conditions to be specified presently, heat may pass in or out through the walls of the chamber.

Since we have only a single equation, with three variables, we must impose additional constraints to obtain a complete structure and define a causal

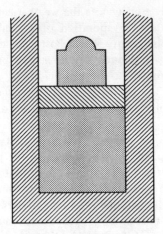

Fig. 1.    The Gas laws.

ordering. We will impose these constraints by assumptions about the possibility of intervention.

*Case I.* We assume that the possibility of heat passing in and out of the chamber can be altered. In the first case (constant temperature), we assume that the heat flows so readily that, at equilibrium, the temperature inside the chamber must always equal the temperature outside. Representing the latter by $\overline{T}$, a constant, we obtain:

(2)          $T = \overline{T}$.

Next, we assume that the weight on the piston is also determined exogenously: the 'experimenter' may impose any weight, $\overline{W}$, he wishes, just as he may maintain any outside temperature, $\overline{T}$, he wishes. From this new assumption, we get:

(3)          $P = \overline{W}$.

Now, Equations (1) through (3) define the complete structure

|     | $P$ | $T$ | $V$ |
|-----|-----|-----|-----|
| (1) | 1   | 1   | 1   |
| (2) | 0   | 1   | 0   |
| (3) | 1   | 0   | 0   |

with causal ordering

Thus, we might make the following kind of statement about the system: 'In order to decrease the volume of the chamber, increase the weight on the piston, or decrease the temperature of the environment.'

Note that we have kept our promise of avoiding dynamics, for these statements do not refer to temporal change, but are statements in comparative statics. They can be put more formally:

"If, in two situations, $\overline{W}_1 > \overline{W}_2$, then $V_1 < V_2$, *ceteris paribus*, and if $\overline{T}_1 > \overline{T}_2$, then $V_1 > V_2$, *ceteris paribus*."

*Case II.* We assume (adiabatic case) that the walls of the chamber have been perfectly insulated so that no energy can pass through. The adiabatic assumption imposes on the system a constraint that was absent in Case I — that the total energy of the system must be conserved. This total energy $\overline{E}$, is the sum of the potential energy $PV$, (since $V$ is equal to the height of the chamber), of the weighted piston, and the heat energy, $Q = qT$; of the gas in the chamber. Hence, the constraint may be written:

(2)′ $\qquad \overline{E} = PV + qT.$

Next, we assume again that the weight on the piston is determined exogenously. From mechanisms (1), (2)′, and (3), we get the new structure:

|     | $P$ | $T$ | $V$ |
|-----|-----|-----|-----|
| (1) | 1 | 1 | 1 |
| (2)′ | 1 | 1 | 1 |
| (3) | 1 | 0 | 0 |

with quite different causal ordering:

$$P \overset{\nearrow T}{\searrow_V}$$

If we regard the interventions themselves, i.e., $\overline{T}$, $\overline{W}$. and $\overline{E}$ as 'variables,' then the causal diagrams for the two cases can be expanded to:

$$\begin{matrix} \overline{W} \to P \searrow \\ \qquad\qquad V \\ \overline{T} \to T \nearrow \end{matrix} \quad \text{and} \quad \begin{matrix} \overline{E} \to E \searrow \\ \qquad\qquad \begin{cases} T \\ V \end{cases} \\ \overline{W} \to P \nearrow \end{matrix} \quad \text{respectively.}$$

In the adiabatic case, it is not immediately obvious in what sense the experimenter can intervene to fix $\bar{E}$. This can be explained as follows. Let the system be in equilibrium for $\bar{E}_1$, $\bar{W}_1$, and let $P_1$, $T_1$, $V_1$ be the equilibrium values of the endogenous variables. Now suppose the weight $\bar{W}_1$ is suddenly replaced by a new weight $\bar{W}_2$. The system, now not in equilibrium, has had its energy increased by the amount $V_1$ $(\bar{W}_2 - \bar{W}_1)$ to the total: $\bar{W}_2 V_1 + kT_1 = \bar{E}_2$. This is the quantity, $\bar{E}_2$, of Equation $(2)'$, and, it can be seen that the experimenter fixes it by setting $V_1$, $T_1$ and $\bar{W}_2$.

In the two different piston cases, how can we specify operationally what variables are being measured and what mechanisms are operating? With respect to the former, the instrumentation required is a thermometer and pressure gauge on the interior of the chamber to measure $T$ and $P$, respectively, and a scale against which to mark the position of the piston, hence to measure $V$. Equation (3) derives from the fact that the observed value of $P$ changes if and only if we change $\bar{W}$. The change in the value of the variable is associated, then, with a change in one specific part of the structure, separated, physically and visually, from the other parts.

In Case I, Equation (2) derives from the fact that $T$ changes if and only if we change the temperature of the surrounding bath. Both $\bar{T}$ and $\bar{W}$ are observable in the same sense that $P$, $T$, and $V$ are observable. Hence, if we can forbid column transformations because they would merge and confuse the operationally distinct measures, $P$, $T$, $V$, we can forbid row transformations because they would merge and confuse the operationally distinct interventions, $\bar{T}$ and $\bar{W}$. Case II is slightly more complicated because of the less transparent status of $\bar{E}$ as an operationally distinct intervention, but its analysis is the same in principle.

In both Cases I and II, Equation (2) also depends on the mechanisms of the boundary between the chamber and its environment. In Case I, the equation implies a law of heat flow that does not admit temperature differentials in equilibrium. In Case II, it implies perfect thermal insulation across the boundary. In a full dynamic treatment of the situation, distinct mechanisms would appear to describe these phenomena across the boundary. Again, particular mechanisms refer to distinct parts — often but not always visually distinct parts — of the total system.

### 7. A DYNAMIC EXAMPLE

Having seen how interventions can be used to define complete structures, and hence causal orderings, we turn next to nonexperimental situations where intervention is not possible. Does the notion of causal ordering apply at all to such situations, and can we identify mechanisms in them?

Let us take a simple example from classical (pre-relativity and pre-Sputnik) celestial mechanics, considering motions in a single dimension to minimize the mathematical complexities. Combining Newton's Second Law with the Inverse Square Law of gravitational attraction, we describe the motion of a set of $n$ mass points by the $n$ equations:

$$(1) \qquad a_i(t) = g \sum_{j \neq i} \frac{m_j}{[x_i(t) - x_j(t)]^2} \qquad (i = 1, \ldots, n),$$

where $a_i(t)$ is the acceleration of the $i$th mass point, $g$ the gravitational constant, $m_i$ the (constant) mass of the $i$th mass point, and $x_i(t)$ the position of the $i$th mass point. Integration of these equations twice gives the time path of the system. Now, to see more clearly what would be the significance of elementary row operations on this system, we consider the discrete approximation; $a_i(t) \sim x_i(t+2) - 2x_i(t+1) + x_i(t)$, and we rewrite the system

$$(2) \qquad f_i[x_i(t+2), x_i(t+1), x_i(t), \{x_j(t)\}_{j \neq i}; \{m_j\}_{j \neq i}, g] = 0,$$
$$(i = 1, \ldots, n).$$

Consider now only those terms of the functions that refer to times other than $t$. In the $i$th function, these terms involve only positions of the $i$th mass point. The form in which the structure is defined by (2) may be regarded as canonical in the sense that elementary row transformations will destroy the property just mentioned. That is, after non-trivial transformations, there will be functions in the structure that refer to the positions at times other than $t$ of more than one mass point.

We may restate the matter differently: Any system of differential equations can be reduced, by introducing additional variables to eliminate higher-order derivatives, to a system of the first order. Let us consider a system of first order, and let us introduce a concept of *self-contained dynamic structure* in analogy to our earlier definition of self-contained structure.

DEFINITION: A self-contained dynamic structure is a set of $n$ first-order differential equations involving $n$ variables such that:

(a) In any subset of $k$ functions of the structure the first derivative of at least $k$ different variables appear.

(b) In any subset of $k$ functions in which $r(r \geq k)$ first derivatives appear, if the values of any $(r - k)$ first derivatives are chosen arbitrarily, then the remaining $k$ are determined uniquely as functions of the $n$ variables.

By performing elementary row operations on a self-contained dynamic structure, we can solve for the $n$ first derivatives — i.e., replace the structure by an equivalent structure possessing the canonical form described above. Our proposal, then, is that the functions of the structure in this form be interpreted as the mechanisms of the system. The $i$th function (the function containing $\partial x_i/\partial t$) is then the mechanism determining the time path of $x_i$. Elementary row operations will be inadmissible since they intermingle first derivatives of variables, just as elementary column operations are inadmissible in intermingling variables.

Notice that a complete dynamic structure is not analogous to a complete structure in the static case. To complete the dynamic structure in the latter sense, we must specify a set of initial conditions, e.g., $x_i(t_0)(i = 1, \ldots, n)$, the values of the $n$ variables for some particular time, $t$. With this addition a causal ordering is defined: for $t_0 < t$ it will be the normal causal ordering, acting forward in time, but for $t_0 > t$ the directions of the causal arrows will all be reversed. Therefore, we may say that a complete dynamic structure defines a causal ordering up to reversal of directionality. Thus, most features of the ordering (i.e., the forms of the functions) are independent of time precedence.

In particular, note that time reversal is *not* equivalent to the contraposition of implication. For if the sense of time is inverted in Equation (1), the accelerations will still be causally dependent on the gravitational constant and the masses (which are exogenous), and on the instantaneous positions of the mass points, and not *vice versa*. What is reversed is just that, in the originally-stated system accelerations and the present state of the system are the causes of *subsequent* states, in the reversed system, they are causes of *prior* states. In both cases, states cause accelerations, by the gravitational mechanism, while accelerations, by definition, are second derivatives of positions.

## 8. EQUILIBRIUM OF DYNAMIC SYSTEMS

Suppose that we observe the behavior of a dynamic system, described in canonical form, over some period of time. We can divide the variables, by rough criteria, in three classes:

1. Variables that have changed so slowly that they can be replaced by constants for the period under observation, deleting the corresponding mechanisms from the system.

2. Variables that have adjusted so promptly that they are always close to (partial) equilibrium, hence their first derivatives always close to zero. We can replace the first derivatives of these variables by zero in their equations – substituting static equilibrium mechanisms for the orginal dynamic mechanisms. We will continue to regard variables whose first derivatives have been set equal to zero as the dependent variables in the corresponding equations.

3. All other variables. We will retain their equations in canonical form.

Returning to the wheat crop example, let us complicate the system, first, by assuming that all processes take time, but that the processes determining $W$ and $P$ are relatively rapid, and second, by introducing additional feedbacks:

> The amount of fertilizer used will adjust (slowly) to previous levels of the wheat price;
> the population will gradually adjust to the amount of wheat available; and
> the weather will be slowly changed by the amount of wheat acreage and the size of population.

We might write the full dynamic system schematically in some such form as:

$$dW/dt = f_W(W, R, F)$$

$$dP/dt = f_P(W, P, N)$$

$$\frac{dF}{dt} = f_F(P, F)$$

$$\frac{dN}{dt} = f_N(N, W)$$

$$\frac{dR}{dt} = f_R(N, R, W).$$

The matrix of coefficients on the right-hand side is given by:

|             | $R$ | $W$        | $F$ | $P$        | $N$        |
|-------------|-----|------------|-----|------------|------------|
| $\dot{R}$   | 1   | $\epsilon$ | 0   | 0          | $\epsilon$ |
| $\dot{W}$   | 1   | 1          | 1   | 0          | 0          |
| $\dot{F}$   | 0   | 0          | 1   | $\epsilon$ | 0          |
| $\dot{P}$   | 0   | 1          | 0   | 1          | 1          |
| $\dot{N}$   | 0   | $\epsilon$ | 0   | 0          | 1          |

where we have introduced $\epsilon$'s instead of 1's as the off-diagonal elements in those processes assumed to be 'slow' relative to the others. That is to say, we assume $R$, $F$, and $N$ can be replaced (approximately) by constants over a period of, say, one year. If we let the $\epsilon$'s approach zero, we are back to the same matrix as in the static case. Moreover, if we then assume that $W$ and $P$ adjust rapidly, we can set their derivatives equal to zero in the dynamic system, obtaining precisely our original static structure.

The notion of 'nearly-ordered' dynamic system illustrated by this example can be appropriately formalized as has been shown by Ando, Fisher, and Simon.[3] Matrices that can be block-triangularized by letting certain elements go to zero at the limit are called *nearly decomposable*. Systems described by nearly decomposable matrices have a number of important special dynamic properties, on one of which the present discussion rests.

We see that the causal ordering in the static case can be interpreted as a set of implicit consequences of assumptions about the relative speeds of various processes in an associated dynamic model. Given these assumptions, the static model represents an approximate short-run equilibrium of the dynamic system.

In moving from the static to the dynamic interpretation of the causal ordering, the exogenous variables, or interventions, in the static system become the 'unmoved movers' of the dynamic system – i.e., variables that act strongly on other variables of the system but are only weakly acted upon by other variables. The definite asymmetry in the matrix of the static system corresponds to relative asymmetry in the matrix of the associated dynamic system.

### 9. DISCRETE VARIABLES

Our final task is to apply the causal ordering notions to the kinds of standard examples that involve discrete variables:

> Striking a dry match in the presence of oxygen, tinder, and fuel will cause a conflagration.

We define the following dichotomous variables: (1), (*S*) struck or unstruck; (2), (*D*) dry or damp; (3), (*O*) oxygen or no oxygen; (4) (*I*) ignited or unignited; (5) (*T*) tinder or no tinder; (6), (*F*) fuel or no fuel; and (7), (*C*) conflagration or no conflagration. The mechanism for lighting matches is specified by the Boolean function.

(1)             $I \equiv S \mathbin{\&} D \mathbin{\&} O.$

The conflagration mechanism is specified by:

(2)        $C \equiv I \& O \& T \& F.$

The exogenous variables are $S, D, O, T$ and $F$, yielding the obvious causal ordering:

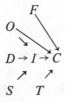

The analysis goes through exactly as in the case of continuous variables, and contraposition creates no problems. The same difficulties as before – but only these difficulties – surround the identification of the individual mechanisms.

## 10. TRANSITION

We now conclude our analysis of causal ordering. It has been shown how such an ordering can be defined formally in a complete structure, and how it is equivalent to identifying the mechanisms of a system. We have explored several ways in which such identification might be accomplished: through prior assumptions about exogenous variables or interventions in the static case, or by employing a standard canonical form of the equations in the dynamic case. Finally, we showed how a causal ordering in a static structure can be identified by deriving the static structure as the short-run equilibrium of an associated dynamic structure. The next task is to show how this explication of causal ordering can be used to provide a basis for the analysis of causal counterfactual conditionals.

## 11. THE APPROACH TO COUNTERFACTUALS THROUGH MODAL CATEGORIZATION

The problem of causal counterfactual conditions can most effectively be formulated in the framework provided by the concept of *belief-contravening hypotheses*, that is, suppositions or assumptions which stand in *logical* conflict with accepted beliefs or known facts.[4] Consider, for the sake of illustration, one of the standard examples from the literature of the subject:

'If the match had been struck, it would have ignited.' The example takes us back to the case discussed in the previous section on 'Discrete Variables.' The case is as follows:

Accepted Facts: $(\sim S_0)$ The match is (in fact) not struck
$(D_0)$ The match is dry
$(O_0)$ Oxygen is present
$(\sim I_0)$ The match does not (in fact) ignite

Accepted Law: $(L)$ Ignition occurs (in the relevant circumstances) if and only if a dry match is struck in an oxygen-containing medium:

$$I \equiv S \& D \& O$$

The counterfactual conditional in question elicits the ostensible consequences of the belief-contravening supposition:

Assume: $(S_0)$ The match is struck

From the standpoint of the abstract logic of the situation, order (i.e., consistency) can be restored in this situation in various ways. We must of course give up the first of the accepted facts, i.e., $(\sim S_0)$. But even then inconsistency remains. We might of course give up the law $(L)$, but this course is obviously undesirable. Retaining $(L)$, three alternatives remain if we wish to maintain the maximum of the accepted facts.

| Alternative 1 | | Alternative 2 | | Alternative 3 | |
|---|---|---|---|---|---|
| Retain | Reject | Retain | Reject | Retain | Reject |
| $D_0$ | $\sim I_0$ | $D_0$ | $O_0$ | $O_0$ | $D_0$ |
| $O_0$ | | $\sim I_0$ | | $\sim I_0$ | |

The choice, in other words, is between three candidates for rejection, namely $\sim I_0$, $O_0$, and $D_0$. A criterion for selecting one of these for rejection is thus needed to vindicate the plausible counterfactual 'If the match had been struck, it would have ignited' over against its implausible competitors

'If the match had been struck it would not have been dry'

and

'If the match had been struck, oxygen would not have been present'

The development of such a *principle of rejection and acceptance* in the face of a belief-contravening hypothesis lies at the heart of the problem of counterfactual conditionals. Note that we have already in effect set up a partial criterion of this kind in our aforementioned determination not to regard the law at issue as candidate for rejection in cases such as that now at issue. In general terms, the procedure to be followed is to sort the various propositions in question into *modal categories* $M_0, M_1, M_2, \ldots, M_n$, devised subject to the conception that the lower the characteristic modal category of the proposition, the less its susceptibility to rejection, and correspondingly the greater the modal index, the greater its susceptibility to rejection.[5]

The leading idea of the line of approach to counterfactuals we are concerned to develop here can now be codified in the following:

*Procedure*: To use the causal ordering of parameters through laws as a basis for allocating the propositions about the facts at issue to modal categories. And specifically to adhere to the: *Rule* — The further down a parameter is in the causal ordering (in terms of its distance from the exogenous variables) the higher the modal category of the proposition about the value of this parameter.

Let us illustrate this procedure in the context of our example.

### 11.1. The Match Ignition Example

Here, the causal ordering of the three parameters is, it will be remembered, as follows:

$$
\begin{array}{l}
O \searrow \\
D \rightarrow I \\
S \nearrow
\end{array}
$$

Using the causal ordering as a basis for modal categorization, we see that $O$ and $D$ will dominate over $I$, so that, forced to a choice between our three alternatives, we retain $D_0$ and $O_0$ and reject $\sim I_0$, thus vindicating the plausible counterfactual 'If the match had been struck, it would have ignited' over against its implausible competitors.

### 11.2. The Gas Law Example

Let us begin with Case I of our piston example, where the experimenter can (directly) adjust the temperature and the pressure, with the result that the

causal ordering is

$$P \searrow$$
$$\quad V$$
$$T \nearrow$$

Assuming that in the case under consideration the actual values are $P_0$, $T_0$, and $V_0$. We thus have the following information-base:

$L$(law):  (1) $PV = kT$
Facts:   (2) $P = P_0$
       (3) $T = T_0$
       (4) $V = V_0$

We are now asked to indicate the counterfactual consequences of the (false) hypothesis: Suppose that the temperature is doubled

$$T = 2T_0.$$

Obviously (1) is to be retained and (3) must be rejected: The question is one of choice between (2) and (4), viz.

(A)      If the temperature were doubled, then the pressure would be doubled.
(B)      If the temperature were doubled, then the volume would be doubled.

Now given the causal ordering at issue, with $V$ as the structurally dependent variable, relatively more vulnerable to rejection because of its higher modal categorization, we would reject (4), with the result of leading to an endorsement of the conditional ($B$).

As before, the adiabatic case is more complex. We recall that in this case, we must include the law of conservation of energy:

(2′)      $E = PV + qT.$

Combining this relation with the gas law, we have:

(4)      $\bar{E} = (k + q)T,$

from which we see that 'If the temperature were doubled . . .' implies 'If the initial total energy were doubled . . .' The causal ordering, previously derived was:

Here also in the comparison between $P$ and $V$, $V$ as the structurally dependent variable is relatively more vulnerable because of its higher modal categorization. And thus again, we are led to an endorsement of $(B)$: 'If the temperature were doubled, then the volume would be doubled.' However, a careful writer might think it more precise and idiomatic to say: 'If the energy were increased *so as to double the temperature*, the volume would also be doubled.'

This example suggests that, in careful English usage, the counterfactual is meant to imply that its conditional stands in a relation of causal precedence to its consequence. As a final example, we shall return to the wheat growing relations to see whether this generalization is warranted.

## 11.3. The Wheat Growing Example

We follow exactly the same procedure as with the previous examples to see what counterfactual assertions can be made about the wheat-growing relations described earlier. The causal ordering among fertilizer $(F)$, rain $(R)$, wheat crop $(W)$, population $(N)$, and wheat price $(P)$, was:

$$F \searrow$$
$$\quad W \searrow$$
$$R \nearrow \quad P$$
$$\quad N \nearrow$$

Supplementing the two laws from which this ordering derives, we have the facts – the actual amount of fertilizer, rain, wheat crop, population, and wheat price last year, say. What follows from the counterfactual premise: 'If the wheat crop had been smaller last year . . .'?

Retaining the laws, and using the causal ordering to determine which factual premises have modal precedence, we obtain readily:

> If the wheat crop had been smaller last year, the price would have been higher.

However, this counterfactual does not resolve all the contradictions, for the hypothesis of the smaller wheat crop is not consistent with the conjunction of the law determining the wheat crop as a function of rain and fertilizer, and the actual amounts of rain and fertilizer. In the usual treatment of the counterfactual, one or the other of the latter facts – the amount of rain or the amount of fertilizer – would have to yield. But both of these have smaller modal indices than the size of the wheat crop. It is reassuring, under these circumstances, that niether of the corresponding counterfactuals is idiomatic:

> If the wheat crop had been smaller last year, less fertilizer would have been applied to it.
> If the wheat crop had been smaller last year, there would have been less rain.

Instead, we would regard it as perfectly idiomatic to say:

> If the wheat crop had been smaller last year, there would have been either less rain or less fertilizer applied.

Even more idiomatic would be:

> (In order) for the wheat crop to have been smaller last year, there would have to have been less rain or less fertilizer.

Thus we see that distinctions are made in English that call attention to the causal ordering among the variables in a counterfactual statement. The ordinary counterfactual corresponds to the case where the cause is the antecedent, and the effect the consequent. Where the causal ordering is reversed, more elaborate locutions, with the modals 'must' or 'have to,' are used.

## 12. CONCLUSION

These examples of the preceding section illustrate the proposed line of attack on causal counterfactual conditionals. First the counterfactual proposition at issue is articulated through the device of a belief-contravening supposition. Then the principle of rejection and retention for the resolution of the resultant conflict of logical contradiction is determined through the mechanism of a system of modal categories. Finally, resort is made to the concept of a causal ordering to serve as a guide for modal categorization of the factual (non-law) propositions at issue.

It is among the merits of this approach that it yields perfectly 'natural' results in underwriting as plausible, in all of the standard examples treated in the literature — just those counterfactuals that are consonant with our informal, presystematic intuitions on the matter. Moreover, reliance on causal orderings also solves in a natural way the problem of the otherwise unnatural consequences of the contraposition of laws.

## NOTES

[1] Technical details underlying the following explication of 'cause' will be found in [5]. The account here has been generalized, however, to encompass nonlinear as well as linear structures.
[2] See [3] and [2].
[3] See [1]. The formal development of the theory is given in Chapters 4 and 5, and a number of illustrative examples in Chapter 6.
[4] This approach to counterfactuals is developed in considerable detail in [4].
[5] In the present context this summary presentation of the matter will prove sufficient. For a more detailed development of the ideas see [4].

## REFERENCES

[1] Ando *et al.*, *Essays on the Structure of Social Science Models* (Cambridge Mass: MIT Press, 1963).
[2] Angell, R. B, 'A Propositional Logic with Subjunctive Conditionals,' *Journal of Symbolic Logic* **27**, 327–343 (1962).
[3] Burks, A. W., 'The Logic of Causal Propositions', *Mind, N.S.* **60**, 363–382 (1951).
[4] Rescher, N., *Hypothetical Reasoning* (Amsterdam: North-Holland Publishing Co., 1964).
[5] Simon, Herbert A., 'Causal Ordering and Identifiability', in W. C. Hood and T. C. Koopmans (eds.), *Studies in Econometric Method* (New York: Wiley, 1953) (reprinted as Chapter 2.1 of this volume).

# THE LOGIC OF IMPERATIVES

The papers of this section, like those of Section 2, had a long gestation period (See note 1 to Chapter 3.1). Since their general theme — the model-theoretic treatment of imperatives — has already been considered briefly in the general introduction to this volume, no extensive comments on that topic are required here. A few notes are in order, however, on some specific points discussed in these chapters.

1. Chapter 3.1 (the last half) and Chapter 3.2 examine the logical structure of means-ends analysis, a central component in most problem-solving algorithms. The application of means-ends analysis to problem solving is taken up again in Chapter 4.3, and then, in its implications for scientific discovery, in the chapters of Section 5.

2. Part IV of Chapter 3.2 contains a discussion of the paradox of the *Meno* — the impossibility of discovering that which we do not already know. The solution proposed here is developed more fully and formally in Chapter 5.5.

3. The thesis of this section — that there is no need for a special modal logic of imperatives — has not gone unchallenged. In the volume from which Chapter 3.2 is reprinted,[1] will be found a lively interchange between Prof. N. D. Belnap, Jr., who was the discussant of my paper, and myself. The three substantive issues raised in that interchange were whether my proposal could handle conditional imperatives, contractual offers, and obligations formulated as sets of rules instead of utility maximization requirements. The answer to all three questions is an unqualified 'yes.' The theory of games and dynamic programming theory, both of which are model-theoretic formulations of problems of action, deal with conditional imperatives, which are called 'strategies' in those contexts. Since contract bridge can be formulated as a game in the game-theoretic sense, contractual offers can clearly also be handled. Finally, the diet problem, used as an example in Chapter 3.1, shows how constraints are expressed within a linear programming framework.

4. Using a special modal logic of action as the central inferential machine for problem solving programs in artificial intelligence has been proposed by John McCarthy and Patrick Hayes.[2] These proposals run into the same difficulties that have been encountered with all modal logics for this purpose,

in particular, difficulty in formulating a principle of composition that is neither too weak nor too strong. I have discussed this difficulty in my paper, 'On Reasoning About Actions', which appears as Chapter 8 in H. Simon and L. Siklossy (eds.), *Representation and Meaning* (Englewood Cliffs, N.J.: Prentice-Hall, 1972). There I reach a pessimistic conclusion about the possibilities of circumventing it within the confines of a modal logic. In Chapter 7 of that same book, Harry E. Pople, Jr., ('A Goal-Oriented Language for the Computer') describes a model-oriented problem-solving system that also has capabilities for modal inference. In Pople's scheme, modal reasoning, even when it has only heuristic value (i.e., may lead to erroneous inferences about the real environment), can be used to aid and supplement means-ends search through the space of a model.

## NOTES

[1] Nicholas Rescher (ed.), *The Logic of Decision and Action* (Pittsburgh: University of Pittsburgh Press, 1967).

[2] See J. McCarthy, 'Situations, Actions and Causal Laws', in M. Minsky (ed.,), *Semantic Information Processing* (Cambridge, Mass.: MIT Press, 1969), and J. McCarthy and Patrick Hayes, 'Some Philosophical Problems from the Standpoint of Artificial Intelligence', in B. Meltzer and D. Michie (eds.), *Machine Intelligence 4* (Edinburgh: Edinburgh University Press, 1969).

# THE LOGIC OF RATIONAL DECISION†*

Philosophy has long struggled with the problem of deducing one imperative sentence from another. Do the same laws of logic govern such deductions as apply to declarative sentences, or different laws? If different, can the laws of logic applying to imperatives be derived from the laws applying to declaratives?

The Infantry Field Manual of the United States Army at one time contained the following passage:

Surprise is an essential element of a successful attack. Its effects should be striven for in small as well as in large operations. Infantry effects surprise by concealment of the time and place of the attack, screening of its dispositions, rapidity of maneuver, deception, and the avoidance of stereotyped procedures.[1]

The second sentence, which contains an explicit 'ought', might be rendered: (1) 'Employ surprise!' This command appears to follow from the first statement combined with another imperative that is left implicit: (2) 'Attack successfully!' (3) Success in attacks implies use of surprise.

An adequate logic of imperatives might well permit the derivation of a sentence like (1) from the conjunction of (2) and (3). Similarly, the last sentence of the quoted paragraph, conjoined with (1), could yield such injunctions as: 'Conceal the time and place of attack!' 'Screen your dispositions!' 'Manoeuvre rapidly!' 'Be deceptive!' and 'Avoid stereotyped procedures!'

There have been numerous proposals for the construction of systems of logic that would permit such inferences to be drawn. Some of these proposals erect systems analogous to, but independent of, the standard systems of demonstrative logic. Other proposals permit chains of inferences only in the declarative mode, but supplement the demonstrative logic by rules of correspondence between certain declarative and imperative sentences, respectively.

What shall be the test of whether a system of imperative logic is adequate? One possible test would be to compare it with the practices of applied

† [*British Journal for the Philosophy of Science* 16, 169–186 (1965)].

scientists who would seem to have frequent occasions for deriving one imperative from another. What logic does a physician use to conclude: 'Give the patient two aspirin tablets'? How does the engineer arrive at: 'Build the bridge according to Plan A'? And by what reasoning does the management scientist advise the business firm: 'Produce 2,000 units of product next month'?

## 1. NORMATIVE AND POSITIVE ECONOMICS

Implicit in the practice of any applied science there lies some form, or forms, of imperative logic. Let us try to find what this logic is, with particular reference to management science, or applied economics.[2]

Normative economics and positive economics (i.e. pure or descriptive economics) live side by side in close symbiosis. Central to the theory of the firm, in its positive version, is the assumption that firms behave so as to maximise profit. But when the applied economist uses the theory as a basis for advising a business firm, he replaces the existential assertion, 'Firms maximise profit', with the imperative, 'Maximise profit!' Often the very same scientist finds himself, on one day, wearing the hat of applied economist, on another day, the hat of pure economist. I have seen no indication that he has any feeling that when he changes his hat he changes his logic — that the rules of inference in the two cases are different. If the profession is faced with a plurality of logics, it is blissfully unaware of it.

### 1.1. The Positive Theory of the Firm

There is no reason, however, why we should limit ourselves to informal tests of this kind. By examining the classical theory of the firm directly we can satisfy ourselves, with as much rigour as we please, as to whether the same or different rules of logic are used when the theory is employed positively and normatively, respectively. The theory is readily put in mathematical form, but for our purposes a non-mathematical version will be adequate.

Stripping the theory to its barest essentials, we assume a firm that manufactures a single product, and sells each month's product during the same period.

1. The total cost ($C$), incurred by the firm during the month is a function of the quantity of product ($X$), and of a variable ($a$) that sums up the effects of supply conditions — wage rates, costs of materials, and so on.

2. The price ($P$) at which the product is sold is a function of the quantity,

($X$), and of a variable ($\beta$) that sums up the effects of demand conditions — e.g. consumer incomes.

3. We define total revenue for the month as price ($P$) times quantity ($X$), and we define profit ($\pi$) as the difference between total revenue ($PX$) and total cost ($C$).

4. The positive theory is completed by the assumption that $X^*$, the quantity actually produced, equals $X^M$, the quantity that maximises profit.

4'. On the other hand, the normative theory is completed by the injunction: Choose the production quantity $X^*$ that will maximise profit!

To avoid irrelevant detail in our exposition, let us simply assume that there is some unique, finite, positive production quantity for which profit assumes an absolute maximum. Then, the positive economist could derive from (4) and (3) the familiar theorem:

5. Marginal cost (change of cost per unit increase in quantity) equals marginal revenue (change in total revenue per unit increase in quantity) when production is set at the level that maximises profit.

## 1.2. The Normative Theory of the Firm

If we now observe what the normative economist, starting with assumptions (1), (2), (3), and (4'), does in practice, we see that he first replaces (4') with (4), derives (5), and then obtains from (5) a new imperative:

5'. Set production at the level where marginal revenue equals marginal cost!

In asserting (5'), he appears to have added to the declarative logic a symmetric rule that permits him to replace an imperative with an existential statement, and an existential statement with an imperative. What is the exact nature of this rule?

Note, first of all, that the rule does not permit us to convert *any* equation in the original system into a corresponding imperative. For example, it would not be correct to convert (3) into:

6. Set the production quantity so that profit equals total revenue minus total cost!

Injunction (6) is meaningless, because (3), being a definition, holds identically in the production quantity, hence (6) gives no command at all, unless it be 'Do something!' Statement (4), on the other hand, is not an identity in the production quantity. The remaining three assumptions are satisfied by all nonnegative production quantities; only a subset of these values (in fact, under our assumptions, a unique value) also satisfies (4). It would appear that the conversion of a declarative into an imperative statement is meaningful only if the former is not an identity in the variable to which the command applies in the latter.

Thus far we have had little to say about the environmental variables $\alpha$ and $\beta$, that appear in our relations (1) and (2). Suppose we had additional empirical information about one or both of these parameters, say:

7. The supply conditions, $\alpha$, lie between $\underline{\alpha}$ and $\bar{\alpha}$. Can we convert (7) into an imperative?

7'. Set the supply conditions, $\alpha$, at some point between $\underline{\alpha}$ and $\bar{\alpha}$!

We would, of course, regard (7') as illegitimate, since the variable whose values the command limits is not a variable controlled by the recipient of the command, the firm.

There appear to be two conditions, then, for the conversion of an existential statement into a command. *First, the statement should not be an identity in the command variable; second, the command variable should be a variable controlled by the recipient of the command.*[3] Note that the operator '!', like the universal and existential operators, binds the variable to which it applies — converts it from a free to a bound variable.

The conversion from imperative to declarative mode has not such restrictions. Given any system containing imperatives, by removing the imperative operators from them, we obtain a positive system in which the erstwhile recipients of commands behave as though they were obeying those commands.

### 1.3. A Restatement of the Positive-Normative Relation

Let us now generalise our results. Normative reasoning always takes place in the context of an empirical system. A set of *variables*, each with a range of admissible values, defines the space of logically possible states of the system — the *state space*. A set of *empirical laws*, specifying certain relations among the variables, restricts the *empirically possible* states of the system to a subspace of the state space. The subspace of empirical possibilities has fewer degrees of freedom than the state space. There is a set of *independent variables*, equal in number to the degrees of freedom of the subspace; fixing a value for each of the independent variables is equivalent to selecting a particular, empirically possible, point in the state space.

The independent variables belong to two mutually exclusive and exhaustive subsets: *environmental variables*, and *command variables*. The command variables are those postulated to be controllable by the actor to whose behaviour the commands apply; the others are the environmental variables.[4]

To this system may now be added additional equations, provided these are consistent with the original set. Alternatively, commands may be added on the conditions: (1) that the variables bound by the command operators are command variables, and (2) that when the commands have all been converted to the corresponding empirical relations, the resulting system of relations is consistent.

After conversion of the commands, new equations may be derived by application of the ordinary laws of logic. Any of these new relations that contains command variables may be converted to a command by binding one or more of its command variables with the command operator. From the method of their derivation, it is clear that the commands so derived will be consistent, in any reasonable interpretation of that term, and realisable.

Let us return now to our example of the theory of the firm. In the system described by statements (1)–(3), the state of the world during any time period is specified by the array of values of the variables: profit, production quantity, price, total cost, supply conditions, and demand conditions. For purposes of this example, it is best to consider all six variables as directly observable. The supply variable might be a statistical index of wholesale prices and wage rates; the demand variable, an index of disposable income; the production quantity, a measure of actual revenue received; cost, the total amount paid out to employees and suppliers; and profit, the actual change in the amount of money in the till from the beginning to the end of the period. Under this interpretation, each of the three equations states an empirical law – Equation (3), for example, denies the operation here of the Scriptural moth and rust.

Consider the admissible sets of simultaneous values of the six variables. Statements (1) and (2) each select out a subset (call them A and B) of this set, by restricting the values of $C$ and $P$, respectively, as functions of the others. These two subsets, A and B, intersect in a smaller subset (call it C) in which both equations are satisfied. Similarly the equation, (3), further restricts the values of the profit, defining a subset, D, of C. Any triplet of values of production quantity, supply conditions, and demand conditions determines a unique element of the subset. Taking the latter three variables as the independent variables of the system, we have the causal ordering:

$$\left.\begin{array}{c}\alpha \\ X \\ \beta\end{array}\right]\begin{array}{c}\to C \\ \to P\end{array}\right] \to \pi$$

Next, we assign each independent variable to an agent, the production quantity to the firm; the supply and demand conditions to its environment or 'nature'. Any additional relation, like (4), that we add to the system, which is consistent with the previous relations, further limits the admissible simultaneous values of $X$, $\alpha$ and $\beta$ to a subset of the subset D previously defined. It defines an additional empirical law. If it is not an identity in a variable assigned to a particular agent, and if it can be solved for that variable, then by binding the variable with the command operator we can convert it into a command to that agent regarding that variable. Statement $(4')$ is such a command.

Although the supply and demand conditions are not mentioned explicitly in Command $5'$, it can readily be seen from the derivation of that statement that it expresses the command variable, the production quantity, as a function of those conditions, hence expresses a conditional command. The command becomes absolute when the state of the environment − the actual values of the supply and demand conditions − are known.

*1.4. Extensions to Uncertainty and Utility*

The particular example we have used is extremely simple. No new problems arise, however, for the logic of imperatives in extending the analysis to the much more complex systems that arise in actual applications of normative economics to real-world problems. I shall therefore only sketch these extensions briefly.

Often, the values of one or more of the environmental parameters are not known with certainty to the decision maker. Instead, he may know certain probability distributions of these variables (the case of *risk*), or even this information may be lacking (the case of *uncertainty*). Here, the profit maximising conditions are simply replaced by conditions that the action be selected so as to maximise the expected value of profits, or to minimax profits − to select that action which will maximise profits for the most unfavourable values of the environmental parameters.

In a still further extension, a whole sequence of decisions is to be made, in successive time intervals. The problem cannot be reduced to the previous one, for new information regarding the environmental variables becomes available as time moves on. Hence, the situation describes a dynamic programming problem, essentially, a problem in the calculus of variations.[5]

Another direction of generalisation takes us into considerations of utility, which is a somewhat more complex and subtle criterion than profit. Unlike profits, utilities are not directly observable. Instead, it is postulated that the consumer exhibits a certain consistency in his choices; if we observe him in a sequence of choices — which bundles he prefers to which others, as his alternatives change — we can infer what his utility function is, and what his probability estimates are of outcomes, from his choice behaviour. Again, the rules for conversion to and from imperatives are exactly the same as before.[6]

## 1.5. Normative Side Constraints

Some additional, highly interesting, considerations are introduced in the linear programming models that are so widely used in both positive and normative economics today.[7] Again, let us consider a very simple example: the optimal diet problem. We are given a list of foods, and for each its price, the calory content, and content of each mineral and vitamin relevant to nutrition. Then we are given a set of nutritional requirements, which may include minimum daily intake of minerals, vitamins, and calories, and may also limit maximum intake of some or all of these components.

The diet problem is to find that sublist of foods and their quantities that will meet the nutritional requirements at least cost. The problem can be formalised along the following lines:

1. The total consumption of each nutritional element is the sum of the quantities of that element for each of the foods consumed.

2. The total quantity of each nutritional element must lie between specified limits.

3. The quantity of each food consumed must be non-negative, although it may be zero.

4. Finally, the total cost of the diet (the sum of the products of the quantities of each food by their prices) is to be minimised.

A diet (the solution is not necessarily unique) that satisfies all the relations (2), (3), (4) is called an *optimal* diet. A diet that satisfies the inequalities (2) and (3) (called *constraints*), but which is not necessarily a minimum cost diet, is called a *feasible* diet (and in this context might also be called a *satisfactory* diet).

Relations (1) to (4) are all declarative in mode. Suppose, for the moment, they have a unique (vector) solution, $\overline{X}^*$. Then, we can make the positive statement that a diet is optimal if and only if the food quantities in it are those specified by $\overline{X}^*$. No unusual kind of logic is involved in arriving at this statement. Suppose we find a (non-unique) vector, $\overline{X}+$, that satisfies relations (1) throught (3). Then we can make the positive statement that the diet described by $\overline{X}+$ is feasible or satisfactory.

Now let us view the situation normatively. Equations (1) and inequalities

(3) are of the nature of technological constraints, imposed by the environment. The prices are also assumed to be environmental givens. There remain the $N + M$ quantities of foods and nutritional elements, subject to the $M$ linear constraints (1), and the $N$ inequalites (3).

We now add to (1) and (3) two simultaneous commands, (2′) and (4′):

2′. Select a diet $X^*$, so that the nutritional requirements are satisfied!

4′. Select a diet $X^*$, so that the cost is minimised!

Note that the command variables in both cases are the quantities of foods that make up the diet, although the variables that appear explicitly in (2) are the nutritional elements. Hence, we see that, as in the previous example, our designation of the command variables depends on a prior specification of the causal structure of the model consisting of (1) and (3), and a selection of the variables that are assumed controllable by the recipient of the command.

Having postulated the commands (2′) and (4′), we convert them to positive statements (2) and (4), as before, and solve the resulting system for a diet that satisfies all the relations. We now perform the inverse conversion to an imperative:

5′. Select a diet, $X^*$. that satisfies both (2) and (4)!

The present example differs from the example of the theory of the firm in two respects. First, instead of a single minimisation (or maximisation) command, we now have a whole set of commands, that operate in conjuction: minimise the cost of the diet *subject to* the condition that it meet the nutritional stipulations of (2). Again we see that reasoning about imperatives requires, as context, a complete system of alternatives and consequences; the conversion operation is defined relative to that complete system, which takes into account the causal ordering of the variables as well as interactions among them.

The second new feature in this model is the notion of feasible or satisfactory actions that we obtain by striking off condition (4). Let us now consider the system consisting of the conditions (1) and (3) and the command (2′). In general, this system will have many solutions, rather than a unique one. Suppose that $X^°$ is one of these solutions. Is it legitimate to convert to the command (5″)?

5″. Select the diet $X^°$!

The distinction between (5′) and (5″) is, of course, the familiar distinction between necessary and sufficient conditions. If we call the solution $X^°$, the means, and the relations to be satisfied – in particular, those relations that were converted from imperatives – the ends, then in the case of the command (5′) the means is both necessary and sufficient to the end, while in the case of the command (5″), the means is only sufficient to the end.

## 1.6.  Summary of Part 1

Before turning to a more thorough investigation of means-end relations, and of sufficiency and necessity of means, let me sum up this first part of our inquiry into the logic of imperatives and rational decision. No different brand of logic is used in normative economics from that used in positive economics. On the contrary, the logic employed is the standard logic of declarative statements.

Imperatives enter the normative systems through the rules of correspondence that permit commands to be converted into existential statements, and existential statements into commands. The conversion process always takes place in the context of a complete model, with the command variables and environmental variables designated, the state of knowledge about the latter specified, and the causal relations among variables determined. In such a context, commands that bind one or more of the command variables can be converted to the corresponding declarative statements; while declarative statements that can be solved for command variables, but are not identities in those variables, can be converted to commands by binding the command variables with the command operator. In the latter conversions, two alternatives are open: the conversion can be allowed always, or it can be allowed only when the decision variables are determined uniquely. The freer rule might be thought to create a danger that contradictory commands will be derived, a question we shall take up in Part 2.

## 2. MEANS AND ENDS

The terms 'means' and 'ends' are common in the literature of problem solving, but rarely occur in normative writings on economics or statistical decision theory. Understanding why this is so will prove enlightening. In the models we have been considering, the decision maker is faced with a *given* set of alternatives. In the theory of the firm, for example, he may choose any positive number, $X$, as the production for the next period. There is associated with each admissible alternative choice a profit, or a utility, or a cost. The decision maker's task is to choose the action that leads to the preferred consequences. This he accomplishes by making a calculation, which may be trivial (as in the simple theory of the firm), tedious (as in a large linear programming problem), or impossible to carry out in practice (as in determining the best move by the minimax criterion in a chess game). The positive theory asserts or implies that the decision maker makes the calculation, or finds the answer without making it. The calculation itself, the process of making it, is not usually a part of the theory.

## 2.1 Consequences and Actions

In the theory of the firm, the quantity produced, $X$, is, after the fact, an observable comparable to the other five observables of the system. But $X$, regarded as a command variable, is not an observable at all; it is an action. In fact, we can say that the after-the-fact observed quantity of goods produced is a consequence of the *action* of producing the goods in exactly the same way that the cost is a consequence of that action. It is these consequences that are represented in the state space, not the actions.

Consider the behaviour of a child who is just learning to speak. The child hears the sound 'ahh', say. There is no built-in connection in his nervous system that allows him, on hearing the sound, to perform the appropriate movements with tongue, lips, larynx and lungs that produce that sound. The connection is a purely arbitrary one between certain stimuli, travelling primarily from sensory organs to brain, and certain responses, travelling primarily from brain to muscles.[8]

The sound as heard by the child belongs to what we have been calling the state space; the signals controlling the muscular actions that produce the sound belong to a (different) space of actions. The child's learning consists precisely in using the feedback through the environment to establish a correspondence between actions – and heard sounds. (A deaf child cannot, for this very reason, learn to speak in this way.) Once the correspondence has been established, and uttering the desired sound is no longer problematic, it is convenient simply to ignore the distinction between the action and its immediate consequence, and represent both in the state space.

A situation is problematic whenever there is a weak link in the chain of learned connections between actions and consequences, between means and ends. For the child, the weak link is often very close to the action end of the chain – his problem is how to produce an 'ahh' sound. Even in the business firm, however, the problem may just as well be 'How do I get the factory to produce at level $X$ ' as 'What is the best level of production?' The classical theory of the firm assumes the answer to the former question is unproblematic, hence it confounds the action with the resulting production.

The language of classical decision theory, then, describes the world as it is experienced, and refers to actions by identifying them with their most direct and invariable consequences. We must now inquire whether the very simple scheme we used for avoiding an independent logic of imperatives in such a language is also satisfactory when we add a second language of actions, and when we consider the mapping of actions upon consequences to be problematic.

## 2.2. A Language of Actions

Let us first propose a general form for a language of actions, fashioned after modern computer languages.[9] Each statement in the language is an imperative directing that a particular action be performed (e.g. that a machine instruction be executed). A programme is a sequence of such instructions – not, however, interpreted simply as a conjunction of the imperatives, for the sequence defines a particular time order in which the instructions are to be executed, and the specified time ordering may cause instructions to be executed more than once.

The relation between the sequence of commands that constitutes a programme and its consequences is seldom unproblematic. Programming is the art of designing sequences that have desired consequences, and programming almost always requires a more or less extended period of 'debugging' during which the programme is tested, and deviations between actual and desired outcomes are gradually removed. Though there is a perfectly definite function of programmes on to consequences (expressed in terms of outputs of calculations), the function is immensely complex, and discovering a programme that has specified consequences may be a difficult or impossible intellectual task.

## 2.3. Logical Inference in an Action Language

Programme instructions follow one another temporally, they do not stand in a deductive relation to one another. Hence, the rules of programme organisation have nothing to do with the logic of imperatives, as that term is usually understood.

Many programming languages, however, allow for the introduction of *closed sub-routines.* A closed sub-routine is a programme to which a name is assigned, and which can be inserted by use of its name, as though it were a single instruction, in another programme. Thus, in an appropriate language, we might have the programme:

> Walk one block
> Step with left foot
> Step with right foot
> Halt if end of block, otherwise repeat

This programme might be used as a closed sub-routine in another programme:

> Go to Times Square
> Walk one block
> Halt if Times Square, otherwise—
> Cross street and repeat

The relation of 'Walk one block!' to the three instructions that define that imperative, or of 'Go to Times Square!' to its defining imperatives is clearly a relation of end to means.

Now we can raise again the question of inferential relations. From the injunction: 'Go to Times Square!' can we deduce the imperative conclusion 'Walk one block; then halt if Times Square; otherwise, cross street and repeat!'? Patently, the deduction is invalid, for there may be many other ways of reaching Times Square, following other sequences of actions — walking by other routes, taking a taxi, taking a subway, and so on. The programme constitutes a *sufficient* condition for execution of the sub-routine it defines; it is not a *necessary* condition.

## 2.4. Heuristic Programmes

The generalisation that means are sometimes sufficient, but seldom necessary conditions to their ends holds not only when the means are described by a programme (a recipe) but even when the means are described in terms of states of affairs to be realised (a blueprint). Thus, means for bridging Puget Sound were specified by the blueprints for the Tacoma Bridge. Many other designs could have been synthesised towards the same end. As a matter of fact, the Tacoma Bridge did not even prove to be a sufficient means, for under high winds it collapsed. The sufficiency of the means is almost always empirical rather than logical.

Standard design processes employ no new rules of inference from imperatives to imperatives. The design, viewed as a set of imperatives, is simply converted to the corresponding empirical statements. Then the latter, together with the other empirical laws that govern the situation, are used as premises to be tested for consistency with other premises converted in the same way from the design criteria.

Programmes of action that are means to ends only in this pragmatic sense are often called *heuristic programmes*. They are not necessary to their ends, they are not sufficient in any strict sense, they satisfy no particular criteria of optimality. Their claim for consideration is that they frequently accomplish the desired goal, and that when they fail, something else can be tried. They are used because there are relatively few real-life situations where programmes of action having stronger properties than these are available. The map of actions on consequences is seldom simple and unproblematic.

## 2.5. *Problem-Solving Programmes*

Thus far, we have maintained the assumption that means are given, however problematic their relations to ends. We have talked about how the Tacoma Bridge design could be tested, not how the design might have been arrived at in the first place. In practical life, an even larger time and effort is involved in arriving at possible courses of action than in evaluating them, once they have been designed. Problem-solving activity is activity aimed at both the synthesis and evaluation of performance programmes for accomplishing desired ends.

In problem-solving activity, we have to consider the relations of three sets of imperatives: (A) imperatives prescribing performance goals and constraints; (B) imperatives prescribing performance programmes for attaining the goals (A); and (C) imperatives prescribing problem-solving programmes for discovering and evaluating the performance programmes (B).

In the normative models considered in Part 1, no line was drawn between the performance programme (B), and the problem-solving programme (C). In the simple model of the theory of the firm, the optimal action (B) is discovered deductively from the equations of the system, and the method of its derivation guarantees that it satisfies the goal as well as any side constraints that have been imposed. Evaluation is complete as soon as the design has been found.

The same may be said of the linear programming model for the optimal diet problem — with one qualification. In this case, the derivation (C) of the optimal solution (B) is not a trivial matter. If the problem is large, it calls for powerful algorithms and powerful computational means. Under these circumstances, a normative theory of linear programming must include prescriptions of effective computation procedures (C). The theory is incomplete if the calculations are not performable by the kinds of information processing systems — humans or computers — available to perform them. Normative theories are concerned with *procedural means*, processes for finding programmes that will attain the ends, as well as with the substance of the programmes themselves.

We may now ask of problem-solving programmes: is there implicit in them a logic of imperatives different from the conversion scheme that we have already examined? By inspecting the structure of normative and positive theories of heuristic problem solving, we reach the same answer as before. No special logic of imperatives is needed; simply rules for converting imperatives to declarative statements, and declaratives to imperatives.

By way of example let us examine the choice of a strategy in a game of chess when the player is in a favourable position. He can set himself the task of 'designing' or discovering a strategy (performance programme) that, in spite of anything his opponent may do, will lead to checkmate of the opponent. The strategy, if discovered, is a *sufficient* means (B) to the goal of checkmate (A).

As a matter of fact, there exists a systematic algorithm that will discover a checkmating strategy in any position where there is one. It can be shown beyond doubt that strong human players do not use this strategy — and for a simple reason: it would require astronomical numbers of calculations. Nor could any computer be made powerful enough to execute it in a reasonable time.

On the other hand, a heuristic computer programme has in fact been written that is quite effective in finding checkmating strategies.[10] Moreover, this programme parallels, in its gross qualitative features, the programmes used by good human players. Many alternative programmes could probably be devised having the same general characteristics. As in the earlier examples of heuristic performance programmes, the logical relation of means to end in this procedural programme is weak. The checkmate search programme is not necessary to the end of discovering a checkmate strategy. It is not even sufficient; there is no guarantee that if a forced checkmate is actually attainable in the position, the programme in question will discover it. There is only empirical evidence that the programme is often efficient — requires only a moderate amount of search — and no evidence whatsoever that other programmes are not more efficient. The strongest claim we can reasonably make for it is that in a number of situations, and with moderate search effort, it has found checkmates that would do credit to a chess master.

In the present instance the criterion of success is relatively specific — the programme finds a checkmate strategy, or it does not. Thus the performance programme (B) here is logically sufficient for achieving the goal (A), while the procedural programme (C) is only a heuristic means for discovering the performance programme (B). If we examine the structure of problem-solving programmes for other tasks — for example, a more general programme for playing chess — we find that even such specificity is usually lacking. No one has devised a chess-playing programme that looks for 'best' moves, and there is reason to believe that construction of such a programme is infeasible.[11]. A programme might, however, play excellent chess by searching for good moves, and terminating its computation as soon as one is found. From all the available evidence, this is precisely what strong human chess players do. Manageable algorithms for discovering solutions to optimisation problems are known for only very restricted classes of problems. If the optimisation goals are replaced by satisficing goals, it often becomes very much easier to discover adequate performance programmes.

The problem-solving process is not a process of 'deducing' one set of imperatives (the performance programme) from another set (the goals). Instead, it is a process of selective trial and error, using heuristic rules derived from previous experience, that is sometimes successful in *discovering* means that are more or less efficacious in attaining some end. It is legitimate to regard the imperatives embodying the means as 'derived' in some sense from the imperatives embodying the ends; but the process of derivation is not a deductive process, it is one of discovery. If we want a name for it, we can appropriately use the name coined by Peirce and revived recently by Norwood Hanson: it is a *retroductive* process. The nature of this process — which has been sketched roughly here — is the main subject of the theory of problem solving in both its positive and normative versions.

### 3. CONCLUSION

This paper has undertaken to throw some light on the logic of imperatives by examining areas of scientific activity where imperatives enter into the scheme of things. Part 1 examined the classical theories of rational decision that have developed in economics and statistical decision theory. Part 2 examined the logical relations of means and end in various programming and problem-solving structures.

In all cases we have seen that the logic used in positive theories is exactly the same as the logic used in normative theories. Speaking strictly, there is never any occasion to deduce one imperative from another. There is frequent occasion, however, to convert an imperative to a declarative statement, and adjoin it to a set of empirical statements. There is occasion, also, to convert a derived empirical statement to an imperative, by binding a command variable. The conditions for carrying out these conversions have been stated.

The final paragraphs of Part 2 show that there is also frequent occasion to obtain one set of imperatives from another set by processes of discovery or retroduction, but that the relation between the initial set and the derived set is not a relation of logical implication.

## NOTES

*The work reported here was supported in part by a grant from the Carnegie Corporation and in part by the Public Health Service Research Grant MH-07722-01 from the National Institute of Mental Health. An earlier version of this paper was delivered at a joint seminar of Western Reserve University and Case Institute of Technology on Rational Values and Decision, 7 October 1964.

[1] *Complete Tactics, Infantry Rifle Battalion* Washington, 1940, *Infantry Journal*, p. 20. The problem treated in Part 1 is stated, but the solution only hinted at in *Administrative Behavior*, New York, 1947, Chapters III and IV, which in turn is based on my doctoral dissertation, *The Theory of Administrative Decision* (University of Chicago, 1942, unpublished). My debt to Jorgen Jörgensen, 'Imperatives and Logic', *Erkenntnis* 7, 288–296 (1938), will be evident. I owe an equally large, but more recently incurred, debt to Nicholas Rescher, who has kindly allowed me to read an unpublished manuscript, *The Logic of Commands* (London: Routledge & Kegan Paul, published, 1966) that develops and formalizes the point of view first suggested by Jörgensen. While I start from a rather different end of the problem than does Professor Rescher, our conclusions, though distinct are not mutually incompatible. In particular, Rescher's notion of the termination statement of a command corresponds to what is here called the declarative statement obtained by conversion of the command. But while Rescher seeks to construct a separate normative logic, I undertake to show that such a construction is not actually necessary.

[2] Applied economics is especially suitable for this undertaking because the field is characterised by a high degree of formalisation and self-awareness about matters methodological. Thus engineering design is only now beginning to approach the level of sophistication in decision theory that has been present in economics and statistics for a generation. While the examples are carried through in this paper in non-mathematical form, the rigour of the analysis can readily be tested (and, indeed, I have tested it) by making a simple mathematical translation.

[3] Rescher, *op cit.* Chapter 8, alludes to this consideration but does not provide an explicit rule.

[4] The assumptions stated here amount to defining a causal ordering on the variables that enter into the empirical laws. See Herbert A. Simon 'Causal Ordering and Identifiability', reprinted as Chapter 2.2 in this volume. The use of state descriptions for the treatment of semantic issues in logic, introduced by Wittgenstein, has been carried furthest by Carnap. For a brief account of his method see Section 18 of his *Logical Foundations of Probability*, (Chicago: University of Chicago Press, 1950). Without some such treatment we cannot be sure when or whether particular empirical propositions are mutually independent.

[5] For an example of a normative theory containing the complications of the two previous paragraphs, see Holt, Modigliani, Muth, and Simon, *Planning Production, Inventories, and Work Force* (Englewood Cliffs, N.J.: Prentice-Hall, 1960). Perusal of Chapters 4 and 6, which contain the mathematical derivations, will show that they are precisely parallel to those of the simpler example above.

[6] For a rigorous development of this theory in its modern form, with applications to statistical decision theory, see L. J. Savage, *Foundations of Statistics*, (New York: Wiley, 1954). Savage is concerned, of course, with the normative form of the theory, but there are no evidences that the logic he uses in his derivations is modified in the least by this. For a less technical introduction to normative statistical decision theory, from which the same conclusion can be reached, see Robert Schlaifer, *Probability and Statistics for Business Decisions*, (New York: McGraw-Hill, 1959). These are only samples. The literature relevant to this and the previous footnote is enormous, and uniformly consistent with the conclusions reached here about imperative logic.

[7] A standard treatise, which works both the positive and normative sides of the street, is Dorfman, Samuelson, and Solow, *Linear Programming and Economic Analysis*, (New York: McGraw-Hill, 1958). See especially their Chapter 6, which develops the linear programming version of the theory of the firm. Note the casual alternation, which creates no logical difficulties, between the positive and normative modes. On p. 162, just preceding three theorems that follow (by ordinary logic) from the maximisation assumption, we find the authors saying: "The profit-maximizing firm, then, seeks that feasible program . . . which makes the profitability . . . as great as possible." On pp. 164–165, they summarise one of these same theorems with the statement: "If a firm's situation can be described adequately by a linear-programming model, then for the firm to maximize its time rate of profits, it *should* use a number of activities which does not exceed the number of the restrictions that limit its operations." (Italics mine.)

[8] I am well aware of the oversimplification in which I am indulging. However, adding all the second-order corrections to this simplified scheme would only complicate the discussion without changing its conclusions.

[9] Even in computer programming languages, the distinction between an action and its consequences is sometimes systematically confounded. Thus, in algebraic languages like ALGOL and LISP, the name of a function – e.g. '(X + 14), – may stand for both the programme of actions required to evaluate that function, and for the value itself, which is the output of the programme when it is executed. In programmes as in life, this confounding is limited to aspects of the situation where the relation between action and consequence is not problematic.

[10] H. A. Simon and P. A. Simon, 'Trial and Error Search in Solving Difficult Problems: Evidence from the Game of Chess', *Behavioral Science* 7, 425–429, (1962).

[11] Some programmes choose a good move by determining which move is 'best' in terms of a computable, approximate criterion. But there is no guarantee that such a move is *objectively* best, since the criterion is necessarily very rough. Hence such programmes in fact only choose good moves – if they play well at all.

# THE LOGIC OF HEURISTIC DECISION MAKING†*

The task of a comprehensive theory of action is to describe or prescribe the occasions for action, the alternative courses of action (or the means of discovering them), and the choice among action alternatives. The task of a comprehensive logic of action is to describe or prescribe the rules that govern reasoning about the occasions for action, the discovery of action alternatives, and the choice of action.

Approaches to the theory of action have often taken their starting point in the modalities of common language: in the meanings of 'ought' and 'must' and 'can.'[1] But because common language is complex, flexible, and imprecise, travellers on this path have encountered formidable difficulties. To the best of my knowledge, no theory based on modalities has been developed sufficiently far to serve as a working tool for a practitioner in a field of action such as engineering or management science.

A different starting point is to ask what the practitioners actually do. How does an inventory manager decide when to reorder stock? How does an engineer design an electric motor? How does a production scheduler choose the appropriate factory employment level for the current and future months? These practitioners reason and reason to action — be it well or badly. Perhaps we shall find that they have already forged satisfactory logics of norm and action. Or perhaps, on analyzing their practice, we shall discover that the ordinary predicate calculus of declarative discourse is adequate to their purposes. By examining their reasonings, we shall perhaps be relieved entirely of the task of constructing a new logic of norm and action; at worst, we shall have to make explicit what is implicit in practice, correct it, and improve it. In any event, we may hope to find that a large part of the work has already been done for us.

For these reasons I have found the logic used by professional decision makers an excellent starting point for inquiry into the requirements of imperative and deontic logic. Particularly useful for the task are areas of practice where the decision-making process has been imbedded in formal

[†Rescher (ed.), *The Logic of Decision and Action*, Pittsburgh: University of Pittsburgh Press, 1967, pp. 1–20].

models: normative economics, statistical decision theory, management science, computer programming, operations research, and certain areas of modern engineering design.

In a previous paper, I reported the results of such an inquiry, concerned in the main with schemes for choosing among given action alternatives.[2] The central conclusion reached in that paper is that there is no need for a special 'logic of imperatives' or 'logic of action'; the basis for the conclusion is that the practitioners in the fields examined clearly get along very well without one.

No different brand of logic is used in normative economics from that used in positive economics. On the contrary, the logic employed is the standard logic of declarative statements.

Imperatives enter the normative systems through rules of correspondence that permit commands to be converted into existential statements, and existential statements into commands. The conversion process always takes place in the context of a complete model, with the command variables and environmental variables designated, the state of knowledge about the latter specified, and the causal relations among variables determined. In such a context, commands that bind one or more of the command variables can be converted to the corresponding declarative statements; while declarative statements that can be solved for command variables, but are not identities in those variables, can be converted to commands by binding the command variables with the command operator.[3]

The best-developed formal models of the decision process — those examined in Part 1 of my previous paper — are concerned largely with choice among given alternatives; the alternatives of action themselves are assumed to be known at the outset. In Part 2 of that paper, I explored in a preliminary fashion the question of whether the reasoning involved in designing possible courses of action could also be subsumed under the standard predicate calculus of declarative statements. Again, the tentative answer appeared to be affirmative. I should like to pursue that question here to a more definite conclusion, and to extend the inquiry, as well, to the reasoning involved in determining the occasions for action. The method, again, will be to point to what sophisticated practitioners actually do: to show that they reason rigorously about action without needing a special logic of action.

## 1. PHASES OF DECISION

The decision models of classical economics do not recognize the need either to identify the occasions of action or to devise courses of action. These models presuppose that there is a well-defined criterion for choosing among possible states of the world (a utility function), and that the actual state of the world is a function of two mutually exclusive and exhaustive sets of variables, which in the paragraph quoted above are called the command variables and the environmental variables, respectively. In the dynamic case, which is the more interesting one, each variable is a function of time; hence, the task of choice is to select a function – a time path for the command variables – for a given value of the path of the environmental variables (or a probability distribution of such paths) that corresponds to the maximum of the utility function. Virtually all of the models of classical economics are variations on this central theme.

In this picture of the world, the distinction between action and inaction is meaningless. The actor is pictured as always in action: each command variable must have some definite value at each moment in time, and there are no particular values that can be identified as 'no action.' Doing nothing, if it can be identified at all, is simply a particular way of doing something, not distinguished in the theory from all other forms of action.

## 2. THE DECISION TO ATTEND

Looking now at actual formal decision models used in industrial management, we may contrast two examples: on the one hand, a scheme for determining each week the aggregate employment level and the aggregate production level (in gallons, say) of a paint factory; on the other, a scheme for replenishing warehouse inventories of particular kinds and colors of paint. Both are dynamic programming schemes, for the optimal action during a particular period depends on future events and actions. In the first example, the decision takes the form of choosing two numbers each week – a number of workmen, and a number of gallons of product. There is no concept of 'inaction' in the model. In the second example, the inventory of an item is reviewed whenever a quantity is taken from inventory for shipment. Two decisions are then made: whether to order a new supply of the item from the factory; and, if so, how much to order. Of course, if the first decision is in the negative, no quantity is calculated and no order placed – no action is taken. Action is quantized, and occurs only intermittently, when the inventory on hand falls below a specified reorder point.

Under what circumstances would we expect to use such a scheme of intermittent actions, interspersed by periods of inaction? One condition is that there be fixed costs associated with each action so that, other things being equal, it is economical to act as infrequently as possible, taking a few large actions instead of many smaller ones. A price will be paid for this economy, for it will require larger average quantities of inventory to be held (the average inventory quantity will vary reciprocally with the average frequency of ordering). In the absence of uncertainty about future sales, the classical inventory problem is to fix the reorder quantity (and consequently the reorder period) so as to minimize the sum of the reordering cost and the inventory holding cost.

A second, and more interesting, circumstance under which we would expect a system to act intermittently is one where there are many different actions to be performed, but where the system is capable of performing only one or a few at a time; where the environment makes parallel demands on the system, but the system can respond only serially. As an important special case, some of the demands may occur only infrequently but may require prompt response when they occur (e.g., a fire alarm). Here the division between action and non-action is dictated by the environment.

Under any of these circumstances, one way to design the action system is to provide inventories to meet most needs for action at the time they occur, and to permit the system to replenish inventories intermittently, thus letting it attend to its several actions serially, as its abilities require. When it is not possible to stock an inventory in anticipation of a certain kind of action, an action can be given special priority, so that the system will perform it immediately on receipt of the signal calling for it. A priority system will work satisfactorily, of course, only if the totality of occasions for high-priority action is small relative to the total action capacity of the system.[4]

In rough outline, the action systems of living organisms with central nervous systems appear to correspond to this scheme. Leaving aside actions that can be carried on in parallel with others (e.g., breathing) most behaviors requiring significant participation of the central nervous system must be performed serially. Since the environment sometimes poses real-time demands on organisms (e.g., the appearance of danger), there must be provision for priorities to interrupt ongoing actions as well as for inventorying stocks (e.g., of food and water) to permit intermittent action along each dimension.

It follows that one requirement for a comprehensive logic of decision making is that it should handle the attention-directing decisions that determine when particular kinds of actions should be initiated. In this case, as in the case of choice models, we find that there already exist formal schemes for making attention-directing decisions, phrased in terms of ordinary mathematical concepts, and making use only of the declarative logic that is used in all mathematical reasoning.[5] No special logic is required.

To be more specific, the typical two-bin inventory scheme operates as follows: Associated with each item stocked are a reorder point and a reorder quantity. Whenever items are drawn from inventory, the remaining quantity is compared with the reorder point; if the latter exceeds the former an order is placed for an amount equal to the reorder quantity. The reorder point is set so as to minimize the sum of costs of holding inventory and suffering outages; while the reorder quantity is set so as to minimize the sum of costs of holding inventory and ordering (there is usually an interaction between the cost functions, so that the two minimization problems must be solved simultaneously). Once the injunction, 'Minimize total expected costs!' is converted to the declarative 'The order point and the reorder quantity are at the levels that minimize expected costs,' the reasoning task becomes a straightforward dynamic programming problem. Its solution is then reconverted to the injunctions: 'Reorder whenever the quantity in stock falls below $x$!' and 'When you reorder, order the quantity $y$!'

Now if there are limits on the number of different items that may be reordered during a given period (e.g., the system may restore its inventory of food or its inventory of water, but not both simultaneously), a possibility arises that the decision rules may lead to a contradiction, that is, may call for both of two incompatible actions to be performed. In actual systems, this difficulty is handled, explicitly or implicitly, by one or more supplementary injunctions: 'If several actions are to be carried out, execute first the one that has been longest on the 'want' list!'; or, 'Actions of class A always take precedence over other actions!' – with or without interruption of the latter; or 'Execute first the action that will replenish the smallest inventory!' – where inventories are measured in expected hours to exhaustion. Rules like these, and combinations of them, can all be found in operation in existing industrial inventory and scheduling systems, and in the programs that control the behavior of animals.

In job-shop scheduling, where each of a large number of orders is to be scheduled through a different sequence of manufacturing processes, the rules determining which order will be processed next on each machine are the heart of the scheduling system. (An especially interesting contemporary class of such systems are large computing systems with provision for simultaneous access and time sharing among many users.) The imperatives in these systems answer the question 'Who's next?' The choice among alternative decision rules is made by converting the imperatives to declaratives (i.e., by assuming that the system is obeying the decision rules in question), and then estimating and comparing the costs that would be incurred under each régime.

The fact that, in these systems, the imperatives say 'when' rather than 'how much' does not in any way affect the logic involved. The standard paradigm for reasoning about decision rules is the same as it is in choice models of the kinds examined in my previous paper.[6] Convert the imperatives to declaratives – that is, consider a system that behaves in accordance with the imperatives. Evaluate the outcomes for that system; and compare them with the outcomes that could be expected with different decision rules.

To illustrate the logic of attention-directing procedures, I have mostly used examples drawn from a rather special area of industrial scheduling practice. I have done so because these decision procedures have been completely formalized, hence leave no doubt as to what logic is employed. Attention-directing imperatives play a large and important role, however, in all human behavior, for reasons that have already been suggested.

Because the central nervous system can do only a few things at a time, and because the human memory and the human environment jointly contain an enormous amount of information potentially relevant to behavior, it is essential that there exist processes to determine what tiny fraction of this totality will be evoked at any given moment, and will, during that moment, constitute the effective environment of thought and behavior. It must be possible to make decisions about what to attend to before making decisions about what to do about that which is being attended to. This factorization is reflected in the basic organization of the decision-making procedures that govern human behavior.

It is easy to construct conceptual abstractions – like those in the literature of economics and statistical decision theory – that describe decision making as a process of choosing among possible states of the world. Whatever their value for conceptualizing certain aspects of the theory of choice, these abstractions cannot be taken as descriptions of actual decision-making systems, since they ignore a central fact of the decision-making process: that it must be carried out by an information processing system whose computational powers are puny in comparison with the complexity of the environment with which they must cope. Factorization of that complexity by the device of selective attention is an indispensable adaptive mechanism.

Attention-directing and priority-fixing schemes like those described work satisfactorily only in a world that is mostly empty: that is, a world in which the demands for action, and particularly for high-priority action, are small relative to the organism's total capacity for action. In such a world, the distinction between 'action' and 'inaction' is meaningful. Most of the time, the organism is inactive, or is attending, at most, to 'background' activities that do not impose severe real-time deadlines. Anyone who has tried to design a monitor system for a time-sharing computer, has discovered that the 'empty world' requirement holds not only for the human condition, but for the condition of any serial processor in a world that makes unexpected and heterogeneous demands upon it.

### 3. DESIGN DECISIONS

The second stage in decision making is to devise or discover possible courses of action. This is the activity that in fields like engineering and architecture is called 'design'; in military affairs 'planning'; in chemistry, 'synthesis'; in other contexts, 'invention'; 'composition'; or — that most approving of labels — 'creation.' In routine, repetitive decision making, design may play a small role, for the alternatives of action may be already at hand, to be taken off the shelf as occasion requires. In slightly less structured and repetitive situations, design may require only relatively unproblematic assembly of action alternatives from prefabricated components. In most human affairs, however, the design stage in decision making occupies a far larger part of the mind's information processing capacity than either the stages of attention directing or of choice.

Design is concerned with devising possible means for ends. In the second part of my previous paper,[7] I outlined briefly some of the characteristics of the design process; its concern with relating actions to consequences, its heavy dependence on heuristics, and the major influence exercised over it by considerations of processing capacity. I should like here to develop somewhat more fully these aspects of design, and to point up their consequences for the logic of decision making.

### 4. THE SPACE OF ACTIONS AND THE STATE SPACE

To introduce adequately the first problem about design that we shall consider, I must digress to the passage of the *Meno* where Meno asks:

And how will you inquire, Socrates, into that which you know not? What will you put forth as the subject of inquiry? And if you find what you want, how will you ever know that this is what you did not know?

We are all familiar with Socrates' answer to the conundrum, his theory of recollection. No intelligent schoolboy today would accept that answer as anything but sophistic, but in our delight in Socrates' clever dialog with

Meno's slave, we forgive his tricking us, and we ignore the force of Meno's still-unanswered question. In particular, Socrates completely avoids, does not even restate correctly, the last part of the question: 'And if you find what you want, how will you ever know that this is what you did not know?' How do you identify the answer as the answer to *that* question?

If the answer to Meno's puzzle seems obvious, you have not felt the full force of the difficulty. Let me undertake a restatement. To define a problem, you must refer to the answer — that is, name it. The name may be nothing more than the noun phrase 'the answer to the problem of . . .' Now in the solution process, certain objects are discovered or created: let us call them *possible solutions.* There must be some way also of naming or referrring to the possible solutions — '*A*', '*B*', and so on. Meno's question is: How do we know that the possible solution we call '*D*', say, is the same as the object called 'the answer to the problem of . . . '?

The reply we give today is not Socrates' but John McCarthy's: "We call a problem well-defined if there is a test which can be applied to a proposed solution. In case the proposed solution is a solution, the test must confirm this in a finite number of steps."[8] In the problem statement, the solution is referred to as 'The object that satisfies the following test: . . .' Each possible solution can then be tested until one is found that fits the definition. Thus, if the problem is: 'What is the smallest prime number greater than 10?' and if someone proposes as possible solutions the numbers 11, 12, and 13, a test can be constructed from the meanings of the terms of the problem statement that will identify 11 as the answer. The full procedure might be: (1) generate integers in order, starting with 10; (2) test each to determine if it is prime; (3) stop when a prime is found; (4) that prime is the solution, for it is the smallest greater than 10. (It is instructive that, in this example, the procedure for generating possible solutions already guarantees that one of the conditions — that it be the *smallest* — will be satisfied without an explicit test. This is a typical feature of solution processes.)

A problem will be difficult if there are no procedures for generating possible solutions that are guaranteed (or at least likely) to generate the actual solution rather early in the game. But for such a procedure to exist, there must be some kind of structural relation, at least approximate, between the possible solutions as named by the solution-generating process and these same solutions as named in the language of the problem statement. Suppose, for example, all the words in the unabridged dictionary are put on cards, which are then placed in an urn and stirred thoroughly. Finding the word 'peanut' in the urn is now rather difficult; for, with the cards randomly distributed, no particular scheme of search has a better chance than any other of finding 'peanut' in a short time.

On the other hand, provided one knows the English alphabet, finding the word 'peanut' in the dictionary is much easier. One program runs as follows: (1) open the dictionary about in the middle; (2) if the letter encountered is earlier in the alphabet than 'p', go halfway to the end; if the letter is later in the alphabet, go half way to the beginning; (3) and so on.

In sum, whenever there is a relatively simple relation mapping the names of actions on the names of solutions that can be used to guide the solution generator, finding problem solutions is simple. There is no reason to expect the world to be constructed in such a way that simple mappings of actions on to states of the world will be common. In fact, there is reason to expect the contrary.

An adaptive organism is connected with its environment by two kinds of channels. Afferent channels give it information about the state of the environment; efferent channels cause action on the environment. Problem statements define solutions in terms of afferent information to the organism; the organism's task is to discover a set of efferent signals which, changing the state of the environment, will produce the appropriate afferent. But, *ab initio*, the mapping of efferents on afferents is entirely arbitrary; the relations can only be discovered by experiment, by acting and observing the consequences of action.[9] This, of course, is what young children begin to do in their early months – to discover the seen, heard, and felt consequences of different patterns of innervation of arms, legs, body, tongue.

When the mapping of actions on states of the world is problematic, then, and only then, are we faced with genuine problems of design. Hence, if we wish to construct a formalism for describing design processes, the formalism will need to contain at least two distinct sublanguages: a sublanguage for actions, and a sublanguage for states of the world. To the extent that these two sublanguages are related simply to each other, so that an expression in the one can be translated without difficulty into the other, the problem of design will vanish. For the problem of design *is* the problem of making that translation.

Let me give an illustration of what I consider an *un*satisfactory formalism for the design process. Consider a world with discrete time, so that points in time can be designated by integers. Denote the state of the world at time $t$ by the vector $x(t)$.

Now, let $A(x_1, x_2)$ be the transition matrix that transforms $x_1$ into $x_2$:

(1)        $x_2 = A(x_1, x_2)x_1$.

If we try, in this formalism, to state the problem of changing the state of the world from $x_1$ to $x_2$, we can immediately write down the answer: 'Apply the action $A(x_1,x_2)$!' This is correct, but profoundly uninteresting, throwing no light on what the design problem really is.

The problem becomes interesting when we have a second way of naming transition matrices, say: $A(a_{11},a_{12},\ldots,a_{21},\ldots,a_{nn})$, where $a_{ij}$ is the element in the $j$th column of the $i$th row of the matrix. Then, the problem of finding an $A$ such that $x_2 = Ax_1$ is nontrivial. In terms of the bilingual formalism of actions and states of the world, the problem now is to find a transition matrix, $A$, in the action language, whose name under translation into the language of states of the world is '$A(x_1,x_2)$.' A design process is a process for finding an object that satisfies this translation requirement.

In natural language, the sublanguage of actions consists largely of verbs and their modifiers; the sublanguage for describing states of the world, of nouns and their modifiers. But natural language tends to blur the distinction wherever the translation is relatively unproblematic. Where the consequences that follow the action are well known, the noun or adjective describing those consequences may be 'verbed' to name the action. Thus 'to clean' is to take action that will produce a state of cleanliness. Conversely, a verb may be 'nouned' to denote consequences that regularly follow from action of a certain kind. Thus 'wash' is a collection of articles that is being subjected to a washing process.

Natural language blurs the distinction, because one of the main goals of learning is to discover programs of action that make the connection between actions and states of the world reliably predictable and unproblematic. Cookbook recipes, for example, are programs of action that, if followed, will produce objects having the properties of taste (and digestibility) promised by their names (assumed to be already defined in the state language). To solve the design problem of baking a pumpkin pie, use the cookbook index to find the pumpkin pie recipe, and carry out the actions prescribed there. If the cookbook is reliable, the object produced by these actions will have the properties usually associated with pumpkin pie.

To summarize the argument to this point: a problem of design exists when (1) there is a language for naming actions and a language for naming states of the world, (2) there is a need to find an action that will produce a specified state of the world or a specified change in the state of the world, and (3) there is no non-trivial process for translating changes in the state of the world into their corresponding actions.

In the decision situations treated by classical economics and statistical decision theory, the problem is considerably simplified (1) because the set of possible actions generally consists simply of the set of vectors of the known command variables; (2) the language of actions (i.e., of command variables) is essentially homogeneous with the language of states of the world; and (3) states of the world are assumed to be connected with the command variables by well-defined, and relatively simple functions. Under these simplifying conditions, algorithms often exist that are guaranteed to find, with only reasonable amounts of computation, actions corresponding to desired states of the world. Thus, the classical maximizing algorithms of the calculus, combined with the newer computational algorithms of linear programming and similar formalisms are powerful enough to handle quite large problems when the prerequisite conditions are met.

One of the earliest problems solved with the classical techniques was the following: given the cost of electricity and the cost of copper, to determine the optimal diameter of copper cable to carry a given amount of current. An early linear programming problem was the so-called diet problem: given the prices of different foods, their known content of different nutrients, and the nutritional requirements of a human being, find the lowest-cost diet that will meet these nutritional requirements. These two examples are prototypes of the wide range of practical decision problems that have yielded to the classical techniques. I have called them problems of 'choice' rather than problems of 'design' because the set of possible actions is given, in a very clear sense, and because the determination of the correct action involves a straightforward, if somewhat tedious, deduction — using the ordinary rules of logic — from the description of possible states of the world. In our discussion of the logic of design we shall put these kinds of problems aside.

It may be objected that our proposed meaning for 'design' excludes almost everything called that in engineering and architecture. The typical solution of an engineering or architectural design problem is not a program in the action space, but a description (or picture) of an object in the state space — a blueprint or an elevation, say. But the reason why this description is regarded as a solution to the design problem is that the steps completing the translation from that description to an action program (a manufacturing or construction program) are nonproblematic. The sole action the engineer or architect has to perform (if I may indulge in a bit of heroic oversimplification) to realize the design is to turn it over to a manufacturing department or construction contractor.

In these complex, real-life situations, we may think of the design process as concerned with weaving a tight web of connections between actual physical actions (the actions of lathe operators and carpenters) on one side, and realized states of the world (electric motors, office buildings) on the other. Many parts of this web can be woven using traditional patterns, without new problem-solving activity that goes beyond choice among known alternatives. At other points in the web, however, weaving together the fabric of means, coming from the left with the fabric of ends, coming from the right, requires exploration for new alternatives. It is at these interfaces (there may be more than one) that design activity takes place. Thus, a blueprint can be regarded as an encoded name for a complex action program, where a routine (in both senses of the word) exists for translating the name into the manufacturing program that corresponds to it. Given such a manufacturing algorithm, from blueprints to action, the design interface lies between the blueprint and the desired properties of the final product.

## 5. HEURISTICS

To make our discussion of the logic of design concrete, I propose to examine the structure of a particular computer program, the General Problem Solver (GPS), that embodies some of the techniques people use in solving design problems that are relatively novel to them. A number of variants of GPS have been programmed and tested on digital computers over the past eight years, with problems drawn from a dozen domains. In this way, a fair amount of experience has been acquired with the problem-solving techniques that are incorporated in GPS. In the discussion, I shall use the name 'GPS' in reference to any and all of its variants.[10]

As a first example of a design problem, consider the task of discovering a proof for a mathematical theorem. The state space here may be taken as the space of syntactically well-formed sentences in the branch of mathematics under consideration, including the conjunctions of such sentences. It may be thought of as the space of 'possible theorems.'

A mathematical proof, as usually written down, is a sequence of expressions in the state space. But we may also think of the proof as consisting of the sequence of justifications of consecutive proof steps — i.e. the references to axioms, previously-proved theorems, and rules of inference that legitimize the writing down of the proof steps. From this point of view, the proof is a sequence of actions (applications of rules of inference) that, operating initially on the axioms, transform them into the desired theorem. The problem of discovering, or designing a proof of the expression, $T$, from the conjunction of axioms, $A$, can be phrased:

Problem: To find a sequence of operators or actions that transforms $A$ into $T$.

GPS attacks such a problem roughly as follows: Compare $T$ with $A$, and list the differences between them (if there are none, the problem has been solved); selecting one of the differences, choose an operator that is relevant to differences of that kind; apply that operator to $A$, transforming it into a new object, $A'$. Now repeat the process, using the pair $(A',T)$. If at any stage $A''$ becomes identical with $T$, then the desired proof is the sequence: $AA'A''A'''A''''\ldots T$. This general process is commonly called *means-end* analysis.

For GPS to operate in this way, it must be able to detect differences between pairs of expressions, and it must be able to associate with each difference one or more operators relevant to that difference. The function that maps differences onto sets of operators is usually called the *table of connections.*

In a problem space with very simple structure, the table of connections may associate with each difference an operator that precisely eliminates that difference, but makes no other change in the expression to which it is applied. In this case, each of the $n$ differences between $A$ and $T$ can be detected in turn, and the corresponding operator in the table of connections applied. After $n$ steps, the problem will have been solved.

Of course the interest of GPS lies in its attack on problems that do not have such simple structure. The operators in an interesting problem domain will not correspond simply with differences. Consider, in ordinary algebra, the distributive law, viewed as an operator for transforming expressions. Suppose $A$ is the expression $(x + y)z$, while $T$ is the expression $(x + z)(y + z)$. We know that the distributive law, applied to an expression like $A$, having three literals, will transform it into an expression having four, hence will remove that particular difference between $A$ and $T$. However, when it does so, it also interchanges the multiplication and addition operations, creating a new difference. Thus, applied to $A$, it produces $(xz) + (yz)$, instead of $(x + z)(y + z)$.

This simple example illustrates, in a microcosm, the nature of heuristic problem solving. The available set of transformations allows only certain kinds of changes to be made in the problem expressions. These changes tend to be complex, so that in seeking to remove a particular difference between the initial expression and the desired expression, new differences are often created. Some kind of search must then be undertaken to find a successful path. Means-end analysis, the central heuristic in GPS, gives direction to the search by repeatedly comparing the state or states reached with the desired state. It does not guarantee, however, that the search will be successful, or that it will not go down a number of blind alleys before it finds a correct path.

The efficiency of means-end analysis, applied to any specific problem domain, depends in the first instance on the quality of the table of connections, as our simple example has shown. The skill of a player in ten-second chess, for example, hinges very largely on his ability to recognize the salient features of a chess position, and to evoke effective standard actions applicable to positions having those particular features. There is good empirical evidence that, even for grandmasters, actual dynamic analysis of the consequences that will follow on particular moves takes a matter of minutes, not seconds, and is therefore relatively unimportant in ten-second chess.

The problem-solving power of means-end analysis can be increased if information is available as to the best order in which to consider differences when there is more than one. The information need not be perfectly reliable — it need only be better than the scheme of taking up the differences in random order. The ordering of differences also provides information as to whether applying a particular operator has improved matters or not — whether the differences removed are more or less important than new differences that have been created. Thus, the information may be used as a *progress* test. In interesting problem domains the progress tests are not perfect; if they were, they would guide search infallibly, and the problems would be trivial. Instead, progress tests are heuristic: they usually help, but they are not guaranteed to do so.

A typical feature of the particular problems we call 'puzzles' is that to solve them we must sometimes search where the progress test tells us not to. In the missionaries and cannibals puzzle, for example, the task is to move three missionaries and three cannibals from the left to the right bank of a river, under constraints aimed at preventing drowning and dining casualties. A plausible progress test is to compare numbers of persons on the right bank before and after a trip. But to solve the problem, at a certain point two persons, instead of a single one, must return with the boat to the left bank. This is the point of difficulty in the problem for most persons who try it.

With a heuristic problem solver like GPS, there is never a guarantee until the last that it is on the right path to the solution. Therefore it must try several paths and gradually generate a branching tree of possibilities. As a generalization of the progress test, we may incorporate heuristics that determine from which terminal branch of the tree already generated the next explorations should be made, and the next branches added. Two simple heuristics, or strategies, for this purpose are the rule of *depth first,* and the rule of *breadth first.*

Under the depth-first rule, the problem solver starts with the initial state, *A,* and generates some possible one-step paths. These are evaluated by a progress test, the best is chosen, and the process repeated. A second test terminates search along a branch if the path becomes very unpromising. In that case, the next branch above is recovered, and the next-best continuation there explored.

Under the breadth-first rule, the problem-solver generates a number of one-step paths from *A.* It then takes up each of the newly-generated states in turn and generates one-step paths from it.

Experience with GPS and other problem-solving programs provides fairly convincing evidence that neither the depth-first nor the breadth-first rules are efficient in state spaces of any considerable size. *Scan-and-search* rules are usually far more effective. With these rules, the problem solver generates one-step paths from *A*, and puts them on a *try list* in an order determined by some progress test. It repeats this, taking its starting point from the head of the try list, and putting the new paths generated back on that same list. Even if the progress test is very crude, these schemes avoid both the single-mindedness and stereotypy of the depth-first strategy, and the plodding, effort-scattering blindness of the breadth-first strategy.

Other examples could be provided of heuristics that affect the power of a problem-solving system. Some of them, like means-end analysis and the scan-and-search strategy, are general and independent of the problem domain. Others, involving improvement of the table of connections and of the progress test, are specific to particular problem domains. Their common characteristic is that, without providing an immediate and sure-fire route to the problem solution, they generally bring about substantial reduction in the amount of search required to find a solution.

Now the output of GPS, when it is successful in solving a problem, is a recipe or program of actions — a sequence of operators, which, if applied to the initial state *A* will produce the terminal state *T.* This interpretation is not limited to theorem proving, but is equally applicable to any of the tasks that can be attacked by means-end analysis. Thus, GPS discovers actions that are *sufficient* to realize goals. In general, there is no guarantee that the actions are necessary, unless the structure of the problem space itself guarantees the uniqueness of solutions. Uniqueness, hence necessity of the actions, will be the rare exception rather than the rule.

What do we learn from GPS about the logic af action, as it appears in the design process? First, we learn, just as in the process of choice, that the ordinary logic of declarative statements is all we need. As we have seen, that logic is adequate for describing the relation between the action programs designed by GPS and the states they are supposed to realize. The actions are sufficient conditions for transforming the initial state of the environment into the desired goal state.

Starting with the imperative: 'Try to achieve the state $T'$,' the design problem is formulated by transforming that imperative into: 'Try to discover a program of action that will achieve the state $T'$,' which is transformed, in turn, to 'Apply GPS to the problem of transforming $A$ into $T'$.' The third imperative is not deduced from the second or the first. The logical nexus that relates them can be stated entirely in the declarative mode. Let us see how.

We consider a model of the world in which the available actions include both planning actions and performance actions. In general, if at time $t_0$ the world is not in state $T$, then it can sometimes be brought into that state at time $t$, by performing the planning action, $P(T)$, followed by the performance action $D(P(T))$, where $P(T)$ means the action of trying to solve the problem of realizing $\overline{T}$, while $D(P(T))$ means the action of executing the program created by $P(T)$.

Now 'Achieve $T$' can be converted to 'The state of the world at $t_1$ is $T$.' Simplifying, in this model it is true that: 'If, at $t_0$, action $P(x)$ is followed by $D(P(x))$, then at $t_1$ the state of the world will be $x$.' If, now, the command variables are so fixed, for the time $t_0$, that $B(t_0) = (P(T)*D(P(T)))$, where '$B$' stands for 'behavior' and '*' is the sign of concatenation of actions, then the sentence, 'The state of the world at $t_1$ is $T$' will be true.

The phrase 'try to' in the earlier statement of the problem was simply there to remind us that in the real world the actions in question usually, or sometimes, but not invariably, produce the goal state. In some cases we may incorporate these contingencies in the model itself, through probabilities or otherwise; in other cases, we may simply be satisfied to have a model that is a simplified, and idealized, representation of reality. The fallibility of the actions in producing the desired state of the world may stem from two causes: (1) the planning process may be heuristic, hence not guaranteed to produce an output in the available time (or ever); (2) the outputs produced by the planning process, the performance actions, may not be fully guaranteed to produce the desired state of the world. Many design processes can be cited suffering from either or both kinds of fallibility.

In terms of a distinction made earlier, to 'try to achieve $T$' is a genuine action, lying clear at the efferent end of the efferent–afferent spectrum, and always capable of execution. Still more exactly, to 'try to achieve $\overline{T}$' could mean: (1) to execute the program $P(T)$; (2) if $P(T)$ has no output, stop; (3) if $P(T)$ has the output $P'$, execute the program $D(P')$. This sequence of steps can always be executed; whether it will produce $T$ depends on the fallibility of $P$ and $D$.

## 6. THE EFFICIENCY OF HEURISTICS

The conclusion reached in the previous section might be restated thus: In those cases (and they will be the rule rather than the exception) where the achievement of a goal calls for a non-trivial planning action (discovery of alternatives) as well as a performance action (execution of alternatives) determined by the former, the model of the state space must include planning actions as well as performance actions as values of the command variables. If, further, planning actions commonly consume scarce information-processing capacity, then the theory of action will be concerned with the design of efficient planning programs as well as the design (by the planning programs) of efficient performance programs.

A considerable and growing body of applied mathematics is concerned with planning actions, or design processes, as we called them earlier. First of all, there is the subject of numerical analysis, in which some of the typical problems are:

1. Prove that, in a number of steps less than $N$, the algorithm $A$, applied to the argument $x$, will produce as output $f(x)$.

2. Prove that, for any epsilon however small, there exists an $N$ sufficiently large that the difference between $f(x)$ and $A(N,x)$ – the result, after $N$ steps, of the operation of algorithm $A$ on argument $x$ – will be less than epsilon.

3. Prove that (with qualifications similar to those stated in the two previous paragraphs) the output of $A$ is the value of $x$, call it $x^*$, that maximizes $f(x)$.

A particular topic in applied mathematics, of great importance today in management science and engineering design, is linear programming – roughly speaking, the theory of maximization of a linear form subject to constraints expressed as linear equations and inequalities. A linear programming *calculation* is a design calculation – that is, it is aimed at discovering the optimal action program in a situation that has been described in a linear programming model. But linear programming *theory* is one step removed from such calculations; it is aimed at discovering algorithms that are efficient for solving whole classes of linear programming problems. Hence, it is aimed at the design of the design processes. A typical problem in linear programming theory is to show that a particular algorithm will, in fact, find the optimum, and to provide exact or approximate estimates of the amount of computing effort that will be required for problems of various sizes.

In the past, design procedures have been formalized principally in areas where algorithms were known – that is, where it could be shown that the design procedure would always arrive at a solution to any design problem in a specified domain. Today, formal design procedures, usually taking the shape of computer programs, have been constructed for many domains where algorithmic procedures are not known to exist, or, if known, are hopelessly exorbitant in their demands upon computing effort. How are such procedures to be evaluated?

Figure 1 illustrates one way in which the *heuristic power* of a design procedure can be evaluated, independently of whether or not it possesses algorithmic guarantees. Consider a domain in which problem solution is an all-or-none matter – in which a given action program either is or is not a solution. Theorem proving is such a domain. Consider, next, some population of problems and a problem-solving program, $S$. We define $p(S, t)$ as the probability that a problem, drawn at random from the domain, will be solved by the program, $S$, in $t$ minutes or less. The function $p(S, t)$ will then be a non-decreasing function of $t$.

Now, for any particular time allowance, say $t_0$, we can define the heuristic power of the program $S$ as $p(S, t_0)$. Hence, we can compare the heuristic powers of different programs for some 'reasonable' amount of computing effort.

We can also use Figure 1 to define various algorithmic guarantees. For example, we might call a program algorithmic if, for some $t_1, p(S, t_1) = 1$. Or, we might call a program asymptotically algorithmic if we can make $p(S, t)$ as close to 1 as we please by making $t$ sufficiently large. The important point is that whether a particular program does or does not possess such algorithmic properties is quite independent of its heuristic power for moderate $t$. For example, the only algorithm for chess (which consists of considering all possible games and minimizing backwards from the end) would almost never

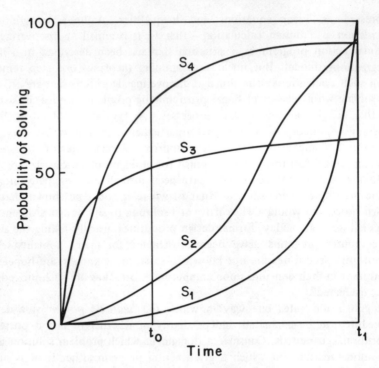

Fig. 1.   The Concept of Heuristic Power. The function $p(S,t)$ is graphed for four hypothetical problem-solving programs. $S_1$ is an algorithm, guaranteed to solve any problem in time $t_1$. $S_2$ is asymptotically algorithmic. $S_3$ is the most powerful of the programs for very small $t$, but $S_4$ has the greatest heuristic power for $t_0$.

find a move during the lifetime of the universe, much less in a reasonable computing time.

If problem-solving in a particular domain is not an all-or-none matter, but solutions of different quality can be distinguished, the measure of heuristic power has to be modified somehow. If there is some way of measuring the value of the improvement in the solution that would be attained by increasing the computing time, and measuring this value in units comparable to the measure of computing cost, then the problem can be formulated of determining the optimal computing time. So-called sequential sampling problems in statistics, and search problems in operations research take this general form.

In many cases of practical importance programs having considerable heuristic power can be obtained by taking care to define the notion of 'problem solution' with an eye to the effect that this definition will have on the computing requirements. An illustration that I find instructive on this point is the problem of finding a needle in a haystack.

Suppose we have a haystack in which needles are distributed at random with a specified density. What procedure can we devise to find the sharpest needle in the stack? The only algorithm that suggests itself is finding all the needles and measuring or comparing their sharpness to determine which is sharpest. If the stack is very large, we shall content ourselves with searching some portion of it, and selecting the sharpest needle of those in that portion. If we search one $n$th of the stack, our chance of finding the sharpest is $1/n$.

How can we tell when to stop searching? One rule is to stop when we have used a specified amount of effort. Another quite different rule is to stop when we have a needle sharp enough to sew with. A good feature of this rule is that it calls for a search time inversely proportional to the density of sharp needles in the stack, and independent of the size of the entire stack. In a world full of haystacks that for all practical purposes are infinite, this is a highly desirable property for a problem-solving procedure.

Now an economist would say that the proper rule is to search until the expected improvement in sharpness per minute of additional search is worth less than the cost of the search. This is true, but not always helpful, because it is often far easier, in practice, to define what is meant by a 'sharp enough' needle than to measure the marginal value of additional sharpness, or to estimate the amount of search that would be required to produce it.

The process of searching for 'good enough' solutions is called *satisficing*. It is one of the most general and effective means for attaining heuristic power with modest amounts of computation. The fundamental reason for its effectiveness is that it does not require the comparison of all possible solutions with each other, but only the comparison of each possible solution, as it is generated, with a standard.[11] It is easy to see how GPS can be made into a satisficer. If differences are signed, so that the directions of better and worse can be distinguished, then GPS can simply be given the task of transforming the initial state into a state that is, along certain dimensions, as good as, or better than, a standard state.

## 7. CONCLUSION

Human beings are information-processing systems operating largely in serial fashion, and possessing very modest computational powers in comparison with the complexity of the problems with which their environment confronts them. Their survival depends on attending selectively to that environment, and on finding satisfactory behavioral alternatives for handling those problems to which they attend.

Hence a theory of decision making is concerned with processes for selecting aspects of the environment for attention, processes for generating alternatives and processes for choosing among alternatives. In the design of these processes, the conservation of attention and of computing effort is a vital consideration. To reason about these matters, models must be constructed that contain command or action variables and environmental variables. With these models, the reasoning used to make decisions, or to design decision-making processes embodies no special logic, but employs declarative logic of the ordinary kind.

Design problems — generating or discovering alternatives — are complex largely because they involve two spaces, an action space and a state space, that generally have completely different structures. To find a design requires mapping the former of these on the latter. For many, if not most, design problems in the real world systematic algorithms are not known that guarantee solutions with reasonable amounts of computing effort. Design uses a wide range of heuristic devices — like means-end analysis, satisficing, and the other procedures that have been outlined — that have been found by experience to enhance the efficiency of search. Much remains to be learned about the nature and effectiveness of these devices.

Our brief survey of the kinds of reasoning that can be applied to the design of planning programs demonstrates again the central thesis of this paper: ordinary mathematical reasoning, hence the ordinary logic of declarative statements, is all that is required for a theory of design processes. The actions in question in a planning theory are the actions of using particular processes as planning programs. The relevant imperatives are of the form: 'Prove this theorem!' and 'Apply GPS to the problem!' The route from the first to the second of these imperatives lies through an empirical or theoretical analysis (requiring no imperatives) of the heuristic power of GPS for theorems of the kind in question.

## NOTES

*The work reported here was supported in part by Public Health Service Research Grant MH-07722-01 from the National Institutes of Mental Health. I am indebted to Allen Newell for numerous comments and suggestions.
[1] An excellent example of this approach is G. H. von Wright's *Norm and Action* (New York: The Humanities Press, 1963).

[2] H. A. Simon, 'The Logic of Rational Decision', *British Journal for the Philosophy of Science* 16, 169–186 (1965), (reprinted as Chapter 3.1 of this volume).

[3] *Ibid.* For fuller discussion of the contextual conditions for a model of an action system see my 'Causal Ordering and Identifiability', (reprinted as Chapter 2.1 of this volume); and J. Marschak, 'Statistical Inference in Economics: An Introduction', in T. C. Koopmans (ed.), *Statistical Inference in Dynamic Economic Models.* Cowles Commission Monograph No. 10 (New York: John Wiley & Sons, 1950). ch. 1.

[4] The requirements for the design of systems of this kind are outlined in my 'Rational Choice and the Structure of the Environment', Chapter 15 of *Models of Man*, (New York: John Wiley & Sons, 1953).

[5] K. J. Arrow, T. Harris, and J. Marschak, 'Optimal Inventory Policy', *Econometrica* 19, 250–272 (1951).

[6] *Op. cit.,* p. 179.

[7] *Op. cit.,* pp. 179–186.

[8] 'The Inversion of Functions Defined by Turing Machines', in C. E. Shannon and J. McCarthy (eds.), *Automata Studies* (Princeton University Press, 1956), p. 177.

[9] Since the organism is a product of evolution, which may already have produced a partial matching between efferents and afferents, the 'arbitrariness' of the relation may be overstated here.

[10] A number of descriptions of GPS have been published. For the purposes of this discussion, I recommend the one in *Contemporary Approaches to Creative Thinking*, Howard E. Gruber, Glenn Terell, Michael Wertheimer (eds.) (New York: The Atherton Press, 1962), pp. 63–119. See also Chapter 5.1 of this volume.

[11] For a more thorough discussion of satisficing see 'A Behavioral Model of Rational Choice', in *Models of Man, op. cit.*

# COMPLEXITY

The subtitle of this section might read 'Is there anything nontrivial, yet quite general, that can be said about complexity?' Its four chapters represent some attempts to give a (qualifiedly) affirmative answer to the question. The contents of the section are perhaps a little more heterogeneous than those of other parts of this book, but there are two unifying concepts. The first of these is *hierarchy* (especially, Chapters 4.1, 4.2, and 4.4). The second is *heuristic search* (especially Chapter 4.3)

## HIERARCHY

Almost all complex systems that occur in nature exhibit an underlying hierarchic structure. There is both a reason for this and a consequence. The reason is given in my paper, 'The Architecture of Complexity', which appears as Chapter 4 in my book, *The Sciences of the Artificial* (Cambridge, Mass.: MIT Press, 1969). The probability that a structure of given size will be assembled from smaller and simpler structures through processes of evolution is greater if the structure is hierarchic than if it is not. The argument is restated briefly in Chapter 4.4, below.

The consequence of a system being hierarchic is that the analysis of its behavior can be (approximately) subdivided into analysis of each of its subparts, combined with an aggregate analysis of their interactions. If a system is made up of five components, each containing, in turn, five parts, and each of these containing five subparts, then the behavior of the whole system can be studied by analysing the behavior of twenty-five systems of five subparts each, five systems of five parts each, and one system of five components — a total of 31 systems of five parts each. This is generally a far simpler matter than analysing the behavior of one system of 125 interacting parts.

The mathematical theory that justifies this assertion is presented in Chapter 4.2, written jointly with Albert Ando, where dynamic systems having hierarchic form are described as *nearly decomposable systems*. Extensions of the theory of nearly decomposable systems and its application to problems of statistical estimation were published by Ando, Franklin M. Fisher, and myself, and reprinted in *Essays on the Structure of Social Science Models* (Cambridge, Mass.: MIT Press, 1963), a volume that is unfortunately now out of print.

The dynamic systems discussed in Chapter 4.2 have matrices that are nearly block diagonal. (These systems are nowadays usually called 'nearly completely decomposable'.) Ando and Fisher found analogous results for nearly block triangular systems. Since block triangular systems are precisely the kinds of systems which, according to Section 2, define causal orderings, the theory developed in this chapter and its extension may be viewed as a theory of systems that are nearly causally ordered. The significance of near decomposability for estimation is that the parameters of systems with this kind of structure can be treated, in first approximation, as though the causal ordering were exact.

Within the past four years, P. J. Courtois of the Catholic University of Louvain has shown that the techniques for approximating the behavior of hierarchic systems described in Chapter 4.2 can be applied to the performance analysis of complex computing systems containing, for example, elaborate memory hierarchies.[1]

Finally, the brief Chapter 4.1 is reprinted here simply out of pride in an early (1950) forecast of the role that hierarchy would play in understanding the human mind. The remarks were comments on a talk by J. von Neumann, who had warned against taking the brain-computer analogy too literally. I observed that the significant analogy was not between the hardware of computer and brain, respectively, but between the hierarchic organizations of computing and thinking systems: what Walter Pitts referred to, a few years later, as "the hierarchy of final causes called the mind." It was this hierarchic organization of mind, together with the feasibility of using the computer to simulate it, that made possible the rapid advances in cognitive psychology and artificial intelligence that have taken place in the past twenty years, and that form the main subject matter of Chapter 4.3, as well as most of the chapters of Section 5 of this book.

## 2. HEURISTIC SEARCH

Problem solvers are systems designed to deal with the complexity of large, poorly understood problem environments. Chapter 4.3 is a survey of the state of the art of problem solving by computers in about 1971. A principal means that has been employed in problem solving programs, heuristic search, is described in the chapter, and some new directions in heuristic search outlined. Chapter 4.3 deals with problem solving wholly from the standpoint of artificial intelligence. The psychological aspects of the same topic will be taken up later, in Chapters 5.1 and 5.2.

NOTE

[1] See his papers, 'Decomposability, Instabilities and Saturation in Multiprogramming Systems', *Communications of the ACM* **18**, 371–377 (1975), and 'Error Analysis in Nearly-Completely Decomposable Stochastic Systems', *Econometrica* **43**, 691–710 (1975).

# THEORY OF AUTOMATA: DISCUSSION[†]

The interest of social scientists in the recent rapid development of automata has two bases: they are interested in powerful computing devices that would enable them to handle complex systems of equations; and they are interested in the suggestive analogies between automata, on the one hand, and organisms and social systems on the other. With respect to the second interest, Mr. von Neumann's strictures on the limitations of the automaton-organism analogy are well taken. The analogies are fruitful in exposing some of the very general characteristics that such systems have in common — for example, characteristics centering around the notions of communication and servomechanism behavior. But it is dangerous to carry such analogies in detail — e.g, to compare specific structures in a computer with specific neural structures.

An important aspect of the theory of automata needs to be further explored. Rationality in organisms often exhibits a hierarchical character. A frame of reference is established, and the individual or social system behaves rationally within that frame. But rationality may also be applied in establishing the frame, and there is usually a whole hierarchy of such frames. Some automata exhibit the rudiments of such hierarchy, but it may be conjectured that the greater flexibility of organismic behavior is somehow connected with the more elaborate development of hierarchical procedures.

† [*Econometrica* 19, 72 (1951)].

# AGGREGATION OF VARIABLES IN DYNAMIC SYSTEMS† *

## (with Albert Ando)

In many problems of economic theory we need to use aggregates. The general Walrasian system and its more modern dynamic extensions are relatively barren of results for macroeconomics and economic policy. Hence, in our desire to deal with such questions we use highly aggregated systems by sheer necessity, often without having much more than the same necessity as our justification. Perhaps the most important result to date for justifying aggregation under certain circumstances is the Lange-Hicks[1] condition, about which we shall say more later.

Concern with actual numerical coefficients in the Leontief input-output model renewed interest in aggregation. It was hoped at first, perhaps, that modern computers would handle matrices of about any desired size, and hence would obviate the need for aggregation. By now it is clear that our ambitions have outstripped the computers, for the time required to invert a matrix by known methods increases with the cube of the number of rows and columns. The high cost of inverting large matrices has led to a number of experiments[2] to determine whether aggregation can be used to obtain approximate inverses more economically.

Hence, aggregation is a topic of considerable importance regardless of whether we are interested in the general mathematical treatment of large systems — in which case aggregation is essential for conceptual clarity and for effective manipulation of the system — or interested in numerical computation — in which case aggregation is often necessary to make computation feasible with available means.

Let us consider an example. Suppose that government planners are interested in the effect of a subsidy to a basic industry, say the steel industry, on the total effective demand in the economy. Strictly speaking, we must deal with individual producers and consumers, and trace through all interactions among the economic agents in the economy. This being an

† [*Econometrica* **29**, 111–138 (1961)].

obviously impossible task, we would use such aggregated variables as the total output of the steel industry, aggregate consumption and aggregate investment. The reasoning behind such a procedure may be summarized as follows: (1) we can somehow classify all the variables in the economy into a small number of groups; (2) we can study the interactions within the groups as though the interaction among groups did not exist; (3) we can define indices representing groups and study the interaction among these indices without regard to the interactions within each group.

When thus explicitly written out, this reasoning appears rather bold. Yet, we implicitly use it almost every day in our analysis of the economy. We should at least make some attempt to specify the conditions that would justify the aggregation.

The conditions for exact aggregation are very severe. Whether these conditions are strictly satisfied in any practical situation is, of course, not important. We would be perfectly satisfied with aggregative models that were only approximate; we have no illusions that *any* model we might employ is more than an approximate description of reality. In exploring the aggregation problem we seek rules and criteria — exact or heuristic — that indicate what variables to aggregate and that show the circumstances under which aggregation will yield satisfactory approximations.

In the more general sense, justifications for approximation must be related to the decisions that depend on the approximating — if the decisions based on the approximate model are not much 'worse' than the decisions based on the more elaborate model according to some criteria, then we may be justified in using the approximate, simpler model. This consideration is strengthened if, while the improvement of the final decision is very slight, the cost of working with a larger model is very much greater than that of working with an approximate, simpler model. Furthermore, the relation between the aggregation problem here discussed and the identification problem when the structural equations are misspecified — a relation pointed out recently by Fisher[3] — can be better understood when both of these problem are viewed as parts of a larger decision problem. We shall come back to this point in the concluding section of this paper, but we must first make the statement of our problem more precise.

## 1. THE PROBLEM

We shall restrict our attention to aggregation defined within the following algebraic model: We have two sets of (not necessarily all distinct) variables,

$x = (x_1, \ldots, x_i, \ldots, x_n)$, and $y = (y_1, \ldots, y_j, \ldots, y_m)$, and a system of equations giving y as a function of $x$; $y = \phi(x)$. We wish to know under what circumstances there exist two sets of functions, $X_I(x)$, $I = 1, \ldots, N$, $N < n$, and $Y_J(y)$, $J = 1, \ldots, M$, $M < m$, such that a set of relations between $X$ and $Y$: $Y = \xi(X)$, can be derived from the given system of equations, $\phi$, relating $x$ and $y$. $X$ and $Y$ are vectors: $X = (X_1, \ldots, X_N)$, and $Y = (Y_1, \ldots, Y_M)$. Sometimes additional conditions are imposed, e.g., that the functions $X$ and $Y$ are given; or that there exist also relations, $y = y(Y)$, such that if, for a given set of values of $x$, $\bar{x}$, $\bar{y} = \phi(\bar{x})$, $\bar{X} = X(\bar{x})$, $\bar{Y} = \xi(\bar{X})$, and $\bar{\bar{y}} = y(\bar{Y})$, then $|\bar{y}_j - \bar{\bar{y}}_j| < \epsilon$ for all $j$, where $\epsilon$ is a given positive number.

In the special case where the relations are all linear and the $y_i$'s are the values of the $x_i$'s in the following period, the function $\phi$ can be written as

(1.1)     $x(t + 1) = x(t)P,$

where $x(t)$ is an $n$-dimensional row vector and $P$ is an $n \times n$ matrix of constants. The question raised above will then be specialized to that of conditions under which there exist $N$ functions,

(1.2)     $X_I(t) = X_I[x(t)]$          $(I = 1, \ldots, N < n)$

and a new set of relations

(1.3)     $X(t + 1) = X(t)Q,$

where $X(t)$ is an $N$-dimensional row vector, and $Q$ is an $N \times N$ matrix of constants. The elements of $Q$ are functions of the elements of $P$. Further, we seek to define an additional set of $n$ functions

(1.4)     $x_i(t) = f_i[X(t)]$          $(i = 1, \ldots, n)$

such that the time path of the $x_i$'s defined by (1.3) and (1.4) can be considered an acceptable approximation of the time path of the $x_i$'s defined by (1.1) according to some predetermined criteria.

The Lange-Hicks condition is a criterion of this kind. It states: if two or more variables always move together they may be aggregated into a single variable, which will be an appropriately weighted average of the original variables. This is a useful criterion, since it tells us that we may aggregate classes of commodities that are perfect substitutes, or that are approximately so.

At another level, the Lange-Hicks condition is unsatisfactory, for it requires that we know in advance which variables move together. In reality, it may be part of our problem to discover this. We may be confronted with a dynamic system of many variables, and may have to infer from the equations of the system which variables will move together — or will move nearly enough together to warrant aggregation. This is the problem we shall set ourselves here: *to determine conditions that, if satisfied by a (linear) dynamic system, will permit approximate aggregation of variables.* Note that we shall be interested in sufficient, rather than necessary, conditions. Hence, we may also view our task as that of discovering one or more classes of dynamic systems whose variables may be aggregated.

In Section 2, we shall present one such class of dynamic systems, which we call 'nearly decomposable' systems, and suggest that in such systems, the aggregation of variables described by Equations (1.1) through (1.4) can be performed. In Section 3, we shall give a physical illustration of such a system. In Sections 4 and 5, the mathematical analysis underlying the propositions summarized in Section 2 will be given in some detail. Section 6 will present a numerical illustration of the behavior through time of 'nearly decomposable' systems, and, as a special case, an application of the aggregation procedure discussed in this paper to the problem of the inversion of matrices. Finally, in Section 7, we shall discuss some further implications of our results and their relations to the recent works of others.

## 2. PROPERTIES OF NEARLY DECOMPOSABLE MATRICES

The dynamic characteristics of the system (1.1) depend on the properties of the matrix of its coefficients, $P = \| P_{ij} \|$. More specifically, we will be interested in the patterns of zeros and near-zeros in the matrix $P$. Since we are concerned with closed systems, we assume $P$ to be a square matrix.

Let us consider a matrix $P^*$, that can be arranged in the following form after an appropriate permutation of rows and columns:

$$(2.1) \qquad P^* = \left\| \begin{array}{cccc} P_1^* & & & \\ & \ddots & & \\ & & P_I^* & \\ & & & \ddots \\ & & & P_N^* \end{array} \right\|$$

where the $P_I^*$'s are square submatrices and the remaining elements, not displayed, are all zero. Then the matrix is said to be completely decomposable.

Let us denote the number of rows and columns in the $I$th submatrix in $P^*$

by $n_I$. Then

$$n = \sum_{I=1}^{N} n_I.$$

We shall also adopt the following notation for the vector $\{x_i^*(t)\}$ on which $P^*$ operates:

$$\cdot\, x^*(t) = \{x_i^*(t)\} = \{[x_{i_1}^*(t)], \ldots, [x_{i_I}^*(t)], \ldots, [x_{i_N}^*(t)]\},$$

where $x_{i_I}[(t)]$ is the row vector of a subset of components of $\{x_i^*(t)\}$, so that if

$$x_{i_I}^*(t) = x_i(t)$$

then

$$i = \sum_{J=1}^{I-1} n_J + i_I.$$

It is clear that if the system (1.1) is specified to

(2.2)        $x^*(t) = x^*(0)P^{*t}$

then the subset $[x_{i_I}^*(t)]$ of $x(t)$ at any stage $t$ depends only on $[x_{i_I}^*(0)]$ and $P_I^*$ and is independent of $[x_{i_J}^*(0)]$ and $P_J^*, I \neq J$.

Let us next consider a slightly altered matrix $P$ defined by

(2.3)        $P = P^* + \epsilon C,$

where $\epsilon$ is a very small real number, and $C$ is an arbitrary matrix of the same dimension as $P^*$. In this introductory discussion, the phrase 'a very small real number' is intentionally left unprecise; it will be defined later. We shall refer to matrices such as $P$ as *nearly decomposable matrices*. Using $P$ thus defined, we restate Equation (1.1) below:

(2.4)        $x(t + 1) = x(t)P.$

It is the dynamic behavior of the system given by (2.4) in which we are interested.

Let the roots of the submatrix $P_I^*$ be designated as: $\lambda_{1I}^*, \lambda_{2I}^*, \ldots, \lambda_{nI}^*$. We assume that these roots are distinct, and the subscripts are so arranged that $\lambda_{1I}^* > \lambda_{2I}^* > , \ldots, > \lambda_{nI}^*$. In addition, if $\lambda_{1_1}^*, \lambda_{1_2}^*, \ldots, \lambda_{1_N}^*$ are all distinct, then without loss of generality, we can arrange rows and columns so that

$\lambda_{1_1}^* > \lambda_{1_2}^*, \ldots, > \lambda_{1N}^*$. When all these conditions are satisfied, i.e., when all roots of $\hat{P}^*$ are distinct, we can analyze the dynamic behavior of (2.4) with relative ease. In most cases, we feel that this assumption is not too restrictive as a description of reality. There is, however, an important exception, namely, the case where $P^*$ is a stochastic matrix in which case all $\lambda_{1_I}^*$ are unity. It turns out, fortunately, that our analysis of the case with all distinct roots can readily be extended to the stochastic case. In the remainder of this section, we shall summarize the results of the more detailed mathematical analysis presented in Sections 4 and 5.

Let us define

(2.5)     $\min_{\substack{i,j \\ i \neq j}} | \lambda_i^* - \lambda_j^* | = \delta^*.$

If $P^*$ is stochastic, the $N$ largest roots of $P^*$ take the identical values of unity. In this case, (2.5) should be interpreted to mean the selection of the minimum of the differences among all roots whose values are not unity and their differences from unity.

Since the roots of a matrix are continuous functions of its elements,[4] we can define, for any positive real number $\delta$, however small, a small enough $\epsilon$ so that, for every root of $P^*$, $\lambda_i^*$, there exists a root of $P$, $\lambda_i$, such that

(2.6)     $|\lambda_i - \lambda_i^*| < \delta.$

We can choose $\delta$ sufficiently smaller than $\delta^*$ so that there is no confusion as to which root of $P$ corresponds to any particular root of $P^*$. The only exceptions to this proposition are the $N$ largest roots of the stochastic $P^*$. If $P^*$ is stochastic, we have

(2.7a)     $\lambda_{1_I}^* = 1$          $(I = 1, 2, \ldots, N),$

(2.7b)     $| 1 - \lambda_{i_I}^* | > \delta^*$          $(i_I = 2, \ldots, n_I; I = 1, \ldots, N).$

Hence, for $P$, we must have

(2.8a)     $| 1 - \lambda_{1_I} | < \delta$          $(I = 1, 2, \ldots, N),$

(2.8b)     $| 1 - \lambda_{i_I} | > \delta^* - \delta$          $(i_I = 2, \ldots, n_I; I = 1, \ldots, N).$

Because of the correspondence of the characteristic roots of $P$ and $P^*$ described above, we expect $x(t)$, when its time path is defined by (2.4), to exhibit the following dynamic behavior:

(1) In the short run, the behavior of $x_{i_I}(t)$ will be dominated by roots

belonging to the $I$th subset, so that the time path of $x_{i_I}(t)$ will be very close to the time path of $x_{i_I}^*(t)$, and almost independent of $x_{j_J}(t)$, $J \neq I$, and $P_J$, $J \neq I$. Here, $P_J$ is defined to be the submatrix of $P$ corresponding to $P_J^*$ of $P^*$. If we are interested in the behavior of the system at this stage, we can treat the system as though it were completely decomposable.

(2) Unlike $P^*$, $P$ is not completely decomposable, so that the weak links among the subsystems will eventually make their influence felt. But the time required for these influences to appear is long enough so that when they do become visible, within each subsystem the largest root, $\lambda_{1_I}$, will have dominated all other roots, $\lambda_{2_I}, \ldots, \lambda_{n_I}$. Thus, at this stage, the variables within each subset, $[x_{i_I}(t)]$, will move proportionately, and the behavior of the whole system will be dominated by $N$ roots, $\lambda_{1_I}, \ldots, \lambda_{1_N}$. Notice that, since the variables in each subsystem move roughly proportionately, the Lange-Hicks condition for aggregation is approximately satisfied.

(3) At the end, however, the behavior of $x(t)$ will be dominated by the largest root of $P$, as in any linear dynamic system.

It is quite clear that all these statements refer to the limiting properties of the system (2.4), and can be made more precise and meaningful only with more careful mathematical analyses of the system, which are presented in Sections 4 and 5.

## 3. A PHYSICAL ILLUSTRATION

Before we proceed with a more complete statement of the mathematics that underlies our analysis, it may be useful to provide an example of a physical system that can be approximately decomposed in the manner just described. We shall see that the principle of aggregation we are employing is essentially that which justifies the replacement of microvariables by macrovariables in classical thermodynamics.

Consider a building whose outside walls provide perfect thermal insulation from the environment. The building is divided into a large number of rooms, the walls between them being good, but not perfect, insulators. Each room is divided into a number of offices by partitions. The partitions are poor insulators. A thermometer hangs in each of the offices. Suppose that at time $t_0$ the various offices within the building are in a state of thermal disequilibrium — there is a wide variation in temperature from office to office and from room to room. When we take new temperature readings at time $t_1$, several hours after $t_0$, what will we find? At $t_1$, there will be very little variation in temperature among the offices within each single room, but there may still be large temperature variations *among* rooms. When we take readings again at time $t_2$, several days after $t_1$, we find an almost uniform temperature throughout the building; the temperature differences among rooms have virtually disappeared.

The well-known equations for the diffusion of heat allow us to represent this situation by a system of differential equations – or approximately by a system of difference equations. Let $F_{il}(t)$ be the temperature of the $i$th office which is in the $I$th room, at time $t$. Let $F(t)$ be the vector consisting of these temperatures as components, $F(t) = [\bar{F}_{1_1}, F_{2_1}, \ldots, F_{il}, \ldots, F_{1N}, \ldots, F_{n_N}]$. Then

(3.1)        $F(t + 1) = F(t)R$,

where $R$ is a matrix whose element, $r_{ij}$, represents the rate of heat transfer between office $i$ and office $j$ per degree difference in temperature.

A temperature equilibrium *within* each room will be reached rather rapidly, while a temperature equilibrium *among* rooms will be reached only slowly, if the $r_{ij}$ are generally large when $i$ and $j$ are offices in the same room, and are close to zero when $i$ and $j$ are offices in different rooms – that is to say, if the matrix $R$ is nearly decomposable. When this is the case, and as long as we are not interested in the rapid fluctuations in temperature among offices in the same room, we can learn all we want to know about the dynamics of this system by placing a single thermometer in each room – it is unnecessary to place a thermometer in each office.

## 4. MATHEMATICAL ANALYSIS

In this section, we shall make precise the meaning of propositions stated at the end of Section 2, and provide their proofs for the case where the roots of $P^*$ are all distinct.

Every matrix with distinct roots is similar to a diagonal matrix whose nonzero elements are those roots. Hence, there exist nonsingular matrices $Z$ and $Z^*$ such that

(4.1)        $PZ = Z\Lambda$,

(4.2)        $P^*Z^* = Z^*\Lambda^*$,

where $\Lambda$ and $\Lambda^*$ are diagonal matrices whose nonzero elements are roots of $P$ and $P^*$, respectively. Since $Z$ and $Z^*$ are defined only up to a scalar factor and permutations, we select $Z^*$ so that the $\lambda_{il}^*$ appear in order of magnitude for each $I$.

From the argument leading to (2.6), it is clear that the $\lambda_i$'s are functions of $\epsilon$. Let us take a particular value of $\delta$, say $\delta_0$, and choose a value of $\epsilon$, $\epsilon_0$, which satisfies (2.6). Then, we can define

$$(4.3) \qquad \delta_i(\epsilon_0) = \lambda_i(\epsilon_0) - \lambda_i^*, \qquad\qquad |\delta_i(\epsilon_0)| < \delta_0;$$

$$(4.4) \qquad v_i = \frac{\delta_i(\epsilon_0)}{\delta_0}, \qquad\qquad |v_i| < 1;$$

and a diagonal matrix whose elements are $v_i$'s, i.e.,

$$(4.5) \qquad V = \left\|\begin{array}{ccc} v_1 & & \\ & v_i & \\ & & v_n \end{array}\right\|$$

We can then write

$$(4.6) \qquad \Lambda = \Lambda^* + \delta_0 V.$$

Substitution of (2.3) and (4.6) with these choices of $\epsilon$ and $\delta$ into (4.1) yields

$$(4.7) \qquad (P^* + \epsilon_0 C)Z = Z(\Lambda^* + \delta_0 V)$$

and

$$(4.8) \qquad P^*Z - Z\Lambda^* = \delta_0 ZV - \epsilon_0 CZ.$$

As $\delta_0 \to 0$, and hence $\epsilon_0 \to 0$, the $Z$'s remaining bounded, the right hand side of (4.8) approaches a matrix whose elements are all zero. Comparison of the left hand side of (4.8) with (4.2) indicates that, if $z_{ij}$ and $z_{ij}^*$ are elements of $Z$ and $Z^*$, we must have a relation

$$(4.9) \qquad \lim_{\delta_0 \to 0} z_{ij} = c z_{ij}^*$$

for all $i$ and $j$, where $c$ is some constant. Since $c$ is arbitrary, we let $c = 1$. Thus we can state:

THEOREM 4.1: *There is a way of selecting the matrices $Z$ such that, for an arbitrary positive real number $\zeta$, there exists $\epsilon_0$ such that, for $\epsilon < \epsilon_0$,*

$$(4.10) \qquad \max_{i,j} |z_{ij} - z_{ij}^*| < \zeta.$$

Let us take a value of $\epsilon$, $\epsilon_1$, that satisfies the condition (4.10).

Corresponding to this $\epsilon_1$, we can define $\lambda_i(\epsilon_1)$, $i = 1, \ldots, n$. These values can then be inserted in (4.1) to yield a specific $Z$. We then define, using this $Z$ and the $Z^*$ given by (4.2), a new set of values

$$(4.11) \qquad \zeta_{ij} = z_{ij} - z_{ij}^*.$$

Because of the way in which the $\zeta_{ij}$'s are constructed, we are assured that $|\zeta_{ij}| < \zeta$ for all $i$ and $j$. Let us further define

$$(4.12) \qquad u_{ij} = \frac{\zeta_{ij}}{\zeta}.$$

We note that $|u_{ij}| < 1$. We can then write

$$(4.13) \qquad Z = Z^* + \zeta U,$$

where $U$ is the matrix whose elements are the $u_{ij}$'s. We know that

$$(4.14) \qquad x(t) = x(0)P^t; \qquad x^*(t) = x^*(0)P^{*t}.$$

Consider next vectors $y(t)$ and $y^*(t)$ defined by

$$(4.15a) \qquad y(t) = x(t)Z^{-1}$$

$$(4.15b) \qquad y^*(t) = x^* Z^{*-1}$$

Substituting (4.15) into (4.14), we obtain:

$$(4.16a) \qquad y(t) = x(0)(Z^{-1}Z)P^t Z^{-1} = y(0)(ZPZ^{-1})^t = y(0)\Lambda^t$$

$$(4.16b) \qquad y^*(t) = x^*(0)(Z^{*-1}Z^*)P^{*t}Z^{*-1} = y^*(0)(Z^*P^*Z^{*-1})^t = y^*(0)\Lambda^{*t}.$$

The inverse transformations of (4.15), when the results of (4.16) are substituted into them, yield:

$$(4.17a) \qquad x(t) = y(0)\Lambda^t Z;$$

$$(4.17b) \qquad x^*(t) = y^*(0)\Lambda^{*t}Z^*.$$

Let us now look at elements of (4.17) more closely. They have the form

$$(4.18) \qquad x_j(t) = \sum_{i=1}^{n} z_{ij}\lambda_i^t y_i(0).$$

It is obvious, from the structure of the decomposable matrix $P^*$, that

$$z_{i_I i_J}^* = 0 \qquad \text{for } I \neq J.$$

This, together with (4.13), implies that

$$(4.19) \qquad z_{i_I i_J} = \zeta u_{i_I i_J} \qquad \text{for } I \neq J.$$

Hence, we can divide the right hand side of (4.18) into five sets of terms according to the scheme:

$$(4.20) \qquad x_{i_J}(t) = \zeta u_{1,i_J}\lambda_{1_1}^t y_{1_1}(0) + z_{1_J i_J}\lambda_{1_J}^t y_{1_J}(0)$$

$$+ \zeta \sum_{\substack{I=2 \\ I \neq J}}^{N} u_{1_I i_J} \lambda_{1_I}^t y_{1_I}(0) + \sum_{i_J=2}^{n_J} z_{i_J i_J} \lambda_{i_J i_J}^t \lambda_{i_J}^t y_{i_J}(0)$$

$$+ \zeta \sum_{\substack{I=1 \\ I \neq J}}^{N} \sum_{i_I=2}^{n_I} u_{i_I i_J} \lambda_{i_I}^t y_{i_I}(0).$$

In the special case where $J = 1$, the first term is absent. In order to discuss the meaning and implications of (4.20), let us give names to each term on the right hand side of (4.20) as follows:

$$(4.21) \qquad x_{i_J}(t) = \zeta S_j^{(1)} + S_j^{(2)} + \zeta S_j^{(3)} + S_j^{(4)} + \zeta S_j^{(5)}.$$

For almost all choices of $y(0)$, each of the five terms on the right side of (4.21) will be nonzero at $t = 0$. We limit ourselves to this case, which is the general one. The following propositions are now self evident, and we state them as a theorem:

THEOREM 4.2. Part (1): *Since* $\lambda_{1_J} > \lambda_{j_J}, j = 2, \ldots, n$, *for any real positive number* $\eta_0$ *there exists an integer* $T_0$ *such that, for* $t > T_0$,

$$(4.22) \qquad \frac{|S_j^{(4)}|}{|S_j^{(2)}|} < \eta_0.$$

*For a given* $T_1 > T_0$ *and arbitrary positive real number* $\eta_1$, *there exists a number* $\zeta_1$, *and hence a number* $\epsilon_1$ *by Theorem 4.1, such that, for* $t < T_1$ *and* $\epsilon < \epsilon_1$,

$$(4.23) \qquad \frac{|\zeta(S_j^{(1)} + S_j^{(3)} + S_j^{(5)})|}{|S_j^{(2)} + S_j^{(4)}|} < \eta_1.$$

Theorem 4.2, Part 1, states that, for a sufficiently small $\epsilon$, the system characterized by a nearly decomposable matrix $P$ behaves in a manner similar to the behavior of the completely decomposable system $P^*$ for small $t$. This is even clearer when we express $x^*(t)$ as

$$(4.24) \qquad x_{iJ}^*(t) = z_{1_J i_J}^* \lambda_{1_J}^{*t} y_{1_J}^*(0) + \sum_{i=2}^{n} z_{i_J i_J}^* \lambda_{iJ}^{*t} y_{iJ}^*(0)$$

and compare (4.24) with (4.20), remembering that

$$z_{i_j} \to z_{i_j}^*, \ \lambda_i \to \lambda_i^* \quad \text{as} \quad \epsilon \to 0.$$

THEOREM 4.2 Part (2): *Given $\epsilon_1$ satisfying condition (4.23), for an arbitrary positive real number $\eta_2$, there exists a number $T_2 > T_1$ such that, for $t > T_2$,*

$$(4.25) \qquad \frac{|S_j^{(4)} + \varsigma S_j^{(5)}|}{|\varsigma S_j^{(1)} + S_j^{(2)} + \varsigma S_j^{(3)}|} < \eta_2$$

*and, for any positive real number $\eta_3$, there exists a number $T_3 > T_2$ such that, for $t > T_3$,*

$$(4.26) \qquad \frac{|S_j^{(2)} + \varsigma S_j^{(3)} + S_j^{(4)} + \varsigma S_j^{(5)}|}{\varsigma |S_j^{(1)}|} < \eta_3:$$

These two inequalities are direct consequences of the fact that we have arranged the index of roots in such a way that $\lambda_{1I} > \lambda_{iI}$ for $i - 1, \ldots, n$, $\lambda_{1I} > \lambda_{1J}$ for $I > J$.

We may summarize the above propositions by saying that the dynamic behavior of the system represented by the nearly decomposable matrix $P$ can be analyzed in the following four stages: (1) $t < T_0$, where $S_2$ and $S_4$ dominate the rest of the terms in the summation (4.20); (2) $T_0 < t < T_1$, where $S_2$ dominates all the rest; (3) $t > T_2 > T_1$ where $S_1$, $S_2$, and $S_3$ together dominate $S^4$ and $S^5$; and (4) $t > T_3 > T_2$, where $S_1$ finally dominates all the rest.

If $|\lambda_{1\,1}| \leqslant 1$ so that the system as a whole is stable, we may use the terminology: stage (1) is the short-run dynamics; stage (2), the short-run equilibrium; stage (3), the long-run dynamics; stage (4), the long-run equilibrium. Note that the terms $S_1$, $S_2$, and $S_3$ involve only the aggregate variables $y_{1_I}(0), I = 1, \ldots, N$.

Thus we conclude: In the short-run, or for stages (1) and (2), we may treat our system as though it consists of $N$ independent subsystems; in the long-run, i.e., for stages (3) and (4), we may look at our system as a set of relations among $N$ aggregative variables, the $y_{1_I}$'s ignoring the relations within each of the subsystems.

Finally, it is perfectly clear how our argument above can be extended to cover the special case where $P^*$ is stochastic. If $P^*$ is stochastic, the largest roots of all $P_I^*$'s are unity, and this violates the condition for the existence of the matrix $Z^*$. However, each submatrix $P_I^*$, will have a similar matrix, $\Lambda_I^*$. Then, we can define $Z_I^*$ such that

$$(4.27) \qquad P_I^* Z_I^* = Z_I^* \Lambda_I^*.$$

Let us now construct, for each $Z_I^*$ and $\Lambda_I^*$, and $n \times n$ matrix appropriately bordered with zeros. We shall designate these bordered matrices by the same symbols as are employed for the corresponding $n_I \times n_I$ matrices. We then define

$$Z^* = \sum_{I=1}^{N} Z_I^*; \quad \Lambda^* = \sum_{I=1}^{N} \Lambda_I^*.$$

Although the bordered $Z_I^*$'s are singular, $Z^*$ defined above is not singular, and we can define $Z^{*-1}$ to be the inverse of $Z^*$. When $Z^*, \Lambda^*, Z^{*-1}$ thus defined are inserted into Equation (4.2) and the following equations, the argument can proceed in the same manner as above.

## 5. A SPECIAL CASE: STOCHASTIC MATRICES

The proof of the basic theorem presented in the preceding section has the advantage that it is straightforward and fairly general. In studying this problem, however, we have found it rather difficult to appreciate the implications of the mathematical results adequately, and we feel that another, somewhat more specialized, but substantially equivalent way of stating our theorems is very helpful. At least, it enables us to follow the dynamic process of the system in more detail. In the present section, we shall state these alternative theorems, leaving their proofs to the Appendix. Having given the general proof in the preceding section, the sole purpose of stating the alternative theorems is to provide for the reader some aid which we ourselves have found useful in getting further insight into the nature of the problem. This being the case, we shall restrict ourselves to the simplest case of the stochastic matrix, and sacrifice mathematical rigor whenever it interferes with the simplicity of our presentation.

Let us restate our systems:

$$(5.1a) \qquad x(t+1) = x(t)P,$$

$$(5.1b) \qquad x^*(t+1) = x^*(t)P^*.$$

These relations are identical to Equations (2.4) and (2.2) except that now $x$, $x^*$, and $P, P^*$ are restricted to probability vectors and stochastic matrices, respectively. We assume that the matrix $C$ in (2.3) has the necessary property to keep both $P$ and $P^*$ stochastic. Thus, we may think of the system as having $n$ possible states, the subscript running over these states; $x_i(t)$ is the unconditional probability that the system is in the $i$th state in period $t$; $P_{ij}$ is the conditional probability that the system is in the $j$th state in period $(t + 1)$, given that the system is in state $i$ in period $t$. We note that the relations (2.8) among the roots of $P$ hold for sufficiently small $\epsilon$.

We wish to express $x(t)$ and $x^*(t)$ in terms of the roots of the respective matrices. In Section 4 we have done so by means of the theorem asserting the existence of a similar diagonal matrix. We shall proceed in a somewhat different manner in this section, as follows: We rewrite (5.1a) and (5.1b) as

(5.2a)        $x(t) = x(0)P^t$,

(5.2b)        $x^*(t) = x^*(0)P^{*t}$.

Now, for any nonsingular $n \times n$ *matrix A* whose roots, $k_1, \ldots, k_n$, distinct, there exists a unique set of $n$ matrices, $\alpha^{(1)}, \ldots, \alpha^{(n)}$ with the following characteristics[5] :

(i)        $\alpha^{(\rho)} \cdot \alpha^{(\rho)} = \alpha^{(\rho)}, \quad \rho = 1, \ldots, n.$   (idempotency),

(ii)       $\alpha^{(\rho)} \cdot \alpha^{(\sigma)} = 0; \quad \rho \neq \sigma; \quad \rho, \sigma = 1, \ldots, n$   (orthogonality),

(iii)      $\sum_{\rho=1}^{n} \alpha^{(\rho)} = I,$

(iv)       $\sum_{\rho=1}^{n} k_\rho \alpha^{(\rho)} = A,$

where 0 in (ii) is an $n \times n$ *matrix whose elements are all zero, and I* in (iii) is an $n \times n$ identity matrix. It is easy to see that, from these properties, it follows that

(v)        $A^t = \sum_{\rho=1}^{n} k_\rho^t \alpha^{(\rho)}.$

Using this representation, we can express $P^t$ thus:

(5.3)      $P^t = \sum_{\rho=1}^{n} \lambda_\rho^t \pi^{(\rho)},$

where the $\pi^{(\rho)}$'s are matrices associated with $P$ that satisfy the conditions (i) to (iv) above. Remembering the classification of roots described by (2.8), we divide the terms in the right hand side of (5.3) into three parts:

$$(5.4) \qquad P^t = \pi^{(11)} + \sum_{I=2}^{N} \lambda_{1_I}^t \pi^{(1I)} + \sum_{I=1}^{N} \sum_{\rho=2}^{n_I} \lambda_{\rho_I}^t \pi^{(\rho I)}.$$

We cannot expand $P^*$ directly into idempotent matrices as above because the $N$ largest roots of $P^*$ are all unity. However, any non-decomposable submatrix $P_I^*$ of $P^*$ can be so expanded, and we may write

$$(5.5) \qquad P_I^{*t} = \pi^{*(1I)} + \sum_{\rho_I=2}^{n_I} \lambda_{\rho_I}^{*t} \pi^{*(\rho I)} \qquad\qquad \text{for all } I.$$

As in the argument we used at the end of Section 4, let us construct $n \times n$ matrices by bordering those in (5.5) with the appropriate number of rows and columns of zeros, and designate these by the same symbols as those used for the $n_I \times n_I$ matrices in (5.5). Then

$$(5.6) \qquad P^* = \sum_{I=1}^{N} P_I^* = \sum_{I=1}^{N} \pi^{*(1I)} + \sum_{I=1}^{N} \sum_{\rho_I=2}^{n_I} \lambda_{\rho_I}^* \pi^{*(\rho I)}$$

and for the $i$th power of $P^*$

$$(5.7) \qquad P^{*t} = \sum_{I=1}^{N} \pi^{*(1I)} + \sum_{I=1}^{N} \sum_{\rho_I=2}^{n_I} \lambda_{\rho_I}^{*t} \pi^{*(\rho I)}.$$

When we compare Equations (5.4) and (5.7) with Equations (4.20) and (4.24), we see that they are analgous expressions, but they also have some differences. Equation (4.20) was very convenient for obtaining information on the variations in the relative influences of various $\lambda$'s as the size of $\epsilon$ varied. Equation (5.4) gives clearer indications of the characteristics of the time path of $x$, as we shall show presently.

We first note that, since the $\lambda_{1_I}^*$'s are unity and the $\lambda_{1_I}$'s are very close to unity for all $I$, the first summation term on the right hand side of Equation (5.7) and the first and second summation terms of Equation (5.4) remain almost unchanged for a relatively small $t$. This means that, for $x$ to behave very much like $x^*$ for small $t$ as indicated by Theorem 4.2, Part 1, $\pi^{(\rho I)}$ must approach $\pi^{*(\rho I)}$ for $\rho = 2, \ldots, n$ and $I = 1, \ldots, N$, as $\epsilon$ goes to zero. Furthermore, if $x$ is to exhibit the behavior described by Part 2 of Theorem 4.2, when $t$ becomes so large that the $\lambda_{1_I}^t$'s are no longer nearly unity, the elements of $\pi^{(1I)}, I = 1, \ldots, N$, must be functions of $j$, $J$, and $I$, but independent of $i$.

Before we proceed to state our basic propositions as theorems, we need a few additional definitions, which we list below:

$P_{ij}^{(t)}$:       elements of the matrix $P^t$, i.e., the $i$th power of the matrix $P$;

$P_{ij}^{*(t)}$:      elements of the matrix $P^{*t}$;

$\bar{x}^*$:         equilibrium value of $x^*$;

$$\bar{x}_{i\mid I}^* = \frac{\bar{x}_{i_I}^*}{\displaystyle\sum_{i_I=1}^{n_I} \bar{x}_{i_I}^*}, \qquad I = 1, \ldots, N.$$

Note that the vector $[\bar{x}_{i\mid I}^*]$, $i = 1, \ldots, n_I$, is the characteristic vector of $P_I^*$ associated with the root of unity.

$$(5.8) \qquad \pi_{IJ}^{(1_l)} = \sum_{i_I=1}^{n_I} \sum_{i_J=1}^{n_J} \bar{x}_{i_I\mid I}^* \pi_{i_{IJ}}^{(1_l)}$$

for $l = 1, \ldots, N$, $I = 1, \ldots, N$, and $J = 1, \ldots, N$.

$$(5.9) \qquad P_{IJ} = \sum_{l=1}^{N} \lambda_{1_l} \pi_{IJ}^{(1_l)}.$$

The subscript of $\lambda$ and superscript of $\pi$ are written $1_l$ instead of the usual $1_I$ to avoid confusion.

In terms of these definitions, the following three theorems are proved in the Appendix.

THEOREM 5.1: *For an arbitrary positive real number $\xi_2$ there exists a number $\epsilon_2$ such that for $\epsilon < \epsilon_2$,*

$$\max_{i,j} |\pi_{ij}^{(\rho_l)} - \pi_{ij}^{*(\rho_l)}| < \xi_2$$

*for $\rho_l = 2, \ldots, n_l$, and $l = 1, \ldots, N$.*

THEOREM 5.2: *For an arbitrary positive real number $\omega$ there exists a number $\epsilon_\omega$ such that for $\epsilon < \epsilon_\omega$*

$$\max_{i,j} |\pi_{i_I i_J}^{(1_l)} - \bar{x}_{j\mid J}^* \pi_{IJ}^{(1_l)}| < \omega$$

*for $l = 1, \ldots, N, I = 1, \ldots, \quad N, J = 1, \ldots, N.$*

**THEOREM 5.3:** *The right hand side of Equation* (5.9) *is the idempotent expansion of the matrix* $P_{ij}$.

The implications of the above theorems are quite clear. Since the $\lambda_{1_l}$ are almost unity for $l = 1, \ldots, N$ as indicated in (2.8), for a relatively small $t$, say $t < T_2, \lambda_{1_l}^t, l = 1, \ldots, N$, will be very close to unity. Hence the first two terms on the right hand side of Equation (5.4) will not change very much while the first term on the right hand side of Equation (5.7) will not change at all. Hence, for $t < T_2$, the time behavior of $x$ and $x^*$ are completely determined by the last terms on the right hand side of Equations (5.4) and (5.7), respectively. But, Theorem 5.1 asserts that the $\pi$'s appearing in the last term of Equation (5.4) can be made as close as we please to the corresponding $\pi^*$'s in Equation (5.7), by taking $\epsilon$ sufficiently small. We may recall that $\lambda_i \to \lambda_i^*$ as $\epsilon \to 0$. Hence, for $t < T_2$ the time path of $x$ must be very close to the time path of $x^*$. Note that $T_2$ can be made as large as we please by taking $\epsilon$ sufficiently small.

Since the $\lambda_{i_l}^*$ are independent of $\epsilon$, and for $i_l = 2, \ldots, n_l$ less than unity as is indicated in (2.7), for any positive real $\xi_1$ we can define $T_1^*$ such that for $t > T_1^*$ the absolute value of the last summation term on the right hand side of (5.7) is less than $\xi_1$. $T_i^*$ is independent of $\epsilon$. On the other hand, (2.8) and Theorem 5.1 insure not only that for any positive real $\xi_1$ there exists $T_1$ such that for $t > T_1$ the absolute value of the lost summation term on the right hand side of (5.4) is less than $\xi_1$, but that $T_1 \to T_1^*$ for the same $\xi_1$ as $\epsilon \to 0$. That is, for any positive real number $\xi_1$, there exist $T_1^*$ and $T_1$ such that

$$(5.10) \qquad | \sum_{l=1}^{N} \sum_{\rho_l=2}^{n_l} \lambda_{\rho_l}^{*t} \pi^{*(\rho l)} | < \xi_1 \qquad \text{for } t > T_1^*,$$

$$(5.11) \qquad | \sum_{l=1}^{N} \sum_{\rho_l=2}^{n_l} \lambda_{\rho}^{t} \pi^{(\rho l)} | < \xi_1 \qquad \text{for } t > T_1 \text{ and } T_1 \to T_1^* \text{ as } \epsilon \to 0.$$

Since $T_2$ can be made as large as we please by taking $\epsilon$ sufficiently small while $T_1^*$ is independent of $\epsilon$, let us take $\epsilon$ such that $T_2$ is very much larger than $T_1$. Provided that $\epsilon$ is not identically zero so that none of $\lambda_{1l}$ except $\lambda_1$ is identically unity, the second summation term on the right hand side of Equation (5.4) will eventually become negligible as $t$ becomes indefinitely large. Let us define $T_3$, corresponding to an arbitrary positive real number $\xi_3$, such that for $t > T_3$

$$(5.12) \qquad \max_{i,j} | \sum_{l=2}^{N} \lambda_{1_l}^{t} \pi_{ij}^{(1l)} | < \xi_3.$$

$T_3$ also increases without limit as $\epsilon \to 0$.

We show the relations among the various $T$'s schematically below:

$$\underset{0 \qquad\quad T_1^* \leftarrow T_1 \qquad\qquad T_2 \qquad\qquad\qquad T_3 \qquad\qquad\qquad\qquad \to t}{\rule{0pt}{0pt}|\rule{4em}{0.4pt}|\rule{0.4pt}{0.6em}\rule{3em}{0.4pt}|\rule{7em}{0.4pt}|\rule{9em}{0.4pt}|}$$

For $T_2 < t < T_3$, corresponding to the period which we called the long run dynamics in Section 4, the last summation term on the right-hand side of Equation (5.4) has very little influence on the time path of $x$. The path is determined by the first and second summation terms on the right hand side of Equation (5.4). But Theorem 5.2 asserts that the elements of $\pi^{(1l)}$, $l = 1, \ldots, N$, are functions only of $j, I, J$, and independent of $i$ That is, for any $I, J$, and $l$, $[\pi_{i_I 1_J}{}^{(1l)}, \ldots, \pi_{i_I j_J}{}^{(1l)}, \ldots, \pi_{i_I n_J}{}^{(1l)}]$, are proportional to the characteristic vector of $P_J^*$ associated with the root of unity, and are the same for $i_I = 1, \ldots, n_I$. Hence, $[x_{1_I}, \ldots, x_{i_I}, \ldots, x_{n_I}]$ will move, for the period $T_2 < t < T_3$, keeping a roughly constant proportionality relationship among individual elements for a given $I$. This permits us, following the Hicks-Lange condition, to replace the $n$-dimensional vector by an $N$-dimensional vector, and the $n \times n$ matrix $P$ by an $N \times N$ matrix $\| P_{IJ} \|$.

The usefulness of Theorem 5.3 will become apparent in the next section when we shall discuss the application of our theorems to the problems of inverting nearly decomposable matrices. Here we merely note that, since (1) $\pi_{i_I}^*$ has $\bar{x}_1^*{}_{|I}$ as its rows where its elements are not zero, (2) $\pi_{1_I}^*$ are orthogonal to $\pi_{i|I}^*$ for $i = 2, \ldots, n$, (3) $\pi_{i_I} \to \pi_{i_I}^*$ for $= 2, \ldots, n_I$, we can express $P_{IJ}$ as

$$(5.13) \qquad P_{IJ} = \sum_{i_I=1}^{n_I} \sum_{i_J=1}^{n_J} \bar{x}_{i_I | I}^* P_{i_I i_J}.$$

### 6. A NUMERICAL ILLUSTRATION

The above results can be understood more readily with the aid of a simple numerical example. Let us consider a nearly decomposable stochastic matrix

$$(6.1) \qquad P = \begin{Vmatrix} .9700 & .0295 & .0005 & 0 \\ .0200 & .9800 & 0 & 0 \\ 0 & 0 & .9600 & .0400 \\ .0002 & .0002 & .0396 & .9600 \end{Vmatrix}$$

and the corresponding completely decomposable matrix

$$(6.2) \qquad P = \begin{Vmatrix} .9700 & .0300 & 0 & 0 \\ .0200 & .9800 & 0 & 0 \\ 0 & 0 & .9600 & .0400 \\ 0 & 0 & .0400 & .9600 \end{Vmatrix} = \begin{Vmatrix} P_{1*} & 0 \\ 0 & P_{2*} \end{Vmatrix}$$

We can compute $\bar{x}_{j\,|\,J}^{*}$:

(6.3)        $[\bar{x}_{j\,|\,1}^{*}] = [.4 \quad .6]$,

(6.4)        $[\bar{x}_{j\,|\,2}^{*}] = [.5 \quad .5]$;

and $P_{IJ}$:

(6.5)        $\| P_{IJ} \| = \left\| \begin{matrix} .9998 & .0002 \\ .0002 & .9998 \end{matrix} \right\|$.

The roots of $P$ and their selected powers are

$$\lambda_1 = 1;$$

$$\lambda_2 = .9996; \quad \lambda_2^{128} = .9511; \quad \lambda_2^{(128)^2} = .001724;$$

$$\lambda_3 = .952004; \quad \lambda_3^{128} = 1.845 \times 10^{-3}; \quad \lambda_3^{(128)^2} = 1.091 \times 10^{-350};$$

$$\lambda_4 = .9202; \quad \lambda_4^{128} = 2.381 \times 10^{-5}; \quad \lambda_4^{(128)^2} = 1.622 \times 10^{-592}.$$

The idempotent expansion of $P$ is given by

(6.6)        $P^t = \pi^{(1)} + \lambda_2^t \pi^{(2)} + \lambda_3^t \pi^{(3)} + \lambda_4^t \pi^{(4)},$

i.e.,

(6.7)  $P^{(t)} = (1.)^t$ $\left\| \begin{matrix} 0.20050125 & 0.29824561 & 0.25062657 & 0.25062657 \\ 0.20050125 & 0.29824561 & 0.25062657 & 0.25062657 \\ 0.20050125 & 0.29824561 & 0.25062657 & 0.25062657 \\ 0.20050125 & 0.29824561 & 0.25062657 & 0.25062657 \end{matrix} \right\|$

$+ (.9996)^t$ $\left\| \begin{matrix} .198685261 & .296522699 & -.248356576 & -.250865228 \\ .202740062 & .302574184 & .253425078 & .255984927 \\ -.199496221 & -.297732997 & .249370276 & .251889168 \\ -.197501259 & -.294755666 & .246876573 & .249370276 \end{matrix} \right\|$

$+ (.952004)^t$ $\left\| \begin{matrix} .6004874 & -.5952777 & .0019774 & -.0807124 \\ -.4030171 & .3995206 & -.0013271 & .0541701 \\ -.0008141 & .0008070 & -.0000027 & .0001094 \\ .0000403 & -.0000399 & .0000001 & -.0000054 \end{matrix} \right\|$

$+ (.92019)^t$ $\left\| \begin{matrix} .0002636 & -.0007692 & -.0062681 & .0062939 \\ -.0000878 & .0002397 & .0020960 & -.0021003 \\ -.0209766 & .0577601 & .5007744 & -.5017791 \\ .0208776 & -.0569881 & -.4983870 & .4993957 \end{matrix} \right\|$

From (6.7), we also readily compute $P^{128}$ (the matrix for the 'middle-run' dynamic system) and $P^{(128)^2}$, the matrix for the long run:

$$(6.8) \qquad P^{128} = \begin{Vmatrix} .390089 & .579037 & .016631 & .014244 \\ .392503 & .586246 & .011831 & .009419 \\ .009465 & .013138 & .487509 & .489888 \\ .011385 & .015999 & .485107 & .487509 \end{Vmatrix}$$

$$(6.9) \qquad P^{(128)^2} = \begin{Vmatrix} .200776 & .298656 & .250286 & .250282 \\ .200782 & .298664 & .250279 & .250275 \\ .200222 & .297829 & .250973 & .250976 \\ .200225 & .297833 & .250970 & .250973 \end{Vmatrix}$$

Note that, if we neglect roots smaller than 0.002, we have

$$(6.10) \qquad P^{128} = \pi^{(1)} + \lambda_2^{128} \pi^{(2)},$$

$$(6.11) \qquad P^{(128)^2} = \pi^{(1)}.$$

The reader's attention is called to the behavior of elements of $P^t$ from $P^{128}$ to $P^{(128)^2}$ — elements of $P_1^t$ and $P_2^t$ maintain the same proportion over the columns and independently of rows within each submatrix while moving toward the full equilibirium.

It is of some interest to see whether or not our results are useful for inverting the nearly decomposable matrix, $P$. We know that

$$(6.12) \qquad P^{-1} = \sum_{l=1}^{N} \sum_{\rho_l=1}^{n_l} \lambda_{\rho_l}^{-1} \pi^{(\rho_l)}.$$

This relation is of little use for computational purposes, since the $\pi$'s are very difficult to compute. But, in the case of nearly decomposable matrices, this leads to a potentially useful approximation. We note that, from Theorem 5.1,

$$(6.13) \qquad P^{-1} \simeq \sum_{l=1}^{N} \lambda_{1_l}^{-1} \pi^{(1_l)} + P^{*-1} - \sum_{I=1}^{N} \pi^{*(1_l)}.$$

Since $P^*$ is completely decomposable, it is much simpler to invert. The $\pi^{*(1_l)}$ are, of course, matrices with identical rows, and their rows are the characteristic vectors of the respective submatrices $P_I$, $I = 1, \ldots, N$, associated with roots of unity. Hence, our problem reduces to that of computing the first term on the right hand side of (6.13). By Theorem 5.2, we can write

$$(6.14) \qquad \sum_{l=1}^{N} \lambda_{1_l}^{-1} \pi_{ij}^{(1_l)} = \bar{x}_{j|J}^* \sum_{l=1}^{N} \lambda_{1_l}^{-1} \pi_{IJ}^{(1_l)}.$$

But, by Theorem 5.3, we have

$$(6.15) \qquad \sum_{l=1}^{N} \lambda_{1l}^{-1} \pi_{IJ}^{(1l)} = P_{IJ}^{(-1)}.$$

Hence,

$$(6.16) \qquad \sum_{l=1}^{N} \lambda_{1l}^{-1} \pi_{ij}^{(1l)} = \bar{x}_{j|J}^{*} P_{IJ}^{(-1)}.$$

To summarize: in order to obtain $p^{-1}$, (i) find the inverses of $P_I^{*}$; (ii) compute $\bar{x}_j^{*} \mid J$ and form $\pi^{*(1l)}$ directly from them; (iii) form the aggregate matrix $\| P_{IJ} \|$ by (5.13); (iv) invert $\| P_{IJ} \|$; (v) substitute these results into (6.13) to obtain $P^{-1}$.

Going back to the numerical example of $P$ and $P^{*}$ given by (6.1) and (6.2), we readily find

$$(6.17a) \qquad P_1^{*-1} = \left\| \begin{array}{cc} 1.031578947 & -.031578947 \\ -.021032617 & 1.021052620 \end{array} \right\|,$$

$$(6.17b) \qquad P_2^{*-1} = \left\| \begin{array}{cc} 1.043478260 & -.043478260 \\ -.043478260 & 1.043478260 \end{array} \right\|.$$

$[\bar{x}_{j|J}^{*}]$ and $\| P_{IJ} \|$ have already been given by (6.3), (6.4), and (6.5). We also have

$$(6.18) \qquad \| P_{IJ} \|^{-1} = \left\| \begin{array}{cc} 1.00020008 & -.00020008 \\ -.00020008 & 1.00020008 \end{array} \right\|.$$

Substituting these results into (6.16), we have

$$(6.19)$$
$$\sum_{l=1}^{N} \lambda_{1l}^{-1} \pi^{(1l)} = \left\| \begin{array}{cccc} .400080032 & .600120048 & -.000100040 & -.000100040 \\ .400080032 & .600120048 & -.000100040 & -.000100040 \\ -.000800320 & -.001200480 & .500100040 & .500100040 \\ -.000800320 & -.001200480 & .500100040 & .500100040 \end{array} \right\|.$$

Further substitutions into (6.13) yield

$$(6.20)$$
$$P^{-1} \simeq \left\| \begin{array}{cccc} 1.031658979 & -.034588990 & -.000100040 & -.000100040 \\ -.020972585 & 1.021172668 & -.000100040 & -.000100040 \\ -.000800320 & -.001200480 & 1.043578300 & -.043378220 \\ -.000800320 & -.001200480 & -.043378220 & 1.043578300 \end{array} \right\|.$$

This result may be compared with the inverse obtained by the perturbation method, which is probably the most efficient way of obtaining the approximate inverse of a matrix of the type treated here.[6]

Let $C$ be defined by

(6.23)        $P = P^* + \epsilon C,$

where $\epsilon$ is a small positive number. Let $\hat{C}$ be defined by

(6.22)        $P^{-1} = P^{*-1} + \epsilon\hat{C},$

where $\epsilon$ is the same number as in Equation (6.21). Then, we have

(6.23)        $P \cdot P^{-1} = (P^* + \epsilon C)(P^{*-1} + \epsilon\hat{C}).$

Ignoring the terms in higher powers of $\epsilon$, we get:

(6.24)        $\hat{C} = -P^{*-1} C P^{*-1}.$

If, in the numerical example of (6.1) and (6.2), we take $\epsilon$ to be 0.0001, we have

(6.25)     $C = \begin{Vmatrix} 0 & -5 & 5 & 0 \\ 0 & 0 & 0 & 0 \\ 0 & 0 & 0 & 0 \\ 2 & 2 & -4 & 0 \end{Vmatrix}$

(6.26)     $\epsilon C = \begin{Vmatrix} -.000011 & .000527 & -.000538 & .000022 \\ .000000 & -.000011 & .000011 & .000000 \\ .000009 & .000009 & -.000018 & .000001 \\ .000211 & .000206 & .000436 & .000018 \end{Vmatrix},$

(6.27)     $P^{-1} \simeq \begin{Vmatrix} 1.031568 & -.031052 & -.000538 & .000022 \\ -.021053 & 1.021042 & .000011 & .000000 \\ .000009 & .000009 & 1.043460 & -.043477 \\ -.000211 & -.000206 & -.043042 & 1.043460 \end{Vmatrix}.$

The direct multiplication of $P^{-1}$ given by (6.27) with $P$ given by (6.1) shows that the approximate inverse obtained by the perturbation method is accurate to the 6th decimal place. The estimate of the inverse given by (6.20), obtained by the aggregation procedure, has an error of about 0.0001 in each element in the product. This relatively large error is caused by the restriction, implicit in the aggregation procedure, that the matrix elements *within* each subset are replaced by the eigenvectors corresponding to the middle-run equilibrium.

On the other hand, the perturbation method assumes implicitly that there is a zero probability that the system will move more than once from a state belonging to one subset to a state belonging to another subset. Hence, we can conclude that, while the perturbation method gives us a good approximation to the short-run behavior of the system, and hence to $P^{-1}$, its approximation to the middle-run behavior (and hence to $(P^{-1})^t$ for relatively large $t$) will be much less good. The aggregation method permits us to study this middle-run behavior, as we have seen earlier in this section.

For those readers who may be interested in the comparison, we give $P^{-1}$ obtained by equating $t = -1$ in Equation (6.7):

$$(6.28) \qquad P^{-1} = \begin{Vmatrix} 1.0306708 & -.0302846 & -.0026491 & -.0783382 \\ -.0206318 & 1.0209660 & -.0019932 & .0492225 \\ .0440999 & -.1027626 & 1.0505158 & -.0510149 \\ -.0408082 & .1067156 & -.0495267 & 1.0505238 \end{Vmatrix}$$

## 7. SOME CONCLUDING COMMENTS

In the preceding sections, we have analyzed the structure of dynamic systems represented by nearly-decomposable matrices. We have seen that such systems may be viewed as composite systems, constructed by the superposition of: (1) terms representing interactions of the variables within each subsystem; and (2) terms representing interactions among the sub-systems. We concluded that, over a relatively short period, the first group of terms dominates the behavior of the system, and hence each subsystem can be studied (approximately) independently of other subsystems. Over a relatively long period of time, on the other hand, the second group of terms dominates the behavior of the system, and the whole system moves, keeping the state of equilibrium within each subsystem – i.e. . the variables within each subsystem move roughly proportionately. Hence, the variables within each subsystem can be aggregated into indexes representing the subsystem.

Thus, the system of variables in the case just described can by represented as a two-level hierarchy, with the aggregative variables at the higher level. Now, there is no reason why we need to restrict ourselves to a two-level hierarchy. For, in such a hierarchy, each of the subsystem variables at the lower level might be an aggregate of variables at a still lower level of aggregation. The matrix of a three-level hierarchy, for example, might look something like this:

$$\begin{Vmatrix} P_1 & Q_1 & S_1 & S_2 \\ Q_2 & P_2 & S_3 & S_4 \\ \hline R_1 & R_2 & P_3 & Q_3 \\ R_3 & R_4 & Q_4 & P_4 \end{Vmatrix}$$

In this matrix, the elements of the submatrices designated as $Q$'s are of the first order of smallness, and the elements of the $R$'s and $S$'s of the second order of smallness. At the first level of aggregation, there will be four aggregative variables corresponding to the four submatrices along the diagonal, respectively. At the second level of aggregation, there will be two aggregative variables, corresponding to the blocks indicated by broken lines.

It is of some interest to consider the implications of our analysis concerning the computation involved in inverting a matrix in this context. To invert a matrix like the one above, we would first invert the matrices $P_i$, then the two aggregative matrices

$$\left\| \begin{matrix} P_1 & Q_1 \\ Q_2 & P_2 \end{matrix} \right\| \quad \text{and} \quad \left\| \begin{matrix} P_3 & Q_3 \\ Q_4 & P_4 \end{matrix} \right\|,$$

and finally the second level aggregative matrix

In ordinary methods of matrix inversion, the number of multiplications increases as the cube of the size of the matrix. On the other hand, under the method of inversion suggested above, if the size of the largest matrix to be inverted at any level of aggregation remains constant as $n$ increases, then the number of matrices to be inverted will increase proportionately with $n$, their size will not increase, and the total number of multiplications will increase only slightly more than proportionately with $n$.

It may be objected that decomposable matrices are rare objects, mathematrically speaking, and nearly decomposable matrices almost as rare. For if the elements of a matrix are selected in any ordinary way by a random process, the probability that the matrix will be decomposable is zero. There is every reason to believe, however, not only that near-decomposability is a very common characteristic of dynamic systems that exist in the real world, but also that many economists and other social scientists conduct their research as through this were the case. As we have pointed out in the introductory remarks, every time economists construct indices representing groups of variables and construct a theory in terms of such indices they are implicitly assuming that the economic system they study is constructed in the hierarchical form described above.

It is interesting to note that many recent discussions on the problems of aggregation can be looked at as studies of various aspects of a system like the one analyzed here.

Interest in the aggregation of the static input-output matrices largely stems from the desire to facilitate the inversion of the matrices involved.[7] As we have shown in Section 6, the method suggested by our analysis is not so efficient as the perturbation method, in the sense that the product of the original matrix with its inverse obtained by our method deviates further from the identity matrix than the product of the original matrix with the inverse obtained by the perturbation method. Our analysis provides, however, a better ground for interpreting the approximate result than the mechanical application of the perturbation method. Furthermore, the goodness of the approximation must be judged in terms of the decisions that will be based on the approximation rather than the closeness of the product to the identity matrix, and in this sense, it is by no means clear that the perturbation method is superior to ours.

Some of the recent work of Theil can also be related to our analysis.[8] One of his aggregation problems may be looked at in the following way: Suppose that we have a set of observations over time on the $x$'s, and estimate from these observations the matrix of coefficients $P$. Suppose further that we classify the $x$'s into a few groups, construct indices representing these groups, consider a new linear system relating these indices, and estimate the new aggregate coefficients from the same set of observations. Theil investigated, among other things, the relations between the micro and macro coefficients then estimated. Theil's results show that the conditions under which there exists a relatively simple relation between micro and macro variables are very severe. Our result suggests that, if the underlying structure generating the $x$'s is nearly decomposable, then, as the $x$'s are aggregated, the unit of time over which observations are made should be changed accordingly. However, a more complete analysis of the relation between our results and those of Theil must be deferred to a future study.

In a paper presented at the December, 1959, meetings of the Econometric Society, F. Fisher explored yet another problem that is closely related to our analysis.[9] The conditions that permit the identification of a structural relationship ordinarily state that a certain set of structural coefficients are identically zero, and the estimation can be carried out on the assumption that there exist no relations among the variables under consideration other than those explicitly stated in the system. Suppose, however, that these conditions are only approximately satisfied. Fisher has shown that, as the approximation of these conditions becomes better and better, the estimates of the structural parameters, obtained by the usual estimation method such as the limited information method or the generalized least squares method, are asymptotically consistent.

In the framework of our analysis, Fisher's problem is analogous to that of specifying the conditions under which one of the subsystems can be treated in isolation from all other parts of the system for the purposes of estimation.

The comparison of our result with that of Fisher immediately raises two important questions. The first has already been suggested by Fisher; since his results apply to what he calls block recursive systems, nearly triangular matrices must possess some properties analogous to those we have shown in nearly decomposable matrices. The investigation of these analogous properties would open a way to generalize Goodwin's justification of partial dynamics to the case where the coupling is only 'nearly-unilateral', as well as to the case where the whole system is 'nearly-block-recursive'.[10] The second is that, according to our analysis, even a very weak link will eventually make its influence felt given a long enough period of time. Thus, in interpreting Fisher's result, we must be careful to choose the appropriate period over which the observations are made.

Finally, we note that there are a number of other discussions in the economic literature upon which the notion of nearly-decomposable systems appears to throw some light. We have already pointed out that the argument here may be regarded as a statement of the circumstances under which the Lange-Hicks condition will be satisfied. It can easily be seen from our analysis that if the micro-system is dynamically stable, this will also be true of the aggregated system, since the characteristic roots of the aggregative matrix are also roots of the original matrix. This stability theorem has been proved earlier by Tamotsu Yokoyama.[11] Yokoyama assumes that the Lange-Hicks condition is satisfied, and derives the stability theorem from this assumption.

Samuelson points out that aggregation of commodities can seek its justification in either of two kinds of principles that, at first blush, appear rather antithetical to each other.[12] On the one hand (the Lange-Hicks condition), we can aggregate the parts of a subsystem when these are much more closely linked with each other than they are with the rest of the system. On the other hand, we can aggregate a set of variables if each of them is linked with the remainder of the system in just the same way as are the others. Our analysis of near-decomposability shows that the former condition is really a special case of the latter. For if $x_i$ and $x_j$ are variables belonging to different subsets of a nearly decomposable system, then $p_{ij}$ is very small, but $p_{ij}^{(t)}$, for sufficiently large $t$, is almost independent of $i$. That is to say, the linkage between $i$ and $j$ is negligible in the short run, and satisfies the second condition in the middle run for which it is not negligible.

## APPENDIX

*Proof of Theorem 5.1:*

We note first that the elements of the $i$th power of a matrix are continuous functions of the elements of the original matrix. Hence, for any positive real number $\xi_2'$ and an arbitrary integer $T_2$ there exists a number $\epsilon_2'$ such that for $t < T_2$ and $\epsilon < \epsilon_2'$

$$(A.1) \qquad \max_{i,j} | P_{ij}^{[t]} - P_{ij}^{*[t]} | < \xi_2'$$

$P_{ij}^{[t]}$ and $P_{ij}^{*[t]}$ are elements of $t$th power of matrices $P$ and $P^*$.

Substituting (5.4) and (5.7) into (A.1), we obtain

$$(A.2) \qquad \max_{i,j} | \sum_{I=1}^{N} \pi_{ij}^{*(1I)} - \pi_{ij}^{(1I)} - \sum_{I=2}^{N} \lambda_{1I}^{t} \pi_{ij}^{(1I)} + \sum_{I=1}^{N} \sum_{\rho_I=2}^{n_I} \lambda_{\rho_I}^{*t} \pi_{ij}^{*(\rho I)}$$

$$- \sum_{I=1}^{N} \sum_{\rho_I=2}^{n_I} \lambda_{\rho_I}^{t} \pi_{ij}^{(\rho I)} | < \xi_2'.$$

Introducing for convenience

$$(A.3) \qquad D_{ij}^{[t]} = \sum_{I=1}^{N} \pi_{ij}^{*(1I)} - \pi_{ij}^{(1I)} - \sum_{I=2}^{N} \lambda_{1I}^{t} \pi_{ij}^{(1I)},$$

we rewrite (A.2):

$$(A.4) \qquad \max_{i,j} | D_{ij}^{[t]} + \sum_{I=1}^{N} \sum_{\rho_I=2}^{n_I} (\lambda_{\rho_I}^{*t} - \lambda_{\rho_I}^{t}) \pi_{ij}^{(\rho I)}$$

$$+ \sum_{I=1}^{N} \sum_{\rho_I=2}^{n_I} \lambda_{\rho_I}^{*t} (\pi_{ij}^{*(\rho I)} - \pi_{ij}^{(\rho I)}) | < \xi_2'.$$

By (2.6), $(\lambda_{\rho_I}^{*t} - \lambda_{\rho_I}^{t}) \to 0$ as $\epsilon \to 0$. Hence, for any positive real $\xi_2$, we can choose a new $\epsilon_2''$ so that for $\epsilon < \epsilon_2''$,

$$(A.5) \qquad \max_{i,j} | D_{ij}^{[t]} + \sum_{I=1}^{N} \sum_{\rho_I=2}^{n_I} \lambda_{\rho_I}^{*(t)} (\pi_{ij}^{*(\rho I)} - \pi_{ij}^{(\rho I)}) | < \xi_2'.$$

But, since $\lambda^*$ are all distinct for $i_I \geqslant 2$, and $D_{ij}^{[t]}$ becomes independent of $t$ as $\lambda_{1I}^{t} \to 1$ for all $I$, this inequality can hold for all $t \leqslant T_0$ only if the coefficients of $\lambda^*$ become vanishingly small; hence, for any positive real number $\xi_2$, we can choose a value of $\epsilon$, $\epsilon_2$ so that for $\epsilon < \epsilon_2$,

$$(A.6) \qquad \max_{i,j} | \pi_{ij}^{*(\rho I)} - \pi_{ij}^{(\rho I)} | < \xi_2$$

for $\rho_I = 2, \ldots, n_I$ and $I = 1, \ldots, N$.

*Proof of Theorem 5.2:*

As indicated in the text and in the above proof of Theorem 5.1, we know that (1) as $\epsilon \to 0$, $T_1 \to T_1^*$ (2) $T_2$ can be made as large as we please for a given $\xi_2$ by taking small enough $\epsilon$, and (3) $T_1^*$ is independent of $\epsilon$. Hence, by taking $\epsilon$ sufficiently small, we can make $T_2$ very much larger than $T_1$ for a given set of $\xi_1$ and $\xi_2$. Then, for $T_1 < t < T_2$, we have

(A.7)    $| P_{i_I i_J}^{[t]} - \bar{x}_{j_J | J}^* \Delta_{IJ} | = | (P_{i_I i_J}^{[t]} - P_{i_I i_J}^{*[t]}) + (P_{i_I i_J}^{*[t]} - \bar{x}_{j_J | J}^* \Delta_{IJ}) |$

$$\leqslant \xi_2' + \xi_1$$

for $i_I = 1, \ldots, n_I,\ j_J = 1, \ldots, n_J,\ I,\ J = , \ldots, N$, and where $\Delta_{IJ}$ is Kronecker's delta.

Let us now consider $P_{ij}^{[t]}$ for a large enough $t$ so that it can be expressed in the following scheme:

(A.8)    $P_{ij}^{[t]} = \sum_k \sum_m P_{ik}^{[t_1]} P_{km}^{[t_2]} P_{mj}^{[t_3]},$

where $t = t_1 + t_2 + t_3$, and

$$T_1 < t_1 < T_2,$$
$$T_1 < t_3 < T_2,$$
$$T_1 < t_1 + t_3 < T_2,$$
$$T_2 < t_2.$$

Then, conditions (5.11) and (A.7) assures us that, for any real positive number $\omega_0$, there exists a value of $\epsilon$, $\epsilon_\omega$, such that for $\epsilon < \epsilon_\omega$, we have

(A.9)    $\sum_{l=1}^{N} \lambda_{1_I} \pi_{ij}^{(1_I)} = \sum_k \sum_m [\bar{x}_{K | K}^* \Delta_{IK}] [\sum_{l=1}^{N} \lambda_{1_I}^{t_2} \pi_{km}^{(1_I)}] [\bar{x}_{j | L}^* \Delta_{MJ}] + \omega_{ij}$

$\max_{i,j} | \omega_{ij} | < \omega_0,$

where the usual $1_I$, the subscript of $\lambda$ and the superscript of $\pi_{ij}$, is replaced by $1_l$ in order to avoid the confusion with the identification of a block of rows and columns of $P$ in this context.

(A.9) becomes, after a rearrangement of terms,

(A.10)    $\sum_{l=1}^{N} \lambda_{1_I}^{t} \pi_{ij}^{(1_I)} = \sum_{l=1}^{N} \lambda_{1_I}^{t_2} x_{j | J}^* [\sum_{i_I=1}^{n_I} \bar{x}_{i_I | I}^* \sum_{j_J=1}^{n_J} \pi_{i_I i_J}^{(1_I)}] + \omega_{ij}$

$\max_{ij} | \omega_{ij} | < \omega_0.$

For this to hold for all permissible values of $t_2$, we must have

$$(A.11) \qquad \lambda_{1_l}^{(t_1 + t_3)} \pi_{ij}^{(1_l)} = x_{j|J}^* \sum_{i_I = 1}^{n_I} \bar{x}_{i_I|I}^* \sum_{j_J = 1}^{n_J} \pi_{i_I j_J}^{(1_l)} + \omega_l,$$

$$\omega_l \to 0 \text{ as } \omega_0 \to 0, l = 1, \dots, N.$$

Comparison of (A.11) with the definition (5.8), remembering that $\lambda_l^t \to 1$ for $l = 1, \dots, N$ and for $t < T_2$, and that $i_1 + t_2 < T_2$, yields the result summarized in Theorem 5.2.

*Proof of Theorem 5.3:*

Let us define

$$(A.12) \qquad \tilde{P}_{ij} = \sum_{l=1}^{N} \lambda_{1_l} \pi_{ij}^{(1_l)}.$$

The omission of terms $2_l, \dots, n_l$ will guarantee that we may write

$$(A.13) \qquad \tilde{P}_{ij}^{[t]} = \bar{x}_{j|J}^* \sum_{l=1}^{N} \lambda_{1_l}^t \pi_{IJ}^{(1_l)}.$$

Suppose that there exists an $N \times N$ nonsingular matrix $Q$ satisfying the condition

$$(A.14) \qquad \tilde{P}_{ij} = \bar{x}_{j|J}^* Q_{IJ},$$

$$(A.15) \qquad \tilde{P}_{ij}^{[t]} = \bar{x}_{j|J}^* Q_{IJ}^{[t]},$$

for all $t$.

Let the idempotent expansion of $Q$ be given by

$$(A.16) \qquad Q_{IJ}^{[t]} = \sum_{l=1}^{N} \mu_l^t \phi_{IJ}^{(l)},$$

where $\mu_l$ are characteristic roots and $\phi^{(l)}$ are corresponding idempotent matrices. Substituting (A.16) in (A.15) and comparing the result with (A.13), we must have

$$(A.17) \qquad \sum_{l=1}^{N} \mu_l^t \phi_{IJ}^{(l)} = \sum_{l=1}^{N} \lambda_{1_l}^t \pi_{IJ}^{(1_l)}$$

for all $t$. As we shall show presently, this implies that

$$(A.18) \qquad \mu_l = \lambda_{1_l} \qquad\qquad (l = 1, \dots, N),$$

(A.19)        $\phi^{(l)} = \pi^{(1_l)}$              $(l = 1, \ldots, N)$.

These conditions obviously imply that

(A.20)        $[P_{IJ}] = [Q_{IJ}]$,

proving Theorem 5.3.

To justify Equation (A.18), we note that $\lambda_{1_1} > \lambda_{1_2} > \ldots > \lambda_{1_N}$.

Let us also assume, without loss of generality, that the subscript of $\mu$ is arranged so that $\mu_1 > \mu_2 \ldots > \mu_N$. Dividing both sides of (A.17) by $\lambda_{11}$ and rearranging terms, we have

(A.21)        $\pi_{IJ}^{(1_1)} = \phi_{IJ}^{(1)} \left( \dfrac{\mu_1}{\lambda_{1_1}} \right)^t + \sum_{l=2}^{N} \pi_{IJ}^{(1_l)} \left( \dfrac{\lambda_{1_l}}{\lambda_{1_1}} \right)^t + \sum_{l=2}^{N} \phi_{IJ}^{(l)} \left( \dfrac{\mu_l}{\lambda_{1_1}} \right)^t.$

Because of the way the matrix $Q$, and hence $\mu$ are defined, $|\mu_l| \leqslant 1$ for $l = 1, \ldots, N$. Hence, as $t$ becomes large, (A.21) may be written as

(A.22)        $\pi_{IJ}^{(1_1)} = \phi_{IJ}^{(1)} \left( \dfrac{\mu_1}{\lambda_{1_1}} \right)^t + \mu_0,$

where $\mu_0$ is an arbitrarily small real number, since $\pi_{IJ}^{(1_1)}$ and $\phi_{IJ}^{(1)}$ are not zero. For (A.22) to hold for all $t$, we must have

(A.23)        $\pi_{IJ}^{(1_1)} = \phi_{IJ}^{(1)},$

(A.24)        $\lambda_{1_1} = \mu_1$

It is clear that this argument can be repeated $N$ times, justifying (A.18) and (A.19).

## NOTES

[1] Lange, O., *Price Flexibility and Employment*, Cowles Commission Monograph 8 (Bloomington, Ind.: Principia Press, 1944), pp. 103 ff.
[2] Balderston, J. B. and T. M Whitin, 'Aggregation in the Input-Output Model', in *Economic Activity Analysis*, ed. by O. Morgenstern (New York: Wiley, 1954).
[3] Fisher, F. M., 'On the Cost of Approximate Specification in Simultaneous Equation Estimation', *Econometrica* **29** (April, 1961).
[4] See, for instance, E. C. Titchmarsh, *The Theory of Functions*, (London: Oxford Univ. Press, 2nd ed., 1939).
[5] See, for instance, J. H. M. Wedderburn, *Lectures on Matrices*, (New York: American Mathematical Society, 1934) pp. 25ff.
[6] See, for instance, Courant, R. and D. Hilbert, *Methods of Mathematical Physics*, (New York: Interscience Publishers, 1953), pp. 42–43 and 343–350.
[7] See, for instance, J. B. Balderston and T. M. Whitin, *op. cit.*; O. Morgenstern and Whitin,

'Aggregation and Errors in Input-Output Models', Logistics Research Project, George Washington University, cited in F. T. Moore, 'A Survey of Current Inter-Industry Models', in *Input-Output Analysis, an Appraisal*, Studies in Income and Wealth, Vol. 18, p. 228 (National Bureau of Economic Research). J. C. H. Fei, 'A Fundamental Theorem for the Aggregation Problem of Input-Output Analysis', *Econometrica*, 400–412 (1956); S. B. Noble, 'Structure and Classification in Resource Flow Models', The George Washington University Logistic Research Project, Serial T-100/59, May 19, 1959; and A. Ghosh, 'Input-Output Analysis with Substantially Independent Groups of Industries', *Econometrica*, 88–96 (1960).

[8] H. Theil, *Linear Aggregation of Economic Relations*, (Amsterdam: North-Holland Publ. Co., 1954).

[9] F. M. Fisher, *op. cit.*

[10] R. M. Goodwin, 'Dynamic Coupling with Especial Reference to Markets Having Production Lags', *Econometrica*, 181–204 (1947).

[11] Tamotsu Yokoyama, 'A Theory of Composite Commodity', *Osaka Economic Papers*, May, 1952.

[12] P. A. Samuelson, *Foundations of Economic Analysis* (Cambridge, Mass.: Harvard Univ. Press, 1947), pp. 144–46.

# THE THEORY OF PROBLEM SOLVING†*

## 1. INTRODUCTION

It is now about fifteen years since the first computer programs were written and tested that used the method of heuristic search to solve problems. Dozens of such programs, some designed for specific task domains, others claiming various degrees of generality, have now been described in the literature, and many experiments with their performance have been reported and analysed. It is an appropriate time to ask what has been learned from these experiments about the general theory of problem solving, and to try to summarize the present state of that theory.

My task is made easier by the fact that several other persons have recently raised the same question, and provided us with their answers (see especially Newell [1], Feigenbaum [2], Banerji [3], Slagle [4], Nilsson [5]). Assuming that you are familiar with their views will permit me to abbreviate my general survey and to focus attention on issues that need more clarification, on extensions to the theory, and on directions for future exploration that appear to be particularly promising.

## 2. HEURISTIC SEARCH

In most theoretical discussions, problem solving is characterized as a process of searching through a tree (perhaps more precisely, a *directed graph*) whose nodes are states of affairs, or situations, and whose branches are operations that transform one situation into another. The graph contains a starting node and one or more goal nodes (alternatively, a test to determine whether any given node is a goal). To solve a problem is to find a sequence of operations that transforms the starting situation into a goal situation — that is, a path from the starting node to a goal node.

If we call a sequence of operations that transforms the starting situation into another situation a *process description* of the latter situation, then we can restate the matter thus: given the state description of a goal situation, we

† [*Information Processing* 71, Amsterdam: North-Holland Publishing Co., 1972, pp. 261–277].

wish to find a process description of that same situation. Problem solving is the activity that seeks to find the mapping between state descriptions and process descriptions of desired situations.

The above description is not as general as we might wish. For instance, without some elaboration, it would not cover problems of selecting moves in competitive games. In a game, a *winning move* is a move that (a) produces a won position, or (b) for every reply of the opponent, leads to a position in which there exists a winning move. The simplest way to represent by a direct graph the problem of finding a winning move in a game is to employ an AND/OR-graph. (The graph in our initial definition of problem can be called an OR-graph, or a simple graph.) In an AND/OR-graph, each node is labelled an AND-node or an OR-node. Solving a problem in such a graph means finding a subgraph such that: (a) each part in the subgraph leads from the starting situation to a goal situation, and (b) for each AND-node in the subgraph, all links leading directly from that node in the original graph are contained in the subgraph.

Applying this representation to the problem of finding a winning move in a game, nodes of the game tree at which the player is to move are labelled OR-nodes, while nodes at which his opponent is to move are labelled AND-nodes. Under this interpretation, the definition of winning move given above coincides with the definition of problem solution in an AND/OR-graph.

The AND/OR-graph has application beyond the realm of games. Consider a problem, P, and suppose that there exist two subproblems, P1 and P2, such that if both subproblems are solved then P is solved. A search for the solution of P via searches for the solution of P1 and P2 can then obviously be represented by an AND-node with P as its state, and the goals of solving P1 and P2, respectively, as its two branches. In this representation, establishing a subgoal is treated as an operation which leads from a given state of affairs *without* that subgoal to the corresponding state of affairs with the subgoal. An unlimited number of subgoals is permitted at an AND-node.

Nilsson [5], following Amarel, regards the distinction between searches in OR-graphs and searches in AND/OR-graphs as fundamental. He calls OR-graphs 'state-space representations' and AND/OR-graphs 'problem-reduction' representations. However, he also groups certain other problem solving representations that are not subsumed under simple heuristic search through a directed graph (e.g., planning methods) within his category of problem-reduction representations. Hence, I find his terminology and classification inconvenient. For this reason, and also because it appears possible to give a unified treatment of OR-graphs and AND/OR-graphs. I will discuss these together.

## 2.1. Selectivity in Search

The graphs in problem domains of interest are usually immense. If they were not, we could solve problems simply by using the brute force of computers to search exhaustively.[1] The size of problem graphs is often characterized thus: We suppose a regular graph, that is, a graph in which all nodes except terminal nodes have the same number, $b$, of branches. We suppose, further, that all paths are $L$ branches in length. The total size of the graph is $G = b^L$. If there is a single goal state in a regular graph of uniform depth, and if the goal state is selected by a random process, with equal probabilities, from the set of all terminal states, then any search process will require, on average, $G/2 = b^L/2$ paths to be generated to find the solution.

Most treatments of the theory assume that the problem solver is a serial search process, limited to looking at one branch at a time, and that the expected cost of the search is proportional to the expected number of branches examined before a solution is found. Apart from the assumption of seriality, the 'pure theory' of search makes no assumptions about specific characteristics of the processor.[2]

Any reduction from the expected search of $b^L/2$ paths must depend on the solution *not* being located at random in the graph. Stated otherwise, a reduction in amount of search depends on the availability and use of information indicating that search along certain paths is more likely to lead to a solution than an equal amount of search along other paths. A pure theory of problem solving is concerned with the different kinds of information that may be available in particular task environments, and with the ways of incorporating this information in the decisions that guide the search.

From the assumption that the search process is serial it follows that the decisions to be made by the problem solver are always decisions as to what to do *next* — which branch to pursue at which node. Given a particular problem graph, we can characterize different problem solvers by different permutations of the branches of that graph. Any set of problem solvers that search the branches in exactly the same sequence can be regarded as equivalent, for they will find a solution after identical amounts of search. A problem solver is the more powerful (has greater heuristic power for this problem) the earlier in its sequence there occurs a branch terminating at a solution node. We are usually interested, of course, in heuristic power averaged in some way over a whole class of problems.

## 2.2.  Information Incorporated in Selection Rules

The information that a problem solver uses to decide what to do next has two parts: (1) information that is available when a problem is posed, and (2) information that becomes available as the search for a solution proceeds. An example will help make this distinction clear.

The checkmate-finding program called MATER takes as initial situations positions in a chess game (Baylor and Simon [8]). MATER's problem is to find a subtree of moves that leads to checkmate for all legal replies of the opponent. Here the problem graph consists of all legal continuations from the given position. In these problems the branchiness, $b$, is typically about 20, and the depth of the checkmate, $L$, typically 6 or 8 (but sometimes as many as 20) steps (plies or half-moves). Even for a depth of six, such a graph has 64 million branches.

MATER's selection processes make use of the information that checkmates can frequently be achieved (when they are achievable at all) by sequences of checking moves. But the number of checking moves at a node (a subset of the legal moves), is typically only 2 or 3. Moreover, the number of legal replies to a checking move is typically also small — say 2 or 3. The graph of checking moves and their legal replies is therefore usually a very small subgraph of the whole graph of legal moves. Reducing $b$ from 20 to 2 reduces the size of a regular graph of length 6 from 64 million branches to 64 branches — from a very large number to a trivial one.

To be sure, MATER pays a price for this selectivity. Not all checkmates can be reached by sequences of checking moves. MATER will sometimes fail to find a realizable checkmate. This is an example of the well-known heuristic (i.e., non-guaranteed) character of many powerful selection rules. MATER adopts the philosophy that it is better to be able to checkmate your opponent frequently *in fact*, even if to do so you must give up the ability always to checkmate him *in principle* (i.e., if you were allowed unlimited search time). In many domains, on the other hand, there exist powerful selection rules which are guaranteed to find a solution if one exists. The simplex method for solving linear programming problems is a highly selective search method (it examines only extreme points, and only some that improve the position already reached); but it never eliminates a path leading to the solution.

Research progress in some areas of problem solving has been slowed by an excessive preoccupation with the completeness of selection rules (i.e., the guarantee that they will not eliminate all solution paths if one or more exist), and by inadequate concern for their heuristic power. Even today, in the realm of automatic theorem proving, new selection rules have generally been incorporated in programs only if they have been shown to possess completeness properties. This has discouraged the search for non-guaranteed heuristic rules, and has also slowed the acceptance of selection rules actually possessing such guarantees until their completeness could be proved. There are some signs that the undesirability of this limitation is now beginning to be recognized, and that the next decade will see a free exploration of heuristic procedures in this and other problem domains.

I should not like to be understood as saying that completeness proofs are uninteresting — much less that they are undesirable. However, there is no reason to suppose that the problem solving processes used by creative mathematicians, or other professional human problem solvers, possess any completeness properties (even when they are solving problems in decidable domains). That being the case, I see no reason for imposing such a restriction on artificial intelligence systems. Probably the best attitude is to regard questions of the completeness of a heuristic as more or less orthogonal to questions of its heuristic power. The theory of problem solving is concerned primarily with questions of the latter kind, rather than the former.

Our method of measuring the selective power of a branching rule depends upon comparing two graphs, one of them a subgraph of the other. In the case of two regular graphs of length $L$, and branchiness $b$ and $b'$ respectively, the ratio of expected amounts of search is given by $(b'/b)^L$. But the larger graph selected for the comparison is, to a certain extent, arbitrary. In measuring MATER's selectivity, why do we compare the size of its subgraph with the size of the graph of all legal moves? We might just as legitimately imbed it as a subgraph in the graph of all moves, legal or not. Since this is a much larger graph than the graph of legal moves, if it were compared with MATER's subgraph, it would show off MATER to even better advantage than the comparison we have actually made.

Presumably, the reason for taking the graph of legal moves as our basis for comparison is that, using as our only information the definition of the game of chess, we could construct a generator for that graph. Hence, this is the 'stupidest' — the least selective — generator that we need consider. In other problem domains the name of 'British Museum Algorithm' has sometimes been applied to a relatively non-selective generator whose problem graphs are used for measuring the selectivity of rules that limit search to subgraphs. The present discussion shows that the selection of the standard graph for the comparison is to a certain extent arbitrary. The arbitrariness does not arise, of course, when we are comparing the relative heuristic power of two different selective rules.

## 2.3. Selection of Node Operator

Earlier, I emphasized that a serial search process is characterized by the way in which it decides what to do next. This decision, which determines what branch will be added to the search tree, has two principal parts: (1) the choice of the node to which the branch is to be added, and (2) the choice of the operator to be applied at that node.

The discussion of selection rules in the previous section has shown how information about the problem domains, built into the problem solver, can be used to select the operator at a node. In the case of MATER, the selection rule we described was only a partial rule, ruling out certain operators (non-checking moves), but not setting priorities among those that remained. In other cases, the rule might determine the exact order of exploration.

A priori information, available when the problem is posed, can also be used to choose the next node. For example, a processor can be programmed to conduct a depth-first search, and such a search might be relatively efficient (in combination with other selection rules) if there are a large number of problem solutions, all of them at the ends of relatively long paths.

The heuristic power of a problem solving system can usually be greatly increased, however, by making the selection of node and operator depend on information that becomes available as the search progresses. A useful taxonomy of problem solvers can be constructed by distinguishing the different ways in which such information is used.

Let us associate with each node that has been generated a *node evaluation*, which is some function of the node. We will not specify, at the moment, the range of the function, except to assume that the values are completely ordered. Let us associate with each operator at each node an *operator evaluation*, which is some function of the node and the operator. Now, we can conduct the search by selecting the node with the highest node value, applying at that node all the operators whose value at that node exceeds some standard value (alternatively, applying the operator with the highest value at that node), and then evaluating the new nodes thus created:

```
SELECT FIRST NODE ON TRY-LIST, AND
   REMOVE IT FROM LIST
SELECT AND APPLY OPERATORS AT
   SELECTED NODE
EVALUATE NEW NODES, AND FILE IN
   ORDER OF VALUE ON TRY-LIST
```

This cycle of actions is repeated until a solution is found or the effort limit is reached. Virtually all of the heuristic search schemes that have attained reasonable power have used some variant of this scheme to guide the branching of the search tree. Moreover, the past three years have seen the beginnings of some mathematical theory, applicable to simple situations, that gives us clues about the properties of good evaluation functions (Nilsson [9], Pohl [10]).

The node evaluation function can depend on properties of the situation at the node. For example, in a theorem prover where the nodes correspond to expressions that have been derived, the promise of a node for further search might be measured by the simplicity of the expression at that node. (Such an evaluator played a role in one version of the LOGIC THEORIST.)

Alternatively, the node evaluation function can depend on a relation between the situation at the node and the description of the goal situation. In most of the theoretical work that has been done on this topic, the node evaluation function has been assumed to be an estimate of the shortest-path distance from the node to a solution state, or a weighted average of that distance and the distance from starting point to the node. Pohl [10] and Nilsson [9] have published theorems showing the optimality of this evaluation function, for an appropriate range of weights, when the distance estimate is accurate.[3]

This search procedure and these theoretical results apply to OR-graphs. The situation for AND/OR-graphs is more complex. Intuitively, it is clear that, other things being equal, an AND-node is a more favorable point for continued search the fewer branches it has — since a solution must be found along each branch before the entire problem is solved. For the moment, I will put aside AND/OR-graphs with this single comment and return to them later.

Several different possibilities also exist for operator evaluation at a node. The evaluation may depend upon absolute properties of node and operator. Alternatively, it may depend on properties of the relation between the node and the goal situation. The GENERAL PROBLEM SOLVER (GPS) embodies, as its principal heuristic, a scheme of the latter kind.

GPS detects the *differences* between the situation at a node and the goal situation. It has stored in memory (as a priori information) a *difference-operator table* which consists, for each difference, of a list of the operators that are relevant to removing or reducing that difference. Thus, GPS operates by applying a succession of operators in order to reduce, progressively, the differences between the current situation and the goal situation. Ernst [11] has demonstrated a set of conditions on the difference-operator table sufficient to guarantee that GPS will succeed in solving a problem.[4]

Up to this point my taxonomy of search schemes can be summarized by two dichotomies: (1) Evaluation functions may be introduced (a) to select nodes and (b) to select operators at nodes; (2) evaluation functions of either variety may depend (a) upon properties of the situation at the node being evaluated (features) or (b) upon relations between those and properties of the goal situation (differences). In general, most effective problem solvers have used evaluators involving differences – estimates of distance from the goal situation in node evaluation, and GPS-like differences in operator evaluation. Little formal theory is available to suggest how such evaluators should actually be constructed for particular task domains, although several authors have proposed schemes for learning evaluations, sets of differences, and difference-operator tables.

In constructing my simple, and over-simplified, four-fold classification of search schemes, I have assumed that node evaluation can proceed independently of operator evaluation. In the schemes described above, this independence was achieved by applying operators to any given node just once and never subsequently returning to that node. If the operator evaluation function selects *all* operators that are relevant at a given node and generates the corresponding branches, then (assuming the relevance criterion is valid) the node can be removed permanently from further consideration; henceforth only its descendants need be considered.

In actual practice, this scheme often works well. It is not terribly costly to generate extra branches at a node provided that they are evaluated immediately, so that (by subsequent node selection) only the promising ones are followed up. Such a scheme may multiply search by an arithmetic constant, but does not increase it geometrically. The extra search cost it entails will often be more than compensated by the simplification of housekeeping it permits. Thus if we distinguish 'sterile' from 'productive' branches at a node, the problem graph size for a scheme that generates $s$ sterile and $b$ productive branches will be $((b + s)/b)b^L$, an expansion of only $(b + s)/b$ over a scheme that generates only the productive branches. This expansion is much less damaging than the expansion, $(b'/b)^L$, produced by a less selective branch generator.

A more elaborate scheme may distinguish different levels of "relevance" of operators. At the first generation from a node, only operators at the top level of relevance are applied. If the standard of relevance is high, a point may be reached where no operators are relevant (at that level) at any of the nodes that have been generated. At that point, the standard of relevance is lowered, and a new cycle of generation begun from each of the nodes already visited.

This strategy is used in the MATER II program (Baylor and Simon [8] ). As we saw in the previous paragraph, essentially the same result can be achieved more simply by generating all the branches at once, controlling the order in which they are explored further by the node evaluation function.

## 2.4. Special Search Strategies

I should like to conclude this brief survey of what is known about tree search by describing briefly three schemes for node evaluation that have attracted some interest: the first two of these are concerned with searching AND/OR-graphs in games, the third illustrates a type of evaluation function somewhat different from those we have considered.

### 2.4.1. Control of search in MATER.
In a game tree, OR-nodes (player's moves) and AND-nodes (opponent's moves) alternate along any path. In general, different criteria of operator selection will be used at the two kinds of nodes. In MATER I, for example, all legal moves are generated at AND-nodes, but only checking (relevant moves) at OR-nodes. Since a checkmating situation is one in which the opponent has no legal moves (and is in check), the number of legal moves at any AND-node is a plausible (inverse) measure of the distance of the node from a goal of checkmate. We may therefore proceed as follows: (see Figure 1).

SELECT POSITION (AND-NODE) ON TRY-LIST WITH FEWEST REPLIES,
     AND REMOVE IT FROM LIST
    FOR EACH REPLY, GENERATE ALL CHECKING MOVES
    AND PLACE ON TEMPORARY LIST
    FOR EACH MOVE ON TEMPORARY LIST,
     GENERAL ALL REPLIES,
     ASSOCIATE THEM WITH MOVE,
     COUNT THEM,
     ASSOCIATE COUNT WITH MOVE,
     AND TRANSFER MOVE FROM TEMPORARY LIST TO TRY-LIST

Fig. 1.

In chess a move is called 'forcing' to the extent that it limits the replies of the opponent. Hence, the search scheme just described is a most-forcing-moves-first scheme. It has proved extremely powerful in practice, although I know of no theorems defining the conditions (if any) under which it is optimal. Notice that there is a two-fold basis for its selective power: (1) number of replies represents — as already observed — an estimate of distance from the goal, and (2) the tree tends to grow first in the directions in which it branches most slowly. Because of the second property, even if the exploration starts off in a wrong direction, the slow branching keeps down the search cost, and as soon as the tree begins to branch more luxuriantly the search in that direction is postponed.

*2.4.2. The alpha-beta heuristic.* Up to this point we have been considering problems of an all-or-none character: a node in the problem graph either is a solution or it is not. In many problem solving domains, situations can be evaluated as better or worse, and the task is to find a path leading to a 'good' situation or the 'best attainable' situation. The interesting problems of this class are those in which exhaustive search is not feasible and there is no efficient algorithm for finding the optimum.

Problems of this kind are sometimes referred to as *satisficing* problems. They are solved by finding a 'good enough' solution, which may mean one whose value exceeds some norm, or may mean the best that can be found after some specified expenditure of search effort. For our present purpose, however, it is not important whether we are dealing with a satisficing problem or with finding a maximum value after exhaustive search in all the nodes.

The alpha-beta scheme for finding the game move having the best value in a minimax sense has been widely discussed in the literature and widely used in game-playing programs. The basic notion is that, in a zero-sum game, the value of a branch at an OR-node cannot be greater than the minimum of the values of the branches from its successor AND-nodes; and the value of a branch at an AND-node cannot be less than the maximum of values of the branches from its successor OR-nodes. As soon as certain branches of the game tree have been evaluated, search along other branches can be cut off if it appears certain, from these principles, that they cannot be better than one of those already evaluated.

Notice that the concept of 'evaluation' used here is somewhat different from the concepts of node evaluation or operator evaluation discussed earlier. The value of a node here is the minimax value of the 'best' path going through the node. The value, in the simplest alpha-beta procedure, is not used to determine where to search next, but to decide that certain parts of the tree need not be searched at all. However, the value can also be interpreted as a measure of closeness to a terminal representing a good path, hence can also be used to order the search.

*2.4.3. Branch-and-bound methods.* Integer programming problems are generally solved by a process of selective search. Because of the mathematical structure of these problems, it is possible to assign upper and lower bounds to the values that are ultimately attainable along a path through any given node. If the upper bound for node A is lower than the lower bound for any other node, then search from node A can be cut off. Moreover, the upper and lower bounds can be used to compute an evaluation function for node selection among the nodes that are not eliminated.

The branch-and-bound principle was apparently discovered independently of the general principle of evaluation for node selection or the alpha-beta principle. It has acquired considerable importance in integer programming, and illustrates the convergence of ideas that is taking place in the study of tree search methods. (See Lawler and Wood [12].)

### 2.5. Summary: Simple Tree Search

I have now mentioned most of the main ideas that have emerged over the past fifteen years for the design of problem solving systems that search through OR-graphs or AND/OR-graphs. I have *not* yet mentioned planning, abstraction, and the operation of substitution, which are usually discussed in this context, for these concepts do not belong to the topic of simple tree search, but involve the choice of problem representation, and should be discussed in relation to the latter subject. I will take them up presently.

What generalizations can we draw from the survey thus far? First, a coherent conceptual framework has emerged for the discussion and analysis of schemes for heuristic search. Alternative schemes can be compared in terms of (1) the nature and heuristic power of their selection rules for operators, and (2) their evaluation functions for (a) node selection, (b) operator selection and (c) cutoff. The effectiveness of existing systems can largely be explained with the help of these concepts. The designers of new systems have available a number of clear and powerful principles to guide *their* heuristic search for a good design.

Second, most of the concepts and principles that have emerged have been the product of empirical work — designing and testing actual problem-solving programs — combined with hindsight diagnosis of why these programs did or didn't work as expected. Few if any of the central ideas were generated in armchairs, and many of them were embedded in operating programs for a considerable time before they were identified and christened. Most of them can be found in programs that were operating by about 1960. Conceptual clarity came much later; Nilsson's [5] monograph being the first systematic book-length treatment of the subject along the general lines set forth here.

Third, what I have called theory still lacks any comprehensive mathematical treatment. In fact, only rudimentary beginnings of an exact mathematical base for parts of it exist at present. Thus it resembles theories in the empirical sciences much more than it resembles mathematics.

Since many of the persons who immigrated into computer science during its early years came from mathematics, they brought into the new field attitudes transported from their previous homeland. In mathematics all knowledge resides (or is sometimes believed to reside) in theorems and their proofs. The relative dearth of theorems about heuristic search has sometimes been thought, erroneously, to imply a dearth of theory. I hope I have said enough to show that there exists, in fact, a simple and moderately strong theory, whose present basis is largely empirical rather than mathematical, and whose most precise statement is to be found in the programs of effective heuristic problem solving systems.

Researchers in artificial intelligence who share the tastes of natural scientists will find this state of affairs quite satisfactory and agreeable, and will push on from it. Researchers having mathematicians' tastes are more likely to deplore the lack of precision of the existing theory, but will presumably be stimulated thereby to try to construct the mathematical adjunct that is called for. Both of these reactions will contribute to the growth of knowledge in the area.

## 3. MULTIPLE REPRESENTATIONS

There is an old adage that 'a problem well stated is half solved.' Thus far I have been talking about the other half — the search that must be carried out to solve a problem even after a representation has been defined. Some investigators have made distinctions between 'ill-structured' and 'well-structured' problems, along these same general lines, but the distinctions themselves have not been very carefully delineated. Let us approach the matter cautiously, simply by trying to extend the previous analysis step by step to less well-structured situations.

The first extension is to problem solving searches that take place in more than one space. At least three species of this general kind can be identified among extant problem solving systems. First, the search may take place partly in the original problem space, partly in a planning space. Second, the search may take place partly in an abstract space. Third, the search may take place partly in a 'semantic' space. We will see that there is considerable overlap among these possibilities, but it is convenient at the outset to consider them separately.

## 3.1. Planning Processes

The basic ideas of planning come directly out of our earlier characterization of the structure of regular directed graphs. Suppose we have to discover a path of length $L$ in a space with branchiness, $b$. The size of the graph we are then concerned with is roughly $b^L$. If we can first establish some intermediate nodes along the path, we can reduce greatly the graph size. For suppose there are $k$ such intermediate points through which the path must pass, with segments of length $L/k$ between sucessive points. Then to find a segment of this length between two successive points, we have to search a graph of size $b^{L/k}$, or, to find the entire path, $k$ such segments with a total size of $kb^{L/k}$. But this quantity will, in general, be much smaller than $b^L$; the precise condition being, of course that $b^{L(k-1)/k} > k$.

To gain this advantage, it is necessary first to find the intermediate nodes on the path between starting node and goal. One scheme for doing this, proposed initially for GPS, is to define a new problem space by abstracting from some of the information contained in state descriptions in the original space. The abstraction produces a many-one mapping of states in the original space into states in the abstract space, and some of the operators in the original space may be mapped into the identity operator in the abstract space. Nodes in the abstract space connected by the identity operator would be merged, so that paths in the abstract space would, in general, be shorter than the corresponding paths in the original space.

The *planning* problem is to find a path from the starting node to a goal node in the abstract space. This problem can be attacked by the usual search procedures and, if it is solved, the solution will pass through a number of nodes in the abstract space. Returning now to the original space, the corresponding nodes can be taken as the starting points and termini for a series of subproblems. Solution of these subproblems will solve the original problem.

But this same factorization of the original problem may be achievable without the use of the planning space. Suppose that there exists an evaluation function for nodes that is computable only for certain nodes but that, when computable, indicates whether or not the node in question lies on a solution path. This evaluation function provides exactly the same information as the plan does, and permits exactly the same kind of factorization of the original search.

To be more concrete about the alternative to planning, I will mention a venerable example — the clicking safe. Consider a combination safe having ten dials, each with 100 possible settings. The search space associated with the problem of opening the safe is of size $100^{10}$. If, however, the safe is defective, so that a click may be heard when any single dial is turned to the right position, then the safe can be opened by means of 10 searches, each in a space of size 100.

The use of a planning space to provide the evaluations at intermediate nodes suggests an important idea that we shall develop as we proceed. The search for a problem solution in the abstract space can be reinterpreted as a search for information that can be used to guide search in the original problem space. In the planning space it would be more correct to say that information is being sought than to say that a problem solution is being sought. If the information could somehow be obtained with actually finding a solution for the planning problem (as it is in the example of the clicking safe), nothing would be lost by the substitution.

This may not be a special situation, but a very general one. The theory of heuristic search has usually been formulated in terms of a search for a *problem solution*. It could be generalized to refer to a search for *information* that will allow the solution to be known. Is there a genuine difference between these two formulations, or a mere verbal distinction without substance? I will leave the question hanging at the moment, but return to it later.

Before I leave the topic of planning and procedures for establishing intermediate "islands" along a solution path, it is worth considering the relation of this idea to AND/OR-graphs. Given a problem described by an OR-graph, planning replaces the original problem by a new one described by an AND/OR-graph. The process can be repeated, and each of the successors to the starting node can become, in turn, the starting point for a new AND/OR-graph. Since searches through AND/OR-graphs are more complicated to manage than searches through OR-graphs, this modification might be thought to be disadvantageous, but, as we have seen, each of the branches of the new graph is much smaller than the original graph.

## 3.2. Abstraction

Our discussion of planning spaces already provides one example of the use of abstraction in problem solving. But abstraction can be introduced in other ways. Suppose that there is a way of partitioning the paths in a problem space into equivalence classes, such that: (1) all members of a given equivalence class have the same number of nodes, (2) the same operation that carries the $i$th node of a particular member of an equivalence class into the $(i + 1)$st node carries the $i$th node of every other member of that equivalence class into its $(i + 1)$st node. Then, by considering the homeomorphism of the paths into their equivalence classes, we obtain a new space that is smaller than the original space. At the very least, by this reduction we gain the ability to solve whole classes of problems simultaneously – a sort of parallel capacity in a serial system.

## 3.3. Semantic Spaces

If the problem space is a space of abstract objects, it may be possible to create a second space in which the objects are instances of those in the first. We call the second space a semantic space for the first. A property which holds in the abstract space will also hold for any instance, though of course, the converse is not true. For many properties it may be cheaper to determine whether they hold in the instance than to prove that they hold in general.

This idea of associating a semantic space with the original problem space was first used by Gelernter and Rochester [13] in their GEOMETRY THEOREM MACHINE. This program, incorporating an AND/OR tree, created numerous subproblems in order to discover proofs for theorems. The program, given a diagram corresponding to the statement of each theorem attempted, could test whether a subproblem was worth attempting by seeing whether the theorem it asserted was satisfied in the diagram. Information obtained from the semantic space, therefore, was used for evaluation in the original problem space.

There is no magic in this semantic process. Any information, valid in the abstract space, that was present in the diagram was also 'present' – in some sense – in the abstract space. The semantic information was valuable because it could often be extracted more cheaply than the corresponding information in the abstract space. For example, the approximate equality of two angles in the diagram could be checked by a simple arithmetic calculation; while this equality could be proved syntactically only by a more or less difficult search.

## 3.4. Variables and Substitution

General theoretical discussions of tree search have not had much to say about representations that employ variables and an operation for substituting constants for variables. If we try to subsume the substitution operation under the general tree search paradigm, we do not gain much insight into what is going on. What kind of evaluation function, for example, tells us whether, at a particular node, we should apply the substitution operation? And how does the evaluation function help us decide what particular substitution to make there?

The use of variables and substitution becomes more comprehensible if we view it as an application of abstraction. From this viewpoint, a search with expressions that contain variables is a search in an abstract space, and substitution of a constant for a variable is a transformation from one search space to another. Instead of an evaluation function that determines when the substitution operation should be applied at a node in a search space, we now require an evaluation function that determines when and how a transformation to a less abstract space should be made.

In many problem domains, the applicable operators contain variables. Thus, if we are trying to solve a single algebraic equation in one unknown (say, $ax + b = cx + d$), we may add, subtract, multiply or divide on both sides of the equation. Call these operators ADD ( ), SUBTRACT ( ), MULTIPLY ( ), and DIVIDE ( ), respectively. In addition, we need a process for collecting terms whenever this is possible. The simple equation above can now be solved by successive applications of SUBTRACT, SUBTRACT, and DIVIDE, but only if the right values are substituted for the variable arguments of the operators $((cx), (b)$ and $(a-c)$, respectively).

We may view the problem solving here as proceeding simultaneously in an abstract and a concrete space. From the fact that the right-hand side of the equation to be solved contains a term in $x$, we can determine that the SUBTRACT operator should be applied. This decision can be made in the abstract space. But before we can apply the operator, we must particularize it, and this requires the information that the term to be eliminated is precisely $cx$.

This trivial example suggests an important general principle. In problem solving with variables, the search is so arranged that substitutions are made when explicit information is available as to *which* substitution to make. If this principle can be observed, all search, heuristic or otherwise, for the correct substitution is eliminated. In the example at hand, we apply the SUBTRACT operation before the DIVIDE operation because it is given explicitly that $cx$ is the correct argument for the former operator, but it is initially only implicit (i.e., would require some calculation to determine) that $(a-c)$ is the correct argument for the latter operator.

The usual great advantage of working-backward searches over working-forward searches derives from this general principle. In theorem proving, the axioms contain variable arguments, which must be instantiated in order to apply them. The terminal expression – the theorem to be proved – contains initially the information as to which substitutions to make. Hence, working backward may make it possible to use this information, and thus to avoid entirely any search in the space of the admissible values of the arguments.

## 4. THE SEARCH PROCESS RECONSIDERED

In my discussion of planning, I suggested that there are perhaps two ways of viewing a problem solving effort. A novel approach is to view problem solving as a search for information that will make the solution known. Our analysis of multiple representations begins to hint what kind of a difference may be lurking behind this distinction, and I should like now to address the question more directly.

Selectivity in search hinges on extracting information from the problem environment, and using that information to answer such questions as: Which node shall we proceed from? Which operator shall we apply next? In each case, we may make the decision with the aid of an evaluation function for each node and for each operator at each node. The evaluation is usually assumed to depend on information derived from the state description of the node in question (features), possibly combined with information derived from the characteristics of the terminal node (differences). The evaluation of each node and each operator is then independent of the evaluation of each other node and operator until the final comparison is made among the values to determine which node and operator will be chosen for processing.

There is nothing in the logic of the situation that imposes this limitation that the evaluations should depend only on information generated at the node being evaluated. There is no reason why information discovered at one node should not be used, if it is relevant, to improve the evaluations at other nodes. The trick is to find out how to do this.

There do exist, in fact, a few heuristic problem solving programs that take at least limited steps in this direction. I will cite three examples: a heuristic first employed in the NSS chess program (Newell et al. [14]); a heuristic employed in MATER II (Baylor and Simon [8]); and a diagnostic procedure employed in a room-layout program constructed by Pfefferkorn [15].

### 4.1. The NO-MOVE Heuristic

In a competitive game, a *threat* is a move that, unless parried, will cause significant loss to the opponent. One way to determine whether a move is a threat is to define a special, extra-legal 'move' – NO-MOVE – for the opponent; or, what is equivalent, to allow one player two moves in a row. Evaluating the position after the NO-MOVE measures the power of the threat, and discovering the most effective move for implementing the threat (i.e., the best second move in the sequence) provides a move that can be given high priority for testing the opponent's alternatives.

Suppose that the threatening move is $A$, and that, after NO-MOVE by the opponent, the most effective follow-up is $B$. Then if the opponent can reply to $A$ with $a'$, $a''$, etc., $B$ can be tried after each of these alternative replies. In this way, information obtained from evaluating the branch that consists of $A$ followed by NO-MOVE can be used to select considerable moves on the branches that consist of $A$ followed by $a'$, $a''$, etc. If the threat is a serious one, then all branches that do not answer it can be eliminated in a hurry.

The MATER II program also uses the NO-MOVE device, in connection with one-move mating threats. A one-move mating threat is a move that, if answered by NO-MOVE, permits a checkmate. MATER II uses the NO-MOVE to discover such threats in order to assign a high priority in the search to the moves creating them.

### 4.2. The Move-permutation Heuristic

The MATER II program incorporates a second departure from the simple tree-search paradigm. The basic move generator in this program is highly selective (in one version, it generates only checking moves). In its exploration beyond an initial check, it often generates moves that it would not have generated in the initial position (e.g., that would not then have been checking moves). To have a name for them, let us call these 'forceful moves.'

MATER II keeps a list of forceful moves that it discovers in its exploration, and if it abandons its search along one line then undertakes a search along a line initiated by a forceful move. Here again, selection of an operator at one node is influenced by information gathered while exploring another part of the tree.

### 4.3. A Diagnostic Procedure

Pfefferkorn [15] has written a program for laying out rooms; that is, for arranging furniture, or pieces of equipment in them. A variety of constraints can be imposed on the arrangements – for example, that certain elements lie within specified distances of each other, or that there be passageways between particular pairs of elements, and so on.

The program, called DPS for 'Design Problem Solver', employs a modified form of heuristic search, each successive operator application adding an element to the design. Constraints are tested as elements are added, so that a satisfactory design is obtained if all the elements can be entered into the room. When serious difficulties arise, however, the search for a solution can be changed into a search for information that will lead to removing the difficulties.

When the attempt to enter a new element into the design leads to repeated violations of constraints, a diagnostic routine is entered. The specific room elements implicated in the violated constraints are identified, and a macroelement is created from them that satisfies all their mutual constraints (removed from the context of the room). The search for a solution to the design problem is now resumed by attempting to enter the macroelement into the room. The diagnostic routine can also be used to reorder the search, so that design elements whose constraints are creating difficulty can be entered into the design earlier.

Clearly, this diagnostic procedure amounts to using information obtained during an (unsuccessful) search along one branch to determine which new branch of the tree to search, and, indeed, by the construction of macroelements, to change the space in which the search takes place.[5]

### 4.4. A Didactic Example of Information Gathering

These three examples from actual problem solving programs illustrate the notion that evaluations on particular branches of a search tree (whether node evaluations or operator evaluations) can be influenced by information gathered along other branches. Although in each of the cases I have cited, the departure from simple heuristic tree search is rather limited, each provides some substance to the distinction between a process of gathering information that may reveal the solution, on the one hand, and a process of seeking the solution directly, on the other.

To make the point more sharply, I should like to give another example which, while only didactic, provides a 'purer' illustration than those already considered. It is a procedure for solving simple algebra word problems, e.g.:

> Given 1 liter of a 90% alcohol-water mixture, how much water must be added to dilute it to an 80% mixture?

Nine quantities are imbedded in this problem, explicitly or implicitly: the initial quantities of alcohol, water, and total liquid ($A1$, $W1$, and $T1$, respectively); the quantities added ($dA$, $dW$, and $dT$, respectively); and the final quantities ($A2$, $W2$, and $T2$, respectively). One way to solve the problem is simply to write down as much information as possible about each of the nine quantities until the quantity in which we are interested ($dW$) is determined. Let us see how this might work.

By the terms of the problem, $T_1 = 1$ liter, and $A1 = 0.9T1$, or $0.9$ liter. Since only water is added, $dA = 0$, hence $A2 = A1$ and $dT = dW$. But $T2 = T1 + dT = T1 + dW = (1 + dW)$ liter. From the terms of the problem, $A2 = 0.8T2$, hence $0.9 = 0.8 (1 + dW)$. Thus, we have arrived at a single equation in $dW$, which can be solved for that quantity.

Now there are various ways in which we could describe the process I have just gone through as a search for a solution in a search space of an ordinary sort. For example, we could define the solution as any algebraic equation containing only $dW$, and the legitimate arithmetic and algebraic operations as the allowable operators. The starting state would be the set of equations corresponding to the information given in the problem statement, together with the implicit conservation assumptions ($A1 + dA = A2$, $A1 + W1 = T1$, etc.).

However, it seems more natural to describe the process as one of accumulating information about the variables. Consider the array of the nine variables:

$$A1 \quad dA \quad A2$$
$$W1 \quad dW \quad W2$$
$$T1 \quad dT \quad T2$$

The problem statement gives us the value of $T1$ and $dA$, the latter being 0. It also gives $A1$ as a fraction of $T1$, and $A2$ *as a fraction of* $T2$. Possible rules for information accumulation are: (1) if $y$ is given as a fraction of $x$, $y$ can be determined if $x$ is known and vice versa; and (2) if two values are known in a row or column, the third can be determined. Since $T1$ is known, we can find $A1$ by the first rule, and then $W1$ by the second. By the second rule, since $A1$ and $dA$ are now known, we can find $A2$, and hence, by the first rule, $T2$. Finally, we can now use the second rule to find $W2$, and by a second application, to find $d/W$.

Again, we have described a process which might better be called a way of accumulating information than a way of searching for a solution. No branching search is created, for any piece of information that is derived is true at all nodes of the search. The process is still sequential, but only a single decision must be made at each step: which operator to apply next. And this decision can be made to depend on any or all of the information thus far accumulated.

Notice that any theorem-proving process that works forward — that is, that finds only true theorems — can be described as an information-accumulating rather than a solution-searching process. In theorem proving by the resolution method, for example, no search tree is generated, but only a gradually growing set of derived expressions. When a working-backward scheme is used, on the other hand, a branching tree is produced because the derived expressions represent points along alternative paths to the goal, and an expression found at a node on one such path does not, in general, remain valid for nodes on other paths.

Solving our simple algebra word problem by accumulating information proved to be a trivial task. Why cannot we just as easily prove theorems in any domain by working forward? The answer, of course, lies in the respective sizes of the spaces of derivable expressions. As we formulated the algebra word problem, there were initially nine unknown quantities, one of them being the quantity in which we were interested ($dW$). Each operator, whenever applicable, had the effect of determining the value of one of these unknown quantities, and at any given point in the process, only one to three operations were performable. Moreover, it did not matter much which permutation of the sequence of allowable operations was selected — they all led in a short time to the same result. (I will leave as an exercise for the reader the demonstration that there are 21 different sequences all leading to the answer in five to seven steps. The shortest path is the one that finds $A1, A2$, $T2, dT$, and $dW$, in that order.)

In theorem-proving by forward search, on the other hand, an indefinite number of expressions may be generated before the desired theorem appears in the sequence, hence the order in which information is accumulated (i.e., in which theorems are derived) is again essential. However, if the representation suggested here is adopted, there is no branching search tree, and the decision as to what to do next can be made to depend on any or all of the information that is present in the expressions derived thus far.

In most problem-solving domains, the operators that add information take a small part of the available information as input (e.g., one or two of the expressions already derived, in the case of a theorem prover), and supply a small increment of information (e.g., one new expression) as output. Hence the principal act of selection – and the one that determines the order in which information accumulates – is to choose the one or two pieces of available information that are to be used as inputs to an operator. The evaluation for this selection can depend, as we have just suggested, on any part of the information already accumulated.

In problem solving by accumulating information, there is no problem of backup in the usual sense – of abandoning the current node on the search tree for another node – nor any notion of size of the search tree. Instead, the efficiency of a search process can be characterized by the amount of *irrelevant information* it generates before it reaches a solution to the problem. That is to say, the total amount of information generated before the solution is found will generally depend on the order of generation. Information is irrelevant if there exists an alternative accumulation sequence that reaches solution without it.

A possible search heuristic is to assume that if the inputs to an operator are irrelevant, the output will usually be irrelevant. If this assumption were valid, then an accurate estimate of which pieces of information were irrelevant would be an excellent evaluation function for selecting inputs to operators. An example of such an evaluator is the procedure, now generally used in theorem proving by the resolution method, of classifying expressions into those that do and those that do not belong to the set of support, and giving the former priority as inputs to the resolution operator.

## 4.5. Models and 'Reasoning' Systems

Our analysis leads us to divide problem solving systems into those that do, and those that do not, employ search trees. The distinction can be characterized in other ways also. The information at the nodes in an OR-tree can be viewed as conditional statements – statements that hold at their respective nodes, but not generally. The information that holds at one node is not necessarily valid at others, hence cannot be used in evaluating other nodes or operators at those nodes. Information accumulated in a non-branching search, on the other hand, is interpretable as universally valid, hence usable for evaluation of operators and inputs at all times.

In problem solving situations with search trees, the information at each node represents a possible state of the system along some possible path of transformation. The information is contingently true – i.e., holds if that particular path is followed and that point reached. Hence, tree search may be viewed as a process of carrying a model of a system through possible histories.

In problem solving by information accumulation, the information represents truths that hold for all possible states of the system, and the transformations are reasoning steps that derive new information from old.

Problem-solving systems belonging to the family of GPS and most game-playing programs are model-manipulating systems. Problem-solving systems like resolution-method theorem provers are reasoning systems. Since our knowledge of the circumstances under which one or the other kind of systems is more powerful is limited, both will need to be explored in the decade ahead.

As we have already seen, hybrid schemes, like those described for some chess programs and the Design Problem Solver, may be quite effective. Pople [16] has built a much more general hybrid, which has capabilities for operating on a given problem in either model-manipulating or reasoning modes. A scheme of this kind appears particularly promising for exploring the relations between these two basic approaches to problem solving. I do not have space here to discuss their respective advantages and disadvantages.

These two categories of problem solvers – model manipulators and reasoning system – do not exhaust the taxonomy of problem-solving systems. We have also, of course, the systems already discussed that use more than one representation. In addition, we have systems of the Advice Taker family, which employ modal reasoning; and we have systems that reason with the help of mathematical induction. I would like to say a few words as to why I separate these two classes of systems – those using modal reasoning and those using mathematical induction – from reasoning systems in general.

It is a fundamental characteristic of a model-manipulating system that it deals in contingent truths – in alternative possibilities. If we wish to handle possibility by reasoning instead of by heuristic search with a model, we must introduce a modal logic containing modal operators like 'can' and 'can cause.' The Monkey-and-Banana problem, for example, may be tackled either with model-manipulating or modal-reasoning methods. In the former-case, we construct a model of the situation in which the monkey finds himself, and operators corresponding to the behaviors open to him for changing the situation. We then seek a sequence of allowable behaviors that allows him to get the bananas.

In the latter case, we construct a set of propositions about properties of the situation and things the monkey can do or cause to be done. We then try to derive the proposition that 'the monkey can get the bananas.' It becomes quite tricky to construct a logic adequate for such reasoning in worlds where the possibility of doing something is contingent on characteristics of the situation in which it is done. (For these difficulties in modal reasoning systems, see my essay 'On Reasoning About Actions', in Simon and Siklossy [17], Chapter 8.)

A recent example of a problem solving system employing the principle of mathematical induction is Waldinger's system [18] which uses theorem proving techniques to discover computer programs. The logic of this system is the predicate calculus, and not a modal logic. Rather than discuss Waldinger's system, however, I should like to consider a rather different and more transparent example to show why systems employing mathematical induction have a rather special flavor.

The Mutilated Checkerboard Problem is frequently evoked in discussions of the limitations of heuristic tree search. (See, for example, Newell [1].) A checkerboard is mutilated by removing squares in its northwest and southeast corners. A set of 31 dominoes is available, each of which covers exactly two squares of the checkerboard. Prove that the mutilated checkerboard cannot be covered by the dominoes.

The problem can, of course, be solved by tree search, but the search, while finite, is enormous. What is needed (and can be provided) is a proof of impossibility that does not require testing all the possibilities. The proof follows from observing that squares on the board, along rows or columns, are alternately black and red (or odd and even). On the whole checkerboard, there are an equal number of black and red squares, but since both the squares removed from the board have the same color (black, say), there are fewer squares of one colour than the other on the mutilated board. However, each domino covers exactly one black and one red square, hence 31 dominoes cover 31 red and 31 black squares; while the multilated board has 32 red and only 30 black squares.

A problem solving system that will discover solutions of this kind must be prepared to handle general propositions like: 'For any number of dominoes, the number of black and red squares covered must be equal.' One way to demonstrate such a proposition is to prove it inductively: that if it is true for $k$ dominoes, it remains true when the $(k + 1)$st domino is added.

The fundamental property of an induction on a search tree is that it involves a hereditary property of nodes: that is, refers to a property which, if it holds at any node, holds also at the immediate successors of that node. A hereditary property that *cannot* belong to a solution provides the basis for a stop rule in tree search; once a node with this property has been reached, there is no need to search further from that node. In the Mutilated Checkerboard Problem, the difference between the numbers of red and black covered squares is an hereditary property of a node, and since the inital node has a different value (zero) of this property from the goal situation (two), search is unnecessary.

A problem solver that could discover hereditary properties and translate them into stop rules would operate in its first phase as an information gatherer, then would use the generally valid propositions it derived to guide its tree search. It would contain a somewhat different blend of search and reasoning from most of the systems we now have.

Becoming still more general (and conjectural), we can contemplate two-phase problem solvers whose first phase employs a variety of information-gathering or reasoning methods, and whose second phase employs tree search or model manipulation guided by this information. In general, we would expect the two phases to operate in different problem spaces – the former, perhaps, usually in a more abstract space than the latter. This sort of alternation of phases (but perhaps with more than a single cycle of alternation) appears to be present in many human problem-solving attempts.

## 5. ILL STRUCTURED AND WELL STRUCTURED PROBLEMS

In discussions of artificial intelligence, distinctions are sometimes made between problem situations that are well defined or well structured, on the one hand, and those that are ill defined or ill structured, on the other. The difference itself is not particularly well defined, for different writers use different criteria to draw the boundary. The distinction may nevertheless have some heuristic value for the study of problem-solving systems.

By one definitional criterion, we might regard a situation as well defined or well structured when a specific problem space has been selected, including a set of operators for working in that space. The structural information implicit or explicit in the definition of the task environment will generally support more than one such formulation of the search space.

A proof of a theorem, for example, means a sequence of expressions possessing three properties: (1) the initial members of the sequence are axioms or previously proved theorems, (2) each remaining member of the sequence is directly derivable, using one of the legitimate operators, from one or two of the preceding members, and (3) the final member of the sequence is the theorem to be proved. Call these three properties of a proof $A$, $B$ and $C$, respectively.

We can define a search space for a theorem prover in a variety of ways. We can construct generators that will generate sequences possessing one or more of the properties *A*, *B*, and *C*, and then test each sequence generated to see if it possesses the remaining properties. Thus, the generators usually produce sequences possessing property *B* (each expression is derivable from preceeding expressions), and hence the sequences produced do not have to be tested for this property. In a working-forward scheme, the generators produce sequences possessing properties *A* and *B*, which then have to be tested for *C*. In a working-backward scheme, the generators produce sequences possessing properties *B* and *C*, which then have to be tested for *A*.

Each of these schemes (and others that might be devised) uses the information present in the task environment in different ways to guide the search. Some of that information is incorporated in generators, so that only nodes satisfying certain criteria will belong to the search space; some of the information is incorporated in tests and evaluating functions to guide search. In general, the more information that can be incorporated in generators (without making them unduly complex and expensive), the less search will be required, and the greater will be the heuristic power of the representation. Since each alternative scheme represents a different definition of the problem, only after a particular scheme is specified is the problem well defined.

There is another notion of 'ill structured' and 'well structured', however, that deserves attention. In real-life problem solving, it does not appear that a problem is always defined, in the sense introduced above, before the search for a solution, or for information, begins. Let us see how this might be.

Consider the Missionaries and Cannibals problem. As it is usually discussed in artificial intelligence research, it is a well defined problem. The objects are specified, together with the legitimate moves, constraints, and starting situation. The state space is, in fact, very small, consisting of only ten allowable states. Whatever difficulty the problem may have either for people or for artificial intelligence systems, that difficulty has nothing to do with the size of the space to be searched.

Contrast this 'laboratory' Missionaries and Cannibals problem with a real-life problem. In the real-life problem, the number of persons the boat will hold may only be determinable by trying it, or at least examining it; and the fact that the boat leaks may be discovered only after it is loaded. The real environment may permit alternative ways of crossing the river — by a ford a few miles further up, on a bridge, by airplane. The actors may be joined by several more missionaries (or cannibals!) while the action is going on.

In real life there is not a single, static, well defined problem, but a constantly changing problem whose definition is being altered by information that the actors recover from memory and by other information obtained from the environment's response to actions taken. Do such ill structured real-life situations pose an essentially different problem for artificial intelligence systems than is posed by the well structured laboratory-defined situations we are accustomed to handle?

Let us imagine a chess playing program that is rather more powerful than any that have thus far been programmed. Let us suppose that it consists of a very large set of productions, combined with a scheme for managing a certain amount of tree search – dynamic look-ahead. The productions are of the usual form: each consists of a condition – a set of tests to determine if the production is applicable to any particular board position – and an action – a move or analysis to be attempted.

We would ordinarily say that we have here a well defined problem solving system operating in a well defined problem environment. And yet, this system can exhibit all the sorts of behavior, and can encounter all the sorts of unexpected situations that we took, above, as evidence that the real-life Missionaries and Cannibals problem is ill defined.

In the first place, certain properties of the situation and certain consequences of actions in it will become apparent only if they are actually tried out in the environment by dynamic analysis. (If we wanted to draw the parallel even closer, we could introduce an approximate, simplified chessboard in the program's calculations – a planning space – in contrast with the actual board on which the real consequences of moves are worked out.)

In the second place, the program 'knows' many things about the situation – possible moves, tests to be applied, and so on – in the sense of having these things stored in memory as part of its complete set of productions. But what it 'knows' only becomes available bit by bit as the information is recalled – that is, as it is evoked from memory by the matching of the conditions of productions. Thus the program may recognize something in the situation (a feature corresponding to the condition of a production) that evokes the idea of seeking a checkmate (the action part of that production). Only when the recognition of the feature evokes the production from memory, does the action 'occur to' the program.

An appearance of ill-structuredness will arise, therefore, whenever a serial search system or information-accumulating system operates in an information-rich situation. Part of the information may lie in the external environment, in which case it becomes available only as that environment is explored; part of the information may lie in the memory of the system itself, in which case it becomes available only as it is evoked from that memory by recognition of appropriate features in the environment. Thus, there is no fundamental difference between this sort of ill-structuredness and complexity of a task environment.

This becomes an important conclusion when we seek to devise intelligent robots that are to explore real physical environments, or automatic architectural design programs that are to create real designs. Almost certainly, the human architect does not begin his work with a well structured problem, in the usual sense. That is to say, one cannot find a sheet of paper or a book full of such sheets in which are specified the totality of design criteria, allowable materials, characteristics of materials, and details of representation. Instead, the activity begins with a very incomplete subset of such elements, and some initial exploratory activities to generate, say, very abstract solutions.

Observing these initial explorations, we would surmise that one of their major goals is to begin to evoke from memory, and to index for future reference, additional considerations — elements of tests and generators — that are relevant to the design process. Thus, the design activity appears to fit our information-accumulating version of the problem-solving process better than the tree-search version.

Even when the whole design process has terminated, and a design is complete, probably only a fraction of the productions available in the architect's memory (and even more probably only a tiny fraction of those available to him in the professional literature he has access to) will have been evoked. Which ones are evoked will depend not only on the problem that was posed initially, but also — and perhaps even more — on the information discovered, in the partially completed design and in memory, along the way to a solution.

It does not appear, therefore, that programs for solving ill structured problems — in this sense of the term, at least — will differ in principle from programs for solving well structured problems. As programs and memories grow larger; and as these programs tend more and more to be organized as production systems, virtually all interesting problem solving will look like ill structured problem solving. The environment will produce a steady stream of surprises, and we will repeatedly ask of the problem solver: 'How did he happen to think of that?' Of course we have already reached this point in the more sophisticated of the existing problem solving programs.

## 6. CONCLUSION

Some of the main directions that will be taken over the next few years by the research on problem solving appear not too hard to discern. The field, having arrived by the year 1971 at a pretty good picture of what tree search is all about, is going to shift its attention -- and is already shifting it -- to the problem of choice of representations.

When problem solving is viewed primarily as tree search, the choice of problem representations looks like a separate, prior, and exceedingly difficult task. That choice of representation is difficult can hardly be doubted, else we would by now know better how to do it. Nevertheless, the gulf between heuristic search and problem representation looks less wide and deep, and the difficulty of bridging it less severe, when we treat problem solving as information accumulation, in which manipulating a model (the usual role of tree search) is only one of several techniques. This shift and broadening of view seems to me an important precondition for rapid progress in the field.

Exploration of the properties and potentialities of hybrid systems -- systems combining capabilities of tree search, reasoning, and perhaps modal reasoning as well -- would appear to be particularly promising. Such hybrids should find themselves much less rigidly confined within a single problem space than systems enjoying only one of these capabilities. Anything that facilitates the use of multiple problem spaces, in turn, promises to facilitate also the generation of representations.

Space has prohibited me from addressing myself to all of the issues that are now current in the discussions of problem-solving research. In particular, I have said little, at least explicitly, about generality. But I think it is implied clearly, particularly by the discussion of ill structured problems, that elements of general heuristic power are auxiliary to, and not substitutable for, subject-matter knowledge appropriately organized in productions. If there is a referent, in artificial intelligence, for general intelligence, it must lie in that phrase 'appropriately organized'.

During the past decade, empirical research on problem solving conducted by programming and testing actual problem solving systems, has kept far ahead of attempts to develop formal mathematical theories. Whether this is a desirable state of affairs or not can be a matter of disagreement between mathematicians and others, but there is little doubt that it is likely to continue during the foreseeable future. Empirical exploration will precede formalization, and for our initial understanding of problem representation and of ill structured problem solving we will have to depend mainly on the continuing construction and testing of an ever-widening range of interesting and sophisticated problem-solving programs.

## NOTES

*This work was supported in whole or in part by Public Health Service Research Grant MH-07722 from the National Institute of Mental Health. In preparing this paper, I have drawn freely upon the work done jointly over the past fifteen years with Allen Newell, and especially upon our book *Human Problem Solving* (Englewood Cliffs, N.J.: Prentice-Hall, 1972).
[1] Problems may be difficult for humans – particularly when they involve AND/OR-graphs – even when the graphs are small. But my concern in this paper is with problem solving in general, and not with the specific characteristics of human problem solving. For the latter, see Newell and Simon [6].
[2] For the reason why such a 'pure theory' may be expected to exist, see Simon [7].
[3] The earliest theoretical work was concerned with optimality of the *path* from start to goal – i.e., with finding shortest-path solutions. More recently, attention has been given to the optimality of the search process – i.e., with finding *a* solution after a minimum amount of search. It is with the latter criterion of optimality that we are concerned here.
[4] Essentially, Ernst's theorem amounts to this: Application of an operator may remove one difference at the cost of introducing one or more new ones. However, if the difference-operator table can be permuted so that it becomes triangular, the operators can always be applied in an order that will remove remaining differences without introducing any that have previously been removed.
[5] Whether forming the macroelements constitutes 'abstraction' is questionable, since a solution of the problem with macroelements is also a solution of the original design problem. Perhaps 'factorization' is a more accurate term than 'abstraction.'

## REFERENCES

[1] A. Newell, 'Limitations of the Current Stock of Ideas About Problem Solving', in: *Electronic Information Handling,* A. Kent and O. Taulbee (eds.), (Washington; D.C.: Spartan Books, 1965).
[2] E. A. Feigenbaum, 'Artificial Intelligence: Themes in the Second Decade', *Proceedings IFIP 68 Congress*, Edinburgh (1968).
[3] R. B. Banerji, *Theory of Problem Solving*, (New York: Elsevier, 1969).
[4] J. R. Slagle, *Artificial Intelligence*, (New York: McGraw-Hill, 1971).
[5] N. J. Nilsson, *Problem-Solving Methods in Artificial Intelligence* (New York: McGraw-Hill, 1971).
[6] A. Newell and H. A. Simon, *Human Problem Solving*, (Englewood Cliffs, N.J.: Prentice-Hall, 1972).
[7] H. A. Simon, *The Sciences of the Artificial* (Cambridge, Mass.: M.I.T. Press, 1969).
[8] G. W. Baylor and H. A. Simon, 'A Chess Mating Combinations Program', *Proceedings, Spring Joint Computer Conference* (1966) pp. 431–447.
[9] N. J. Nilsson, 'Searching Problem-Solving and Game-Playing Trees for Minimal Cost Solutions,' *Proceedings, IFIP Congress 68*, Edinburgh (1968).
[10] I. Pohl, 'First Results on the Effect of Error in Heuristic Search', in: *Machine Intelligence 5*, B. Meltzer and D. Michie, (eds.), (New York: Elsevier, 1970).
[11] G. Ernst, 'Sufficient Conditions for the Success of GPS', *Journal of the ACM* 16, 517–533 (1969).

[12] E. Lawler and D. Wood, 'Branch and Bound Methods: A Survey', *Operations Research* 14, 699–719 (1969).

[13] H. Gelernter, 'Realization of a Geometry Theorem-Proving Machine', *Proceedings of an International Conference on Information Processing* (Paris: UNESCO House 1959) 272–282.

[14] A. Newell, J. C. Shaw and H. A. Simon, 'Chess Playing Programs and the Problem of Complexity,' *IBM Journal of Research and Development* 2, 320–335 (1963).

[15] C. Pfefferkorn, 'The Design Problem Solver', unpublished Ph.D Disseration, Carnegie-Mellon University (1971).

[16] H. E. Pople, Jr., 'A Goal-Oriented Language for the Computer', in *Representation and Meaning*, H. A. Simon and L. Siklossy (eds.), (Englewood Cliffs, N.J.: Prentice-Hall, 1972).

[17] *Representation and Meaning*, H. A. Simon and L. Siklossy (eds.), (Englewood Cliffs, N.J.: Prentice-Hall, 1972).

[18] R. J. Wallinger, 'Constructing Programs Automatically Using Theorem Proving,' unpublished Ph.D dissertation, Carnegie-Mellon University (1970).

CHAPTER 4.4

# THE ORGANIZATION OF COMPLEX SYSTEMS†

The Nobel Laureate Hideki Yukawa earned his prize by observing that the neutron and the proton required a strong, localized force field to hold them together in the atomic nucleus, and that this field should have the properties of a particle – the particle we now know as the pi-meson or pion. The organizers of this series of lectures, having described it as "an experiment in communication between physicists and biologists", evidently concluded that those two kinds of particles – physicists and biologists – also required a binding force to hold them in stable communication. Borrowing Yukawa's idea, they invited me – a behavioral scientist by training – to serve as the pion for the series.

Although I am neither physicist nor biologist, I cannot claim complete innocence of the subject of complex, hierarchic systems, for human administrative organizations – business firms, governments, universities, churches – to which I have devoted a considerable part of my research , are excellent examples of such systems. Since human organizations are staffed by human beings, and since human beings are biological organisms, it might be argued that my research problem is indeed biological. And since biological organisms are constructed from molecules, and those molecules from atoms, and the atoms from elementary particles – all obeying the laws of quantum mechanics – it might even be argued that research on human organizations is merely a rather baroque branch of physics.

I do not intend, however, to talk specifically about either biology or physics. The main point of my paper will be that there are properties common to a very broad class of complex systems, independently of whether those systems are physical, chemical, biological, social, or artificial. The existence of these commonalities is a matter of empirical observation; their explanation is, in a broad sense, Darwinian – they concern properties that facilitate the evolution and survival of complexity. I will leave to the other speakers in the series the specific applications of a general theory of complexity to biological phenomena.

My remarks will fall under four main headings. First, I will define what

† [Pattee (ed.), *Hierarchy Theory*, New York: G. Braziller, 1973, pp. 3–27].

I — and I hope the other speakers in the series — mean by 'hierarchy'. Second, I will review briefly two extant pieces of mathematical theory about hierarchies: One has to do with the time required for their evolution, the other with the interaction of their parts. Third, I will explore some consequences of the fact that biological organisms have hierarchic structure. Fourth, I will draw implications from the hierarchies of nature for the hierarchy of the sciences.

In dealing with each topic, I will turn to two main sources of illustration and example, making my discourse into a sort of two-part fugue. On the one hand, I will draw examples from biology, and occasionally from chemistry and physics. On the other hand, I will draw examples from computer science, and specifically from the structure of computer programming languages and programs. I hope that the relation between these two sets of examples will become clear as I proceed.

## 1. HIERARCHY

In discussions of the theory of complex systems, the term 'hierarchy' has taken on a somewhat generalized meaning, divorced from its original denotation in human organizations of a vertical authority structure. In application to the architecture of complex systems, 'hierarchy' simply means a set of Chinese boxes of a particular kind. A set of Chinese boxes usually consists of a box enclosing a second box, which, in turn, encloses a third — the recursion continuing as long as the patience of the craftsman holds out.

The Chinese boxes called 'hierarchies' are a variant of that pattern. Opening any given box in a hierarchy discloses not just one new box within, but a whole small set of boxes; and opening any one of these component boxes discloses a new set in turn. While the ordinary set of Chinese boxes is a sequence, or complete ordering, of the component boxes, a hierarchy is a partial ordering — specifically, a tree.

It is a commonplace observation that nature loves hierarchies. Most of the complex systems that occur in nature find their place in one or more of four intertwined hierarchic sequences. One partial ordering of boxes starts with observable chemical substances. Analysis of these discloses sets of component molecules. Within the molecules are found atoms, within the atoms, nuclei and electrons, and finally — or is it momentarily? — within the nuclei are found elementary particles.

A second important hierarchy runs from living organisms to tissues and organs, to cells, to macromolecules, to organic compounds, to a junction with the molecules of the first hierarchy. A third, intertwined hierarchy leads from the statistics of inheritance to genes and chromosomes, to DNA, and all that.

A fourth hierarchy, not yet firmly connected with the others, leads from human societies to organizations, to small groups, to individual human beings, to cognitive programs in the central nervous system, to elementary information processes — where the junctions with the tissues and organs of neurobiology largely remain to be discovered.

In this fourth hierarchy, I have included components called 'programs' and other components called 'elementary information processes'. Walter Pitts once referred to this system as 'the hierarchy of final causes called the mind.' Until about twenty-five years ago, programs and elementary information processes were to be found only as components of biological organisms. Since that time, programs and elementary information processes have been occurring with growing abundance in the artificial complex systems called digital computers. Since programs are much more readily accessible to study in their artificial than in their natural environments, we have learned enormously more about them in our generation than in all previous history. For this reason, the digital computer is taking its place alongside Drosophila, Neurospora, and bacteriophage as an experimental system of the greatest importance. It is for this reason, also, that I shall parallel my biological examples with examples drawn from computer science.

## 2. SOME THEORY OF HIERARCHY

Several theoretical results are available today on the general behavior of hierarchic systems. I wish to mention two: One providing some explanation for the frequent occurrence of hierarchies in nature, the other showing that there are certain general properties that all hierarchic systems can be expected to possess, wherever they fit in the ordering of Chinese boxes, and whatever they are made of. I will review these two results here only briefly because I have previously treated them at some length in an essay recently reissued as the fourth chapter of my Compton Lectures at MIT, '*The Sciences Of The Artificial*'.

### 2.1. *The Speed of Evolution*

One can show on quite simple and general grounds that the time required for a complex system, containing $k$ elementary components, say, to evolve by processes of natural selection from those components is very much shorter if the system is itself comprised of one or more layers of stable component subsystems than if its elementary parts are its only stable components. The mathematics of the matter is a straightforward exercise in probabilities, but the gist of it can be given even more simply in a parable.

Two watchmakers assemble fine watches, each watch containing ten thousand parts. Each watchmaker is interrupted frequently to answer the phone. The first has organized his total assembly operation into a sequence of subassemblies; each subassembly is a stable arrangement of 100 elements, and each watch, a stable arrangement of 100 subassemblies. The second watchmaker has developed no such organization. The average interval between phone interruptions is a time long enough to assemble about 150 elements. An interruption causes any set of elements that does not yet form a stable system to fall apart completely. By the time he has answered about eleven phone calls, the first watchmaker will usually have finished assembling a watch. The second watchmaker will almost never succeed in assembling one — he will suffer the fate of Sisyphus: As often as he rolls the rock up the hill, it will roll down again.

It has been argued on information-theoretic grounds — or, what amounts to the same thing, on thermodynamic grounds — that organisms are highly improbable arrangements of matter; so improbable, in fact, that there has hardly been time enough, since the Earth's creation, for them to evolve. The calculation on which this argument is based does not take account of the hierarchic arrangement of stable subassemblies in the organisms that have actually evolved. It has erroneously used the analogy of the second, unsuccessful watchmaker; and when the first watchmaker is substituted for him, the times required are reduced to much more plausible magnitudes.

Specifically, on the simplest assumptions, the mathematical model shows that if a system of $k$ elementary components is built up in a many-level hierarchy, and $s$ components, on the average, combine at any level into a component at the next higher level, then the expected time of evolution for the whole system will be proportional to the logarithm to base $s$ of $k$. In such a hierarchy, the time required for systems containing, say, $10^{25}$ atoms to evolve from systems containing $10^{23}$ atoms would be the same as the time required from systems containing $10^3$ atoms to evolve from systems containing 10 atoms. The form of the generalization is interesting, in that it describes a relation between two levels of a system that is independent of absolute level.

We conclude that hierarchies will evolve much more rapidly from elementary constituents than will non-hierarchic systems containing the same number of elements. Hence, almost all the very large systems will have hierarchic organization. And this is what we do, in fact, observe in nature.

## 2.2. Near-Decomposability

Most interactions that occur in nature, between systems of all kinds, decrease in strength with distance. Hence, any given 'particle' has most of its strong interactions with nearby particles. As a result, a system is likely to behave either as made up of a collection of localized subsystems or to form a more or less uniform 'tissue' of equally strong interactions. An example of the former would be a system of molecules; an example of the latter would be a crystal or a piece of rock. Systems of the former kind are, again, hierarchies.

Thus, protons and neutrons of the atomic nucleus interact strongly through the pion fields, which dispose of energies of some 140 million electron volts each. The covalent bonds that hold molecules together, on the other hand, involve energies only on the order of 5 electron volts. And the bonds that account for the tertiary structure of large macromolecules, hence for their biological activity, involve energies another order of magnitude smaller – around one-half of an electron volt. It is precisely this sharp gradation in bond strengths at successive levels that causes the system to appear hierarchic and to behave so. As Melvin Calvin has put it: 'This is one of the fundamental things we have to teach freshmen: What is the difference between an atom and a molecule? An atom interacts at one energy level and molecules interact at the other, and that is how we tell the difference.' (See Ramsey, 1967.)

Suppose we were to write down and solve the equations describing the behavior of a hierarchic system having $n$ degrees of freedom. We would obtain $n$ frequencies, not necessarily all distinct, in terms of which we could describe the dynamic behavior. We could arrange these frequencies in a sequence, beginning with the lowest frequencies corresponding to the slowest oscill-ations, and going down through medium-range frequencies, to very high frequencies at the end of the list. As is well known, in the case of the physical system I described a moment ago – a system of macromolecules – Planck's Law prescribes a strict proportionality between bond energies and the associated frequencies.

If we now observe the behavior of the system over a total time span, T, and our observational techniques do not allow us to detect changes during time intervals shorter than $\tau$, we can break the sequence of characteristic frequencies into three parts: (1) low frequencies, much less than $1/T$; (2) middle-range frequencies; and (3) high frequencies, greater than $1/\tau$. Motions of the system determined by the low-frequency modes will be so slow that we will not observe them – they will be replaced by constants.

Motions of the system determined by the high frequency modes will control, for the reasons already given, the internal interactions of the components of the lower level subsystems in the hierarchy, but will not be involved in the interactions among those subsystems. Moreover, these motions will be so rapid that the corresponding subsystems will appear always to be in equilibrium and most of their internal degrees of freedom will vanish. In their relations with each other, the several subsystems will behave like rigid bodies, so to speak.

The middle band of frequencies, which remains after we have eliminated the very high and very low frequencies, will determine the observable dynamics of the system under study – the dynamics of interaction of the major subsystems. As we have seen, these dynamics will be nearly independent of the detail of the internal structure of the subsystems, which will never be observed far from equilibrium. Hence, we can build a theory of the system at the level of dynamics that is observable, in ignorance of the detailed structure or dynamics at the next level down, and ignore the very slow interactions at the next level up. The goodness of our approximation will depend only on the sharpness of the separation of the high frequencies from the middle-range frequencies, and of the middle-range frequencies from the low frequencies. We will, of course, want to select the boundaries so as to make that separation as sharp as possible. I will have a little more to say about the relation between the layered structure of natural phenomena and the layered structure of theories.

Systems with the sorts of dynamic properties that I have just described are called 'nearly-decomposable' or sometimes 'nearly completely decomposable' systems. A rigorous mathematical basis exists for reaching the conclusions I have just stated about such systems, but I think our intuitions will suffice for present purposes. (See Ando *et al.*, 1963 and Chapter 4.2 above.)

### 3. HIERARCHIES IN COMPUTING SYSTEMS

So far I have used natural systems as my examples of hierarchies. I could as well have used modern computing systems and their behavior. I should now like to describe a computer program called EPAM with which I am familiar. EPAM simulates human laboratory subjects in certain simple learning tasks, but just what it does is of no concern to us here. What is important is that it is a large, complex computer program.

EPAM consists of lists of instructions organized as 'routines'. It is written in a computer programming language called IPL-V, to which I will return in a moment. The instructions — there are about 3000 — are of two kinds: (1) primitive instructions, corresponding to a fixed, basic set of IPL-V instructions, and (2) higher-level instructions. Whenever I write an IPL-V routine consisting of a list of primitive instructions, I can give that routine a name. I can then use that name just as though it were an instruction — a higher-level instruction — in any other routine I wish to write. Whenever the system, during execution, encounters such a higher level instruction, it simply executes the subroutine that the instruction names. There is no limit to the allowable number of levels of subroutines, and at various points EPAM is five or even ten levels deep.

But that is not all. The IPL-V primitives, in terms of which the EPAM routines are ultimately defined, are themselves not very primitive. They correspond, in fact, to routines — some of them fairly complex — written in the instruction language of the particular kind of computer on which EPAM is to be run. For each distinct machine there must be a translation of IPL-V into the language of that machine; but the behavior of EPAM is substantially independent of that translation and indifferent to what machine it is run on. We can say that EPAM has a 'meaning' that is independent of the particular machine language in which it is expressed.

We are still far from having probed the bottom levels of our hierarchy. Having reached the level of machine instructions, we can analyse how these instructions are realized in the logical organization of the computer itself. The study of that logical organization leads, in turn, to lower hierarchic levels, where we first encounter the actual physical devices that implement the behavior and the actual physical laws that govern those devices. Just as the same language — for example, IPL-V — can be implemented on vastly different computers (more than a dozen translations exist today), so the same computer design, at the logical level, can be implemented with entirely different hardware devices. From a programming standpoint, the IBM 709 and the IBM 7090 were almost identical machines, although the former made extensive use of vacuum tubes, while the latter was a solid-state system. From a physical standpoint, they were radically different machines.

The system I have described is a nearly-decomposable system. Its highest frequencies are those associated with the physical components of the computer — nowadays, microsecond or nanosecond frequencies. Frequencies associated with the logical organization of the machine and its machine instructions might be, for a fairly fast machine, say, in the range of ten microseconds. IPL-V instructions are executed at millisecond rates (one or two orders of magnitude slower than machine instructions). Some of the higher-level routines of EPAM take seconds to execute – even on a fast modern computer, EPAM requires several second to memorize a nonsense syllable.

Now just as we can reach an approximate understanding of a physical system at the level of chemical reactions, ignoring what is going on within the atoms and nuclei, so we can reach an approximate understanding of EPAM by considering only a few of the highest levels of the program, not going down even to IPL-V primitives, much less to machine language, logical design, or computer physics. As a matter of fact, since IPL-V translators are explicitly constructed to make behavior machine-independent, we should be able to describe EPAM *exactly* (apart from some speed parameters) in terms of IPL-V. How much accuracy we lose in disregarding all but the high-level routines depends on how carefully we have sealed off each level from those below.

What do I mean by 'sealing off'? Each year when I fill out my income tax form, I am instructed to perform certain additions and subtractions, and even a few multiplications. I am told where to find the operands and where to enter the sum, difference, or product. Later, the Internal Revenue Service audits my return, and if I have made a mistake – as I sometimes do – corrects it. So the IRS can tell whether I have done the arithmetic correctly, but it cannot tell *how* I did it – what subroutine I use to define 'addition' or 'multiplication'. Perhaps I multiply with paper and pencil, from right to left, or from left to right; perhaps I do it in my head, or on a desk calculator, or on my university's computer; perhaps my wife does it. The only communication between my arithmetic routines and the IRS's auditing routines is through the inputs and outputs of my processes; the processes themselves are immune from scrutiny.

When I multiply two four-digit numbers together, I have to keep the multiplier and multiplicand in memory or on paper. Then I have to store temporarily the four partial products – four or five digits each. When I am done, I have to retain only the seven or eight digits of the final product. The unobservability (to the IRS) of the intermediate results that I create, but hold only temporarily, is precisely analogous to the unobservability of the high-frequency dynamics of a hierarchic system, the disequilibrium dynamics of the smallest components. All of this detail is simply irrelevant to the lower-frequency interactions among the larger segments. No matter which of several processes I use to obtain the product, and which intermediate results I obtain *en route*, the final information I obtain and pass on to other routines is the same. Hence, hierarchy is associated with a very fundamental form of parsimony of interactions. The art of subroutining, in writing complex computer programs, consists in discovering the points of cleavage at which the least information needs to be passed from one subroutine to another.

## 3.1. Loose Horizontal Coupling

In describing the behavior of nearly-decomposable systems, I emphasized 'vertical' separation — the segregation of the low-frequency from the high-frequency dynamics. The last examples suggest that the theory of near-decomposability can be extended to say something about the horizontal relations among subsystems at the *same* hierarchic level.

Consider, again, the frequencies of a nearly-decomposable system arranged in order from low to high. We now observe the behavior of the system much more microscopically than we did before, so that we need consider only the roots of frequency greater than $1/\tau$. This is equivalent to ignoring the weak interactions among the subsystems of the nearly-decomposable system and treating the subsystems as completely decoupled from one another. But then we can take the remaining high-frequency roots and assign them to their respective subsystems. Particular frequencies describe the behavior of particular subsystems.

Returning to our original system, we see that the frequencies describing its dynamics can be *partially* ordered, and each subset of frequencies in the partial ordering (formally, an equivalence class at some particular level of the ordering) can be associated with a specific subsystem in the partial ordering of system components. There will be, essentially, an isomorphism between the hierarchy of subsystems and the hierarchy of equivalence classes of frequencies describing the system, and particular frequencies will 'belong' to particular subsystems.

To a first approximation, the behavior of any given subsystem will depend only on the frequencies belonging to it, together with the lower frequencies belonging to systems at higher levels of the hierarchy. It will be independent of the frequencies associated with other subsystems at the same or lower levels of the hierarchy. (I am sorry the high 'frequencies' correspond to low 'levels', but it can't be helped.)

The loose horizontal coupling of the components of hierarchic systems has great importance for evolutionary processes just as the loose vertical coupling does. The loose vertical coupling permits the stable subassemblies to be treated as simple givens, whose dynamic behavior is irrelevant to assembling the larger structures, only their equilibrium properties affecting system behavior at the higher levels.

The loose horizontal coupling of the components of hierarchic systems permits each to operate dynamically in independence of the detail of the others; only the inputs it requires and the outputs it produces are relevant for the larger aspects of system behavior. In programming terms, it is permissible to improve the system by modifying any one of the subroutines, provided that the subroutine's inputs and outputs are not altered.

When the same outputs can be obtained from the same inputs by two or more different paths, we usually speak of 'functional equivalence'. Functional equivalence, of course, is not peculiar to computer programs, for it occurs frequently in natural phenomena. In chemical reactions, for example, isotopic variants of atoms of the elements are usually functionally equivalent – as long as two atoms present to the surrounding environment the same configuration of outer-shell electrons and differ only slightly in atomic weight, their chemical behaviors are almost indistinguishable.

In biological systems, innumerable examples of functional equivalence are provided by multiple reaction pathways. The equivalence can refer to the reaction itself – for example, the two pathways for synthesis of lysine, one used by some fungi and euglenids, the others by most plants. Alternatively, the equivalence can refer to the enzymic apparatus controlling the reaction – for example, the wide variety of chemically distinguishable protein molecules that serve as functionally equivalent hemoglobins, both among different species and even in a single species.

The various functional equivalents may, of course, vary widely in their metabolic efficiency, and their relative efficiencies may depend on environmental circumstances as well – horse hemoglobin seems to work better for horses and human hemoglobin for people, although perhaps that is only for immunological reasons. But, of course, it is precisely because they may vary in efficiency that functional equivalents have significance for natural selection. Functional equivalence permits mutation and natural selection to go on in particular subsystems without requiring synchronous changes in all the other systems that make up the total organism.

The loose horizontal coupling of components can be observed at all levels of hierarchic structures. Thus, a mammal's circulatory system is loosely coupled to other systems. It receives oxygen from the respiratory system and nutrients from the digestive system. It delivers these to the muscles, say, from which it receives carbon dioxide, and other wastes. These it delivers, in turn, to lungs and kidneys, and so on.

Just how the circulatory system accomplishes these tasks is of no concern, so to speak, to the other systems, as long as it does accomplish them. Appropriate evolutionary changes may take place in any one of these systems without necessarily, or immediately, disturbing the others. Natural selection may improve a horse's locomotion without necessarily changing his digestion, although changes in the metabolic rates associated with one subsystem may, on a longer time scale, bring about natural selection of new adaptations of other subsystems.

The same kind of argument as that used to show that nearly-decomposable systems will evolve more rapidly than others can be used to demonstrate that the advantage in adaptation will be increased if different components of the organism are coupled to different components of the environment. The point is most easily shown by analogy with problem solving efficiency.

Consider the problem of cracking a safe that has 10 dials, each with 10 possible settings. To find the combination by trial and error would require, on the average, testing half the total number of possible settings – half of $10^{10}$, or 5 billion. If each dial emits a faint click when it is set to the correct number, the safe-cracking job becomes trivially simple. Now, on average, only $5 \times 10 = 50$ settings will have to be tried.

## 3.2. Production Systems

The loose horizontal coupling of subsystems can be exploited in another way: to make each subsystem independent of the exact timing of the operation of the others. If subsystem B depends upon subsystem A only for a certain substance, then B can be made independent of fluctuations in A's production by maintaining a buffer inventory of the substance upon which B can draw. The storage of fat is a well-known and important biological example of this principle. Buffer inventories permit many interdependent processes to operate in parallel, at fluctuating rates and under only feedback control – as in the familiar mechanism by which the inventory of the substance produced by the last enzyme in a chain inhibits the activity of the first enzyme.

Most digital computers are organized, more or less, as serial one-process-at-a-time devices. The idea of loosely coupling their processes in the way just described can be employed to simulate parallel systems. To do this each routine is written as a 'production' in two parts: The first part tests for the presence or absence of certain conditions; if and only if the conditions are satisfied, the second part carries out its characteristic process. Clearly, there is a close logical relation between such productions and the operons of molecular genetics. If one wanted to write a computer simulation of operons, one would represent them by productions. Because their components are so loosely coupled, production systems are much more easily modified, component by component, than are computer programs written as more traditional subroutine structures. As a result, complex programs are increasingly being organized in this form.

## 4. ALPHABETS

The flexibility of coupling among subsystems can be further enhanced by limiting the variety of different kinds of components that are incorporated in the larger systems. When the numerous component elements (called 'tokens') of the subsystems of a hierarchy all belong to a small number of basic types, we call this set of types an 'alphabet'. A common milk protein contains 5941 'tokens' — atoms. All of these atoms belong to the five elements — types C, H, O, N, and S. These five types are drawn from the 92-letter alphabet of natural elements.

The alphabet of primitive instructions in IPL-V is more baroque than the atomic alphabet. It contains about 150 instructions, but if we treat certain similar instructions as isotopes, the number remaining is not far from the number of elements. As Turing and others have shown, a computing system — even a completely general one — can get along with a far smaller alphabet than that. In fact, about five instructions like 'write', 'erase', 'move left', 'move-right', and 'test and branch' will suffice for complete generality. It is convenient and efficient, but not logically necessary, for computer instruction codes to contain more operations than these.

Two alphabets have supreme importance for biology: The alphabet of twenty-odd amino acids, and the alphabet of four (or five) nucleic acids. I will confine my remarks largely to the former, for we know today how the one can be translated into the other.

### 4.1. Alphabets, Languages, and Programs

Not every level in a hierarchic structure is characterized by a small alphabet of components. There are only 92 natural elements, but innumerable molecules at the next level up; there are only about 20 amino acids, but innumerable protein molecules. There are only 150 primitive IPL-V instructions, but innumerable routines written in terms of them – at least thousands. What significance can we attach to the fact that only certain hierarchic levels are alphabetic?

We must distinguish between alphabets and languages, on the one hand, and programs or messages, on the other. Alphabets and languages are systems that provide a potentiality for communicating any of a large number of programs or messages. They consist of elements, and rules for the combination of the elements into messages. We may regard alphabets simply as those languages that are based on small numbers of different elements (as distinct, for example, from natural languages, which typically contain hundreds of thousands of morphemes or words).

Members of a single organization may share a set of common messages – standard operating procedures, say. Interaction throughout a language community takes place by means of a common language, messages being constructed and transmitted as needed. Alphabets, because of their restricted set of elements, are even shared across the boundaries of language communities. Most of the Western European languages use the Roman alphabet.

If we knew in advance just what messages were to be sent, we could always find a special encoding that would be more efficient than constructing the messages from a general-purpose language. If we knew in advance the subject of the messages, a lexicon could provide a more efficient encoding of messages than is provided by the combinations of a small alphabet. The 'inventory' of elements we would have to keep on hand would be much greater, however, for the lexicon than for the alphabet.

To realize its potential advantages for communication, a language should have these characteristics: (1) sufficient variety in its primitive processes so that no meaning is absolutely excluded from expression, and (2) sufficient flexibility in its rules of combination so that any nuance can be expressed by building up composite structures. What is required of the amino acids, and of the nucleic acids, is that they provide sufficient variety so that their combinations, proteins, and chromosomes, respectively, can perform all of the basic kinds of chemical functions that need to be performed in the cell.

This does not explain, however, why the nucleic acid and amino acid languages are based on alphabets. If this characteristic has significance for evolutionary success, the significance appears to be different in the two cases. What is needed in the genetic case is a simple code that is isomorphic to the set of amino acids – hence nothing is to be gained from a large alphabet. But what about the amino acids themselves?

An organism can only survive in an environment containing appropriate nutrient matter. Unless it can control that environment, or unless the environment is controlled beneficently by a higher-level system, it cannot rely on finding in the environment highly particular substances. We would expect alphabetic languages to be prominent in communication at subsystem boundaries where each subsystem experiences considerable uncertainty as to what it will find in its environment – where it cannot count on the environment to provide inputs tailored to its exact needs.

(I may observe that manufacturing concerns behave in exactly the same way. They tend to hold their in-process inventories in the form of generalized intermediate products that are capable of being formed into a variety of final products – ingots rather than special steel shapes, for example.)

It is hardly surprising, therefore, that the transactions of an organism with its environment (and even remote internal transactions via its circulatory system) are handled with an amino acid currency, and not with a protein currency. Proteins are far too specific in function, and far too closely adapted to a particular type of organism, to be exchanged satisfactorily among organisms. An amino acid molecule in the bloodstream of an animal may have come from many different sources. It may have been obtained by digestion of protein foods of various kinds; it may have been synthesized from other amino acids; it may have been hydrolyzed from proteins in the animal's own tissues. Two molecules of the same amino acid are functionally equivalent, however derived.

An organism will have access to a supply of components if it maintains itself in a broth of potential replacement parts. It would be hard-pressed – at least without cannibalism – to find such a broth of appropriate proteins.

### 4.2. Summary: Loose Coupling

Our whole discussion to this point underscores the crucial significance of hierarchic organization to the synthesis and survival of large, complex systems. To a Platonic mind, everything in the world is connected with everything else – and perhaps it is. Everything is connected, but some things are more connected than others. The world is a large matrix of interactions in which most of the entries are very close to zero, and in which, by ordering those entries according to their orders of magnitude, a distinct hierarchic structure can be discerned.

By virtue of hierarchic structure, the functional efficacy of the higher-level structures, their stability, can be made relatively independent of the detail of their microscopic components. By virtue of hierarchy, the several components on any given level can preserve a measure of independence to adapt to their special aspects of the environment without destroying their usefulness to the system.

## 5. REDUCTION

I will close with some remarks about reductionism and the structure of the sciences. The general tenor of these remarks should now be predictable. There are at least two versions of the concept of explanation in science. In both versions, of course, explaining a phenomenon involves reducing it to other phenomena that are, in some sense, more fundamental.

But with agreement on this point, the two concepts of explanation branch. The one concept — let me call it Laplacian — takes as its ideal the formulation of a single set of equations describing behavior at the most microscopic, the most fundamental level, from which all macrophenomena are to flow and to be deduced. No one, of course, believes that the program could actually be carried out — the equations, when written, would be far too hard to solve. In spite of that, the concept has practical consequences in the real world, for it influences some scientists' choices of research problems — their view of what is 'really' fundamental.

The second concept — for lack of a better name let me call it Mendelian — takes as its ideal the formulation of laws that express the invariant relations between successive levels of hierarchic structures. It aims at discovering as many bodies of scientific law as there are pairs of successive levels — a theory of particle physics, one of atomic physics, one of molecular chemistry, one of biochemistry, and so on. Since the world of nature is a nearly-decomposable system, and since the invariant properties of a nearly-decomposable system have this layered quality, the fundamental scientific laws must take this form also.

Since, in the second view, nature is only *nearly*-decomposable, not *completely* decomposable, many of the most beautiful regularities of nature will only be approximate regularities. They will fall short of exactness because the properties of the lower-level, higher-frequency subsystems will 'show through' faintly into the behavior of the higher-level, lower-frequency systems. Thus for example, there is a fundamental truth in Prout's hypothesis — that the atomic weights of all the elements can be expressed as integers — even though we know it is not an exact truth, and know the relativistic explanation for the mass deficiency. We know the vicissitudes that Prout's hypothesis suffered: How it was descredited by the 19th century's measurement, with continually increasing accuracy, of fractional atomic weights; how it was triumphantly vindicated by the discovery of isotopes; how further increases in the accuracy of measurement put it in doubt again.

If we were to make a list of the most important, the most beautiful laws of natural science that have been discovered in the past three centuries, we would see that the vast majority of them hold only approximately, and only if we are willing to ignore details of microstructure. The pattern expressed by these laws is simply not present in the underlying, detailed Laplacian equations.

I do not want to present a one-sided case. The fact that nature is hierarchic does not mean that phenomena at several levels cannot, even in the Mendelian view, have common mechanisms. Relativistic quantum mechanics has had spectacular success in dealing with phenomena ranging all the way from the level of the atomic nucleus to the level of tertiary structure in organic molecules.

Perhaps a balanced way to state the matter is this: Suppose you decided that you wanted to understand the mysterious EPAM program that I have, without explaining, alluded to several times in this paper. I could provide you with two versions of it. One would be the IPL-V version — the form in which it was actually written — with its whole structure of routines and subroutines. If you were curious about its implementation on a computer, I could supplement the EPAM program with a listing of the program that translates IPL-V instructions into machine-language instructions for some particular machine.

Alternatively, I could provide you with a machine-language version of EPAM after the whole translation had been carried out — after it had been flattened, so to speak, and spread out in all its Laplacian detail. I don't think I need argue at length which of these two versions would provide the most parsimonious, the most meaningful, the most lawful description of EPAM. I will not even propose to you the third, and truly Laplacian possibility — of providing you with neither program, but instead, with the electromagnetic equations and boundary conditions that the computer, viewed as a physical system, would have to obey while behaving as EPAM. That would be the acme of reduction and incomprehensibility.

Notice that in my plea for a hybrid Laplacian-Mendelian approach to fundamental science I have given no defense of vitalism, nor have I alluded to the Heisenberg Uncertainty Principle. Both of these seem to me red herrings across our particular path of inquiry. Scientific knowledge is organized in levels, not because reduction in principle is impossible, but because nature is organized in levels, and the pattern at each level is most clearly discerned by abstracting from the detail of the levels far below. (The pattern of a halftone does not become clearer when we magnify it so that the individual spots of ink become visible.) And nature is organized in levels because hierarchic structures — systems of Chinese boxes — provide the most viable form for any system of even moderate complexity. I have tried in this paper to show some of the deeper reasons why this is so.

## REFERENCES

Ando, A., Fisher, F. M., and Simon, H. A. *Essays on the Structure of Social Science Models* (Cambridge, Massachusetts: MIT Press, 1963). (See also Chapter 4.2 in this volume.)

Ramsey, Diane M., ed., *Molecular Coding Problems*, (New York: New York Academy of Sciences, 1967) pp. 120–121.

Simon, H. A., *The Sciences of the Artificial*, (Cambridge, Mass.: MIT Press, 1969).

# THEORY OF SCIENTIFIC DISCOVERY

The theory of scientific discovery has both an empirical part and a formal part. As an empirical theory, it seeks to describe and explain the psychological and sociological processes that are actually employed to make scientific discoveries. As a formal theory, it is concerned with the definition and logical nature of discovery, and it seeks to provide normative advice and presciptions for anyone who wishes to proceed rationally and efficiently with a task of scientific discovery. The chapters of Section 5 treat of both the empirical and the formal theories of scientific discovery.

## 1. THE EMPIRICAL THEORY

Chapters 5.1 and 5.2 are concerned with the empirical theory of scientific discovery. The first of these chapters provides an overview of the psychological theory of problem solving (as contrasted with the normative theory described in Chapter 4.3) that has emerged from modern research using information processing concepts and the techniques of computer simulation. The reader who wishes to look at this theory in greater detail may consult my *Sciences of the Artificial* (Cambridge, Mass.: MIT Press, 1969), especially Chapter 2. From that, still brief, account, he can go to such books as Norman and Ramsay's *Human Information Processing*,[1] Newell and Simon's *Human Problem Solving*,[2] and Anderson and Bower's *Human Associative Memory*.[3]

The quotation from Leibniz that introduces Chapter 5.1, supplied by the editor of the volume in which this essay first appeared, illustrates how hard it is for authors to communicate even with editors. When we talk about using computers to simulate human thinking, we are *not* taling about making human thinking more efficient or 'logical'. Nor are we talking about teaching people to think mathematically or formally. We are talking about imitating, with the help of a computer, human thought processes as they actually occur in the human brain during problem-solving (and other cognitive activities) of all sorts. Computers have no intrinsic properties that require them only to proceed 'logically'. After all — as the saying goes — they do only what you program them to do. And this chapter is concerned with programming computers to think in the same unsystematic, inductive, heuristic ways that human beings think, to simulate human error as well as successful problem solving.

Chapter 5.2 uses the information processing theory of problem solving to sketch an explanation of the processes of scientific discovery. The central thesis is stated succinctly in the second paragraph: "that scientific discovery is a form of problem solving, and that the processes whereby science is carried on can be explained in the terms that have been used to explain the processes of problem solving." In selecting a quotation to introduce this essay also, the editor either misunderstood the thesis or sought to avoid scandal by suggesting on the authority of Einstein that the chapter represented a Quixotic attempt to penetrate 'eternal mysteries'.

The subject of scientific discovery (and creativity generally) has always been surrounded by dense mists of romanticism and downright know-nothingism. Even well-informed persons, who do not believe that the stork brings new babies, and who are prepared to accept an empirical account of biological creation, sometimes balk at naturalistic explanations of the creation of ideas. It appears that the human mind is the final citadel of vitalism.

It goes without saying that Chapter 5.2 does not pretend to give a definitive account of the processes of scientific discovery. I would be quite satisfied if it persuaded some readers of the *possibility* that the processes required to produce scientific discoveries, great and small, may not be dissimilar to the processes we observe in everyday, garden-variety problem solving and for which we now have the core of an information processing theory.

The argument is carried a little further in Chapter 5.3, which looks at the kinds of problems that are called 'ill structured'. Most of the empirical information-processing research on problem solving has used well-structured, and often puzzle-like problems as its experimental tasks. We might well wonder how far a theory based on behavior in such tasks can be extrapolated to more complex and less structured domains. Chapter 5.3 provides a characterization of the ways in which problems may be ill structured, and uses that characterization to argue that the processes that have been found to account for the main features of human problem solving in well-structured domains may in fact be adequate to explain behavior in ill-structured domains as well.

## 2. THE FORMAL THEORY

Chapters 5.4 and 5.5 are formal and normative in intent, hence belong to philosophy rather than psychology. The dominant view in the philosophy of science has been that, while it is entirely feasible to construct a normative theory of processes for verifying or falsifying scientific theories, no comparable normative theory of processes of scientific discovery can be constructed. The possibility of a normative theory of discovery has been urged by Pierce, Norwood Hanson,[4] and a few other writers, but it has been denied by many philosophers of science — very emphatically, for example, by Popper.[5] Chapter 5.4 takes the side of Hanson against Popper. It defines a law-discovery process as a process for recoding, in parsimonious fashion, sets of empirical data; and a normative theory of scientific discovery as a set of criteria for evaluating law-discovery processes. Using this definition, it then proceeds to show that theories of the efficiency of heuristic search, and similar theories of computational efficiency in artificial intelligence are normative theories of discovery. Since concrete examples of such theories exist (and some are cited in the chapter), it becomes a little hard to argue against their possibility.

Chapter 5.5 deals with a formal rather than a normative question. Plato explains problem solving with his famous theory of recollection. This explanation, of course, is very different from the information-processing explanation proposed in the earlier chapters of this section. Chapter 5.5 seeks to show, on logical grounds, that Plato's theory of recollection is simply wrong. Since the chapter itself is quite brief, I will not recapitulate its argument here.

## NOTES

[1] New York: Academic Press, 1972.
[2] Englewood Cliffs, N.J.: Prentice-Hall, 1972.
[3] Washington, D.C.: Winston, 1973.
[4] *Patterns of Discovery* (Cambridge: Cambridge University Press, 1961).
[5] *The Logic of Scientific Discovery* (London: Hutchinson, 1959)

# THINKING BY COMPUTERS†*

> That is the aim of that great science which I am used
> to calling *Characteristic,* of which what we call
> Algebra, or Analysis, is only a very small branch, since
> it is this *Characteristic* which gives words to languages,
> letters to words, numbers to Arithmetic, notes to
> Music. It teaches us how to fix our reasoning, and to
> require it to leave, as it were, visible traces on the
> paper of a notebook for inspection at leisure. Finally,
> it enables us to reason with economy, by substituting
> characters in the place of things in order to relieve the
> imagination. . . .
>
> Leibniz, *On the Method of Universality* (1674)

It is hardly possible to talk about thinking by computers without saying something first about thinking by people. There are two reasons why this is so. First, the only definitions of thinking that are of any use at all are ostensive ones. We can point to a person in a certain state of activity and say, 'Thinking is a set of processes like those now taking place in the central nervous system of that person.' Alternatively, we can point to the statement of a problem and to its solution and say, 'Thinking is a set of processes like those that enabled a person to produce this problem solution from this problem statement.' I do not mean that these two definitions are necessarily equivalent, but they might serve equally well as a basis for delimiting the set of phenomena we wish to understand when we investigate thinking.

The second reason why we must talk about thinking by people in order to talk about thinking by computers is that the history of the latter phenomenon is inextricably interwoven with research efforts to understand the former. In most cases where a computer has done something that might reasonably be called 'thinking,' the occasion for this activity was an investigation aimed at explaining human thinking.

† [R. Colodny (ed.), *Mind and Cosmos*, Pittsburgh: Pittsburgh University Press, 1966, pp. 3–21].

## 1. HUMAN THINKING

J have defined human thinking as a set of processes occurring in the central nervous system, and *par excellence* in the human central nervous system. What do we know about these processes? It is conventional to refer to our abysmal ignorance of them. It would not surprise me if a word count revealed that the adjective most commonly associated with the phrase 'thought processes' is 'mysterious'.[1]

That adjective is no longer appropriate. Today we have a substantial and rapidly growing body of knowledge about thinking processes, both at the neurological level and at the level of what I shall call elementary information processes. There are still very large gaps in this knowledge – and particularly gaps between the two levels, as I shall point out. But I think it more useful to follow the example of the physical sciences – to describe what we already know before moving on to the frontier of knowledge – than to observe the vow of ignorance that has been traditional in the social sciences.

## 2. NEUROLOGICAL AND INFORMATION PROCESSING EXPLANATIONS

The notion of levels of explanation is familiar from physics, chemistry, and biology. From classical Greek times, if not before, unobservable atomic particles have been hypothesized to explain the observable processes going on in chemical reactions. The atomic hypothesis, quantified by Dalton and his contemporaries at the beginning of the nineteenth century, led to one triumph after another in the regularization, systemization, and explanation of chemical phenomena during the course of that century. Only in our own century did atoms acquire an existence partially independent of their hypothesized participation in chemical reactions. Thus, we had a highly developed explanation of chemical reactions at the level of atomic processes long before the latter processes received explanation and confirmation, in turn, at the level of nuclear physics.[2]

Genetics provides an example of levels of explanation that is even more instructive than atomic theory for our purposes. In its intial introduction as the unit of inheritance, the gene had exactly the same hypothetical status as did the atom in Dalton's theory.[3] If one assumed there were genes with certain properties, one could explain some of the gross macroscopic phenomena of inheritance. The gene hypothesis, in its initial form, did not require the genes to be localized in space or to have any specific existence as chemical or protoplasmic entities. The gene hypothesis was compelling because it regularized, systemized, and explained those macroscopic phenomena.

The gene, like the atom, turned out to be 'realer' than any of those who proposed it had defensible reasons for predicting. Some of the most beautiful achievements of biology in our generation have been the advances toward the explanation of genes in terms of more microscopic and fundamental levels of biochemical process. The great strides toward deciphering the so-called genetic code within the past few years are only the most recent of these achievements.

Two lessons can be drawn from these examples. First, explanation in science is frequently achieved in successive levels. We explain reactions in terms of atoms and molecules, atoms and molecules in terms of the so-called 'elementary' particles. We explain inherited characteristics in terms of genes, genes in terms of organic molecules and their reactions.

Second, the fact that we have succeeded in 'reducing' a first-level explanation by means of a more fundamental explanation of its entities and laws does not make the original explanation otiose or dispensable. It is important and gratifying to know that complex chemical reactions can *in principle* be explained by the laws of quantum mechanics. In practice, of course, the chemist could not get along without an intermediate level of chemical theory, for the in-principle reduction has been carried out *in practice* only in the very simplest cases.[4] Similarly, there is no reason to suppose that direct explanation of inheritance in terms of cellular bio-chemical processes will ever in practice replace explanations in terms of genes. Hierarchy is as essential to the organization and application of knowledge as to its original discovery.

These two examples provide encouraging historical precedents for what is now going on in psychology. Today, the explanation of thinking is progressing at two levels. We are succeeding in explaining ever-widening spheres of human metnal activity in terms of hypothesized 'atoms' called *elementary information processes.* At the same time, we are making substantial progress toward explaining the fundamental electrochemical processes of synaptic action and nerve signal transmission, and the organization of these processes in various parts of the peripheral and central nervous system.[5] If there is a significant difference between these developments in psychology and the corresponding developments that I have described in genetics and chemisty, it is that the work of constructing explanations at the two levels is going on more nearly simultaneously in psychology than it did in the two other instances cited.

Perhaps the greatest gulf of ignorance today is not *within* neurophysiology or *within* information-processing psychology — although there is no lack of work to be done in each of these areas — but *precisely between them.* Although we can give a considerable account of thinking in terms of elementary information processes, we know almost nothing about the specific physiological basis for these information processes. We do not know what the engram is — how and where symbolized information is stored in the brain. We do not know how symbols are compared, copied, or associated. Neurophysiologists boring from one side of the mountain have not yet made contact with information-processing psychologists boring from the other side.

Yet this state of affairs should be no cause for discouragement, especially for the psychologist who is interested in using psychological theory to understand and work with human higher mental processes. He is no worse off, in his theoretical foundations, than chemists were during the period of most vigorous development of their science. He is no worse off than geneticists were during the twenties of this century. And basing his prognostications on those sciences, he can look forward to a future in which the symbols and symbolic processes hypothesized by information-processing theory will be encased in such hard 'reality' as chemistry can provide to entities.

There is one respect in which the information-processing psychologist today is distinctly better off than the geneticist was a generation ago. Belief in the possibility of a mechanistic explanation for the gene hypothesis was then largely an act of faith.[6] Today, although we do not know what protoplasmic processes correspond to the elementary information processes, or how these processes fit into the architecture of the brain, we do have a proof that such processes *can* be provided with mechanistic explanations, for although we do not know how the elementary symbolic processes that are capable of explaining thinking are accomplished physiologically in the brain, we do know how these processes can be accomplished electronically in a digital computer. The possibility of providing a mechanistic explanation for thinking has been demonstrated by programming computers to think.

## 3. AN INFORMATION-PROCESSING EXPLANATION OF THINKING

Thinking is a dynamic process — using that term in its technical sense. Classical dynamical theories, of which Newtonian mechanics is the standard example, have generally taken the form of differential equations. The *state* of the system at any given moment of time is specified by the values of a set of variables, the state variables, at that moment. Then the differential equations determine how the state variables will change; they predict the state of the system at the 'next' moment as a function of the present state.[7]

Before a system can be described in differential equations of the classical sort, a set of state variables must be discovered. One of the difficulties that has plagued psychology is that no satisfactory way has been found for characterizing thought processes in terms of the kinds of state variables that are suitable for classical differential equations. That difficulty has now been bypassed with the invention of information-processing languages, a special class of computer programming languages, whose variables are not numbers but symbolic structures.[8]

A computer program is quite analogous, at an abstract level, to a system of differential equations (more precisely, of difference equations). Given the memory contents of the computer at any given moment of time (these characterizing its state at that moment), the program determines how the memory contents will be at the end of the cycle. Thus, a computer program can be used as a theory of a dynamic system in exactly the same way as can a set of differential equations. The basic methodological problems of theory construction and theory testing are identical in the two cases. The theory is tested by providing a specific set of intial and boundary conditions for the system, using the equations to predict the resulting time path, and comparing this predicted path with the actual path of the system.

The advantage of an information-processing language over classical mathematical languages for formulating a theory of thinking is that an information-processing language takes symbolic structures rather than numbers as its variables. Since thinking processes are processes for manipulating symbols and structures of symbols (Figure 1), these processes can be represented directly, without requiring elaborate translations or scaling techniques, in an information-processing language.

Let us make this point more specific by considering a particular thinking task.[9] Suppose that a human subject in the psychological laboratory is confronted with a sequence of symbols – ABMCDMEFM, say – and asked to contine it. After a few moments, he will very likely give the continuation GHMIJM, and so on. Now one way in which he might accomplish this – and, from the available evidence, the way in which most subjects do accomplish it – is the following:

1. He scans the original list looking for repetitions of identical symbols, discovering that each third symbol is M.

2. He constructs a symbolic structure in memory that represents the

A ⟶ B ⟶ M ⟶ C ⟶ D ⟶ M

A *list*. Each item is associated with the previous one by the relation of *next* ( → ).

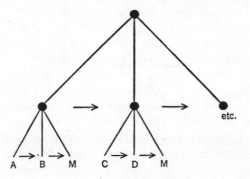

A *tree*, or list of lists. Each item on the main list is itself a list (in this case, a list of three items).

**Fig.** 1.    Some simple symbol structures.

periodicity and the recurrence of the M. In order to talk about this structure, let us represent it as (**M), where the asterisks stand for unspecified symbols. Of course, we should not suppose that the symbolic structure in memory 'looks' like this sequence in any literal sense, but we can use the sequence in our theory as a fairly straightforward representation of the structure in memory.

3. Now the subject again scans the original list to see whether there are consistent relations between pairs of symbols that occupy corresponding positions in different periods of the sequence. We may think of him as now representing the given sequence thus: ABM CDM EFM, so that A, C, and E are in the first positions in their respective periods, and B, D, and F in the second positions. The relations he searches for are relations of *identity* and of *next on a familiar alphabet* (Figure 2). In the example before us, he will discover that the second symbol in each period is next to the first symbol, in the English alphabet, and that the first symbol in each period is next to the second symbol in the preceding period. These relations, then, provide a general description of the sequence, as well as a means for extrapolating it. Leaving out details, we might describe the sequence symbolically as (nnM), where 'n' stands for 'next on the English alphabet'. Given one period of the

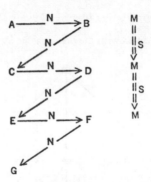

Fig. 2.    A *pattern*. Each triad (list) can be generated from the previous one by using the relations of next ( — — ⟩ ) and same ( = = ⟩ ) on the English alphabet.

sequence, the subject can now construct an indefinite number of the following periods.

It is easy to write a program in an information-processing language that explains this dynamic process in terms of elementary information processes. We need processes for copying symbols, for constructing compound symbols (lists and 'trees') from simple symbols, for comparing symbols for identity, for finding the next symbol on a list, and a few others.

A review of the steps that the subjects were described as taking in the illustrative example above shows that these processes are essentially the ones mentioned. In step 1, the original list of symbols could be scanned by a process for finding the *next* symbol on a list. The repetitions of the letter M could be detected by a process for comparing symbols for identity. Step 2 could be carried out by a process for constructing compound symbols – in this case, the list **M. Step 3 again calls for processes that compare symbols for identity and find the next symbol on a list, and processes that construct the final pattern nnM from the incomplete pattern **M. The extrapolation of the sequence, finally, calls for applications of the same kinds of processes, under the control of the pattern.

Thus, the program constructed from these processes, and organized to carry out the steps 1 through 3, provides an explanation of how humans detect the patterns in sequences like the one illustrated, how they represent such patterns in memory, and how they use the pattern representations to extrapolate the sequences. It is a theory of human information processing in the series generation task.

This theory has been tested by programming a computer to behave in the manner described and examining the behavior of the computer when it is given the same series completion tasks that were given to the human subjects. The predictions of the theory − that is, the output of the computer under these conditions − can be compared directly with the human behavior. No mathematization of the human behavior is required. One gross test is to check whether the problems the program solves are the same ones that were solved by the largest number of human subjects. Much more specific tests − comparison, for example, of the specific errors made by program and subjects − are possible. With the evidence available to date, the theory has given a fairly good account of itself.

The information-processing explanation of series completion would have only rather narrow interest if it were not for the fact that the same small set of processes that represents the core of this explanation also turns up in a central role in the information-processing theories that have been devised to explain human thinking in quite different contexts. In the first place, the program for the series completion task can be generalized without too much difficulty to apply to a much wider range of pattern recognizing tasks:

1. With a few additions (primarily of the numerical operations of addition, subtraction, multiplication, and division), it will handle number series − e.g., 1 4 9 16 25 . . .

2. It can be extended to various kinds of analogy tasks − e.g. '$a$ is to $c$ as $r$ is to ──?' or 'a rectangle is to a square as a parallelogram is to a ────?'

Similar programs, employing the same elementary information processes, have had considerable success in explaining subjects' behavior in partial reinforcement experiments.[10]

Finally, quite distinct information-processing programs which, however, employ essentially the same elementary processes, explain a considerable number of other kinds of human thinking: among them, discovering proofs for theorems in logic, geometry, and trigonometry, playing chess and bridge, harmonizing a musical theme, making investment decisions, memorizing nonsense syllables, or learning foreign language vocabulary.[11]

On the basis of experience with these theories, it now appears highly probable that elementary processes like the ones described, operating on symbols and structures of symbols (that is, lists and trees of symbols), are the fundamental means by which human thinking is accomplished. Because the theories take the form of programs in information-processing languages, and because we can program digital computers to execute such programs, we have incontrovertible evidence that these processes are *sufficient* to account for performance of the kinds of tasks that have been mentioned. And because the computers so programmed do prove theorems, play games, compose music, make investment decisions, and memorize, the theories provide examples of thinking by computers that, from the evidence at hand, closely parallel some kinds of thinking by human beings.[1 2]

## 4. SOME CHARACTERISTICS OF THINKING PROCESSES

What are some of the generalizations about thinking that have emerged from the information-processing theories? It will not be necessary, in stating these generalizations, to distinguish particularly between human thinking and computer thinking, because the computer thinking referred to occurs in the context of programs designed to simulate human thinking as closely as possible. The generalizations apply to both.

One qualification should be made, however. Existing information-processing theories of thinking undoubtedly fall far short of covering the whole range of thinking activities in man. It is not just that the present theories are only approximately correct. Apart from limits on their correctness in explaining the ranges of behavior to which they apply, much cognitive behavior still lies beyond their scope.

The first generalization – that all thinking processes are constructed out of a small set of elementary information processes – has already been sufficiently stressed. Nothing has been said about the organization of these processes, the way in which they are put together in programs. Two additional generalizations apply here:

1. The processes are organized hierachically.[1 3] A sequence of elementary processes can be combined into a compound process. Sequences of compound and elementary processes can be combined again into still more elaborate and complex processes, and so on. If there is a limit on the number of levels in such a hierachy, experimentation thus far has not revealed that limit – or even indicated that it exists.

In the example of the sequence completion program, the three major program steps represent compound processes organized from elementary ones. The first step determines the periodicity of the sequence; the second step constructs an incomplete representation of the pattern; the third step completes the representation. These three 'subroutines', to use computer terminology, are combined into the complete pattern-detection process. The pattern-detection process, in turn, is combined with the extrapolation process in order to carry out the experimental task – continuing the series.

2. The processes are executed serially. Implicit in the principal information-processing theories that have been constructed is the hypothesis that the central nervous system can only do one or a few things at a time. 'At a time' means in an interval of a few milliseconds.

Because existing digital computers are serially organized devices, it is simplest to construct information-processing theories that operate serially.[14] However, there is considerable evidence that the human system is organized in the same way — or at least that large parts of it are. The observably narrow limits on span of human attention are one symptom of the serial organization of thinking. There exists also some contrary evidence — for example, the ability of a person to hear his own name softly spoken even when he is attending to something else. On balance, however, it does not appear inaccurate to describe thinking as essentially a serial process.

The generalizations stated thus far — that thinking is a hierarchically organized, serially executed symbol-manipulating process — apply to virtually all the information-processing theories that have been constructed to date. There are several additional important generalizations that refer more specifically to the kinds of thinking activities called 'problem solving'.

1. Problem solving involves a highly selective trial-and-error search of solution possibilities. The terms 'highly selective: and 'trial and error' may seem contradictory. They are not. Problem-solving searches require trial and error in that they generally do not go directly to the solution without traversing and retracing some blind alleys — sometimes many, sometimes few. When a person solves a problem without any backtracking whatsoever, we are apt to deny that he needed to think at all. We say, 'He knew the answer', or 'he didn't have to think; he did it by rote.'

Problem-solving searches are selective in that they generally explore only a miniscule fraction of the total (and usually immense) number of possibilities. In most cases of interest, the selection of the paths to be searched is not governed by foolproof, systematic procedures, but by rules of thumb we call *heuristics*.

In a few cases a good deal is known about the size of the problem space, about the heuristics that are used to explore it selectively, and about the quantitative reduction in search that these heuristics achieve.[15] The game of chess is one such case. It is known that a player typically has freedom to choose among about twenty or thirty legal moves. To each of these, the opponent may have a similar number of replies. Thus, the tree of possible game continuations branches geometrically nearly a thousand-fold for a single

set of move possibilities and their replies. A complete analysis of continuations two moves deep would typically require the exploration of nearly one
million branches; three moves deep, one billion, and so on.

It is now pretty well established that experienced chess players, even in
difficult middle-game postions or in exploring deep combinations, seldom
examine as many as one hundred continuations. The number examined
appears to be almost independent of the player's skill. What distinguishes very
good players from less good players is not the amount of exploration they do,
but their relative success in identifying the significant continuations to be
explored — the selective power of their heuristics.

A detailed investigation of this question has been made for mating
combinations — sequences of moves that force a checkmate.[16] An information-processing program has been written that examines continuations in
potential mating positions very selectively, using heuristics gleaned from the
chess literature and chess experience. This program is able to find
combinations as many as eight or more moves deep by examining far fewer
than one hundred branches of the game tree. The program, examined in
comparison with records of historical chess games, appears to capture
successfully some of the main heuristics that are actually used by strong
players in complex mating positions.

The positions to which the mating combinations program is relevant allow
the players less freedom than many other chess positions, and our previous
estimate of the branching rate of the game tree — a thousand-fold per
move — is probably too high when applied to them. Let us take one hundred
as a more conservative estimate. With this branching rate, *exhaustive*
exploration of an eight-move combination would mean examing $10^{16}$
positions! A program that examines only one hundred is therefore more
efficient by a factor of $10^{14}$ — one hundred thousand billion — than a
random search program that tries all possibilities.

Similar calculations have been made for the power of the heuristics in some
of the theorem-proving programs, with the finding again, of gain factors of
orders of magnitude similar to those in chess.

2. Means-end analysis is one of the basic heuristics in human problem
solving.[17] Means-end analysis, as it appears in human behavior, and as its is
formalized in information-processing theories of problem solving, is organized
somewhat as follows:

(a) The present situation is compared with the desired situation (problem
goal), and one or more *differences* between them noticed. (E.g., 'I have a
board five feet long; I want a two-foot length; there is a difference in length.')

(b) Memory is searched for an *operator* or operators associated with one of the differences that has been detected. By 'operator' is meant some process that will change the present situation. (E.g., 'sawing', 'planing', 'drilling'.) Operators become associated with particular differences as a result of experiences that show that these operators are capable of reducing or eliminating the differences in question. (E.g., 'Sawing changes lengths.')

(c) An attempt is made to apply the operator to change the present situation. Sometimes, in the course of making the attempt, it is discovered that the operator cannot be applied until some other aspect of the situation has been altered. (E.g., 'A board must be held fast in order to saw it.') In these cases a new goal of type (a) may be set up, with satisfaction of the conditions for applying the operator as the 'desired situation'. (E.g., 'Hold the board fast.')

Examination of a large number of human protocols in problem-solving situations reveals that the largest part of the activity is means-end analysis. Considerable success in simulating such problem-solving behaviour has been achieved in an information-processing program called the General Problem Solver.

Means-end analysis is a special case of a selective heuristic. By identifying the specific differences between the present and desired situation, it becomes unnecessary to consider all possible ways in which the situation might be changed. Only those operations need be examined that are relevant (at least potentially, on the basis of past experience) to the actual differences that exist. When a tailor alters a suit, he obtains at the fitting, not only the qualitative nature of the difference – whether the sleeves are too short or long – but the precise amount of the alteration that is needed. He thereby achieves a laudable reduction in the amount of trial and error that is required to make the suit fit.

Intermingled with means-end analysis in problem solving are heuristics that may be called *planning*.[18] Planning consists in omitting some of the detail of the actual problem by abstracting its essential features, solving the simplified problem, then using the solution of the simplified problem as a guide, or plan, for the solution of the full problem. Again, it can be shown quantitatively that planning can increase speed of solution in favorable circumstances by many orders of magnitude. Speaking generally, the larger the number of steps in the complete problem solution, the greater the increase in efficiency achievable through planning.

3. Another heuristic of wide applicability is the procedure of factoring a problem into subproblems, and tackling first the subproblems containing the

smallest number of 'unknowns'. In this way the number of combinations of possible solutions that have to be examined is greatly reduced. Consider, for example, puzzles of the following kind:

$$
\begin{array}{r}
D\,O\,N\,A\,L\,D \\
+\ G\,E\,R\,A\,L\,D \\
\hline
R\,O\,B\,E\,R\,T
\end{array}
$$

The problem task is to substitute distinct digits – from 0 to 9 – for distinct letters in such a way that the resulting expression will be a correct example of addition. The hint is given that $D = 5$.[19]

Only one unknown now remains in the last column, and this is immediately solved to give $T = 0$, with a carry to the fifth column. Also, the value 5 for $D$ can be substituted in the first column. Now, subjects generally turn their attentions to columns two, four, or five, since each of these has a duplication of letters, hence, only two unknowns each. They soon discover that $E = 9$, and that $R$ must be an odd number greater than 5, hence $R = 7$. The process is continued until the answer is obtained:

$$
\begin{array}{r}
526485 \\
+197485 \\
\hline
723970
\end{array}
$$

The significant point about the example is that successful subjects almost never explore at random or consider possible combinations of digits that might 'work'. They carry through the solution with a minimum of combinations by always working at points where there are only a few unknowns to be determined.

4. In some very well-structured problem domains, formal procedures, usually called algorithms, are available for finding systematically the solution that is best or maximal by some criterion. Elementary calculus provides an example of a simple algorithm of this kind: to find the maximum of a function, take the first derivative, set it equal to zero, and solve the resulting equation.

In most problem-solving domains of everyday life, however, and even in many formal ones, like chess, no such algorithm has been discovered. A modest number of possible solutions can be considered, and there is no way of telling whether a given solution is the best, since many other possibilities must, perforce, go unexamined. In these domains, human problem solvers and the computer programs that simulate them do not search for the 'best' solution. but for a solution that is 'good enough' by some criterion. Heuristics that proceed on this basis are sometimes called 'satisficing' heuristics.[20]

Suppose, for example, that someone wishes to sell a house. He does not know exactly how much he can get for it, but he can make an estimate. If bids come in close to this figure, he holds to it; if they do not, he gradually reduces it. When a bid comes in that meets the revised figure, he accepts it.

The criterion of 'good enough' that adjusts in this way is called an *aspiration level*. Satisficing behavior that makes use of aspiration levels is prominent in the selection of chess moves. We have already seen that there is no practical possibility of evaluating all possible moves. Instead, the player can form a preliminary estimate of the value of his position and look for a move that meets this estimate. As his search continues, if he does not find such a move, he revises the estimate downward. Satisficing heuristics are widely applicable and widely applied in problem domains where the number of possible solutions is far too great to permit exhaustive search and where an efficient maximizing algorithm is not available.

## 5. MOTIVATION AND EMOTION IN THINKING

Satisficing heuristics bring us to a consideration of the relation between thinking processes and those aspects of human behavior that we call motivation and emotion. Thinking is activity directed toward goals, and as we have just seen, involves considerations of whether a proposed solution is the best, or is good enough, in terms of a criterion. If the level of aspiration is very high, search for a satisfactory solution will be more prolonged than if it is low. The thinking program will also contain parameters, or constants, that determine how long exploration will continue in a particular direction and when it will turn to a new direction. (E.g., 'If not successful in five minutes, try something else.') It may contain procedures to determine which of several alternative subproblems will be explored next (the 'minimize-unknowns' heuristic is an example of this).

Thus, thinking programs, whether for human or cumputer, contain motivational components.[21] This is not to say that the aspects of motivation that have been represented in information-processing theories to date come anywhere near to representing the totality of motivational factors in human behavior. Ulric Neisser has pointed out that, as compared with human behavior in the large, the behavior predicted by existing information-processing theories is exceedingly single-minded, stubborn, but otherwise unemotional.[22] He observes that human beings are capable of turning from one activity to another and of being interrupted in an activity.

Can information-processing theories be broadened to encompass the motivational and emotional mechanisms we observe in human behavior? Although there has been little concrete progress in this direction, there have been some speculations suggesting the directions that progress might take.

Imagine a computer with a rather large memory — a combination of magnetic core and tape, say — that contains, among others, the general problem-solving program augmented by programs for specific tasks like playing chess, detecting serial patterns, solving differential equations, inverting matrices, calculating correlation coefficients, and so on. Each job that is input to the computer is examined and assigned a priority (on some basis that need not concern us) that gradually changes with the length of time the job has been waiting to be processed. When the priority of a job reaches a sufficiently high level, the job that is currently being processed is interrupted and replaced by the high priority job.

Such a computer (and, of course, systems organized in this general way are already in existence) would exhibit, in its behavior, motivation and a set of values. If we noticed that it gave high priorities to matrix inversions, we would say that this was an activity it preferred. Suppose we also noticed that when certain brief new jobs were input, it immediately interrupted what it was doing to undertake one of the new tasks before returning to the original one. We might say that it was easily distracted, or even that it was exhibiting emotion.

I do not propose here to develop in detail the idea that the core of the behavior we call emotional derives from a mechanism for interrupting the ongoing stream of activity. However, this notion is consistent with a good deal of empirical evidence about the nature of emotion and provides an interesting avenue of exploration into the relation of emotion to cognitive activity. It suggests that we shall not be able to write programs for computers that allow them to respond flexibly to a variety of demands, some with real-time priorities, without thereby creating a system that, in a human, we would say exhibited emotion.

## 6. CONCLUSION

In the foregoing I have tried to describe some of the general characteristics of human thinking, as we know them from constructing and testing information-processing theories. These are also, of course, the characteristics of computer thinking, since most computers that think, think in simulation of man.

I have not tried to answer the standard objections that 'of course' computers do not think at all. To most of these objections, very satisfactory answers have been given by others – the delightful article by Alan Turing, for example, and the paper by Prof. J. J. C Smart.[23] The best answers, probably, are given by the structure of the programs themselves that embody our information-processing theories of human thinking.

I cannot forebear, however, a brief comment on one of the commonest objections: that computers do only what they are programmed to do. The assertion is undoubtedly true, but it does not imply that computers cannot think. That conclusion would only follow if it were true that human beings, when they are thinking, do *not* do what they are programmed to do. The progress of information-processing theories of human thinking requires a denial of this latter premise. The processes of human thinking, in fact, can be very effectively stated in the form of programs. We do not know what physiological mechanisms store these programs in the brain and execute them; but we have as much reason to believe there are such mechanisms as earlier generations had to believe that there are mechanisms underlying the valences of atoms and the control of heredity by genes.

A human being is able to think because, by biological inheritance and exposure to a stream of experience in the external world, he has acquired a program that is effective for guiding thought processes. If we wish to seek an efficient cause for his behavior, it lies in that program in its interaction with ongoing stimuli.

We know a great deal today about the structure and content of human thinking programs. We know very little about which parts of these programs are inherited and which parts are acquired. We know little about the biological substrate for the programs. We know far less than we need to know about how thinking programs can be modified and improved through education and training. Computers, programmed to simulate human thinking, continue to offer a powerful research tool in investigating these unanswered questions. And programs in information-processing languages offer powerful means for expressing our theories of human thought processes.

## NOTES

*The work on which this chapter is based was supported in part by a grant from the Carnegie Corporation and in part by Research Grant MH-07722–01 from the National Institutes of Health. Several of my examples are drawn from joint work with K. Kotovsky, P. A. Simon, and L. W. Gregg. My debts to Allen Newell are too numerous to acknowledge in detail. To all of these, I give thanks and offer absolution for the particular conclusions reached here, which are my own.

[1] A typical example is Edna Heidbreder's concluding comment in her article on 'Thinking' in the 1960 Encyclopedia Brittanica: "Thinking remains one of the unsolved problems of psychology."

[2] It might be mentioned that although there was much resistance to the atomic hypothesis through the first two-thirds of the nineteenth century, the grounds for this resistance were not what a radical operationalist might suppose. There were few objections to atoms because of their hypothetical character — only a few philosophers of science like Mach, Poincaré, and Russell, anachronistically stressed this toward the end of the century. The main objection was to the neglect of the 'qualities', like color, in a theory that took mass as the significant atomic property. The sceptics were humanists, not operationalists. See Stephen Toulmin and June Goodfield, *The Architecture of Matter* (New York: Harper & Row, 1962), pp. 234–37, 263–68; or *Harvard Case Histories in Experimental Science,* ed. by James B. Conant and Leonard K. Nash, Vol. I, 215–321 (1950).

[3] Toulmin and Goodfield, pp. 365–68.

[4] Compare Kekulé's prescient observation, "Should the progress of science lead to a theory of the constitution of chemical atoms, it would make but little alteration in chemistry itself. The chemical atoms will always remain the chemical unit . . " (Quoted by Toulmin and Goodfield, p. 265.) 'Little alteration' sounds too strong in the light of modern physical chemistry, but the import of the statement, that there is a distinct 'chemical' level, is still substantially correct.

[5] Symbolic of this progress was the award of the 1963 Nobel Prize in Physiology and Medicine to Eccles, to Hodgkin, and to Huxley for their work on transmission of neural signals. See the brief appreciation of this work, by M. G. F. Fuortes, in *Science* 142, 468–70 (1963).

[6] See Note 3 above.

[7] Of course 'next' must be put in quotation marks since the differential equations describe the changes in the limit as the time interval is taken shorter and shorter.

[8] Allen Newell *et al., IPL-V Programmers' Reference Manual* (New York: Prentice-Hall, 2d ed.. 1964).

[9] The analysis here is based on H. A. Simon and K. Kotovsky, 'Human Acquistion of Concepts for Serial Patterns', *Psychological Review* 70, 534–46 (1963). For similar theories applied to closely related tasks, see J. Feldman, F. Tonge, and H. Kanter, 'Empirical Explorations of a Hypothesis-Testing Model of Binary Choice Behavior', in *Symposium on Simulation Models*, ed. by Hoggatt and Balderston (Cincinnati: South-Western Publishing, 1963), pp. 55–100; and K. R. Laughery and L. W. Gregg, 'Simulation of Human Problem-Solving Behavior,' *Psychometrika* 27, 265–82 (1962).

[10] In the partial reinforcement experiment, the subject is asked to predict whether the next stimulus in a series will be a 'plus' or 'minus'. The sequence is in fact random, each symbol having a certain probability of occurring. Subjects, however, typically search for patterns: 'a run of plusses', 'an alternation of plus and minus', or the like. See the chapter by J. Feldman in *Computers and Thought*, Feigenbaum and Feldman (eds.), (New York: McGraw-Hill, 1964).

[11] For a survey of these theories see A. Newell and H. A. Simon, 'Computers in Psychology', *Handbook of Mathematical Psychology,* ed. by Luce, Bush, and Galanter (New York: Wiley, 1963), I, and the references therein.

[12] See references in 'Computers in Psychology', to the work of Hiller and Isaacson on musical composition, Clarkson on investment decisions, and Feigenbaum and Simon on memorizing.

[13] See H. A. Simon, 'The Architecture of Complexity', *Proceedings of the American Philosophical Society* 106, 467–82 (1962), Noam Chomsky, *Syntactic Structures* (The

Hague: Mouton, 1957); and Toulmin and Goodfield, pp. 301–02. See also Section 4 of this volume.

[14] For reasons both of economics and organizational simplicity, a typical computer has only a few 'active' memory locations (sometimes called accumulators) where processing can be carried out. Information is brought in from 'passive' storage locations, processed, then returned to storage. Thus, the steps involved in adding the number in storage location A to the number in storage B and storing the sum in C might be the following: (1) copy contents of A into accumulator, (2) add contents of B to contents of accumulator, (3) store contents of accumulator in C. With only one or a few active accumulators, the action of such a system is necessarily serial rather than parallel. Increasing the number of accumulators is expensive; it also creates an extremely difficult problem of co-ordinating their activity.

[15] For some quantitative analysis, see A. Newell, J. C. Shaw, and H. A. Simon, 'The Processes of Creative Thinking', *Contemporary Approaches to Creative Thinking*, ed. by Gruber, Terrell, Wertheimer (New York: Atherton Press, 1962), Chapter 3; and H. A. Simon, and P. A. Simon, 'Trial and Error Search in Solving Difficult Problems: Evidence from the Game of Chess', *Behavioral Science* 7, 425–29 (1962). In general, see A. Newell and H. A. Simon, *Human Problem Solving*, (Englewood Cliffs, N.J.: Prentice-Hall, 1972).

[16] Simon and Simon, *op. cit.*

[17] The organization of thinking around means-end analysis has been extensively explored with a program called the General Problem Solver (GPS). Descriptions of GPS have been published in several places, including *Human Problem Solving, op. cit.*

[18] The planning heuristic is described briefly in 'The Processes of Creative Thinking', pp. 91–96.

[19] Data on the behavior of subjects performing the Donald-Gerald task will be found in Sir Frederic Bartlett, *Thinking* (New York: Basic Books, 1958), Chapter 4.

[20] A discussion of satisficing heuristics and aspiration levels will be found in H. A. Simon, *Models of Man* (New York: Wiley, 1957), Introduction to Part IV and Chapters 14 and 15.

[21] D. W. Taylor, 'Toward an Information-Processing Theory of Motivation', *Nebraska Symposium on Motivation,* ed. by Jones (Lincoln: Univ. of Nebraska Press, 1960); Walter R. Reitman, 'Personality as a Problem-Solving Coalition', and Silvan S. Tomkins, 'Simulation of Personality', *Computer Simulation of Personality,* ed. by Tomkins and Messick (New York: Wiley, 1963).

[22] Ulric Neisser, 'The Imitation of Man by Machine', *Science* 139, 193–97 (1963).

[23] A. M. Turing, 'Computing Machinery and Intelligence', *Mind* 59, 433–60. (1950), reprinted in *The World of Mathematics,* ed. by James R. Newman (New York: Simon & Schuster, 1956), IV, and in Feigenbaum and Feldman, *op. cit.*: J. C. C. Smart, 'Gödel's Theorem, Church's Theorem, and Mechanism', *Synthèse* 13, 105–10 (June 1961).

# SCIENTIFIC DISCOVERY AND THE PSYCHOLOGY OF PROBLEM SOLVING† *

> The very fact that the totality of our sense experiences is such that by means of thinking (operations with concepts, and the creation and use of definite functional relations between them, and the coordination of sense experiences to these concepts) it can be put in order, this fact is one which leaves us in awe, but which we shall never understand. One may say "the eternal mystery of the world is its comprehensibility." It is one of the great realizations of Immanuel Kant that the setting up of a real external world would be senseless without this comprehensibility.
>
> Albert Einstein, *Out of My Later Years*

In the previous chapter a theory of human problem solving was put forward with references to some of the evidence for its validity. The theory has been formalized and tested by incorporating it in programs for digital computers and studying the behavior of these programs when they are confronted with problem-solving tasks.

The thesis of the present chapter is that scientific discovery is a form of problem solving, and that the processes whereby science is carried on can be explained in the terms that have been used to explain the processes of problem solving. In particular, I shall undertake to show how the theory of problem solving described in the previous chapter can account for some of the principal reported phenomena of scientific discovery.

For a description of these phenomena, the analysis will draw heavily upon previous published accounts. Discussions of scientific discovery have always been highly anecdotal, most of our specific information on the subject deriving from reports of specific examples, recorded in some instances by historians and philosophers of science, in some instances by psychologists, but often by the discoverers themselves. The classics in the latter category are Henri Poincaré's celebrated lecture, translated as 'Mathematical Creation' (New York: The Science Press, 1913), and the delightful essay by Jacques

† [R. Colodny (ed.), *Mind and Cosmos*, Pittsburgh: University of Pittsburgh Press, 1966, pp. 22–40].

Hadamard, *The Psychology of Invention in the Mathematical Field* (Princeton: Princeton Univ. Press, 1945). Chapter 10 of Max Wertheimer's *Productive Thinking* (New York: Harper & Row, enlarged ed., 1959) reports a series of interviews with Albert Einstein on the course of events that led to the invention of the theory of special relativity.

The literature on the topic produced by philosophers of science is substantial, but has been for purposes of this analysis, on the whole, less useful. (I will mention two important exceptions in a moment.) The reason is that philosophers of science tend to address themselves to the normative more than to the descriptive aspects of scientific methodology. They are more concerned with how scientists *ought to* proceed, in order to conform with certain conceptions of logic, than with how they *do* proceed. Notions of how they ought to proceed focus primarily on the problem of induction: on how generalizations might validly arise from data on particulars and on the degree to which a corpus of data logically confirms a generalization. These are interesting questions of philosophy, but they turn out to have relatively little relation to the actual behavior of scientists – and perhaps less normative value than has been supposed.

In the past few years, two philosopher-historians of science, both originally trained in physics, have made particularly significant contributions to the psychology and sociology of scientific discovery. Both have been quite explicit in distinguishing the processes of discovery from the traditional canons of 'sound' scientific method. I shall make considerable use of their work and ideas. One of these men, Norwood Russell Hanson, has set forth his views most extensively in *Patterns of Discovery* (Cambridge: Cambridge University Press, 1958). The other, Thomas S. Kuhn, has produced an original and stimulating account of *The Structure of Scientific Revolutions* (Chicago: University of Chicago Press, 1962).

To explain scientific discovery is to describe a set of processes that is sufficient – and *just* sufficient – to account for the amounts and directions of scientific progress that have actually occurred. For a variety of reasons, perhaps best understood by psychoanalysis, when we talk or write about scientific discovery, we tend to dwell lovingly on the great names and the great events – Galileo and uniform acceleration, Newton and universal gravitation, Einstein and relativity, and so on.[1] We insist that a theory of discovery postulate processes sufficiently powerful to produce these events. It is right to so insist, but we must not forget how rare such events are, and we must not postulate processes so powerful that they predict a discovery of first magnitude as a daily matter.

On the contrary, for each such event there is an investment of thousands of man-years of investigation by hundreds of talented and hard-working scientists. This particular slot machine produces many stiff arms for every jackpot. At the same time that we explain how Schrödinger and Heisenberg, in 1926, came to quantum mechanics, we must explain why Planck, Bohr, Einstein, de Broglie, and other men of comparable ability struggled for the preceding twenty years *without* completing this discovery. Scientific discovery is a rare event; a theory to explain it must predict innumerable failures for every success.

The great events do not, of course, represent sudden leaps forward, unrelated to previous exploration. While modern quantum mechanics clearly did not exist in 1924, and clearly did in 1926, the approach to it was gradual and steady, involving all the illustrious scientists mentioned in the previous paragraph and many hundreds more. And the particular advance that we identify as 'the discovery' was followed by many man-years of exploitation and consolidation, just as it was preceded by man-years of exploration and anticipation. The central point remains: scientific discovery, when viewed in detail, is an excruciatingly slow and painful process.

Related to the rarity of great discoveries – and relevant to our understanding of the process – is the rarity of great discoverers. If there are only a few great discoveries, and if a great discoverer is someone who makes a great discovery, then such persons must be rare by definition. But there is a substantive question too. Does science depend, for its major progress, upon heroes who have faculties not possessed by journeymen scientists? Or are the men whose names we associate with the great discoveries just the lucky ones – those who had their hands on the lever at the precise moment when the jackpot showered its rewards.

A case could be made for either view, and my own hunch is that the truth lies somewhere between. If it is luck, a few men in each generation appear more skillful in wooing the goddess than are their fellows. On the other hand, I have encountered no evidence that there exist significant differences between the processes that great scientists use in achieving their discoveries and the processes used by those men we regard merely as 'good' scientists.

The theory of scientific discovery I propose to set forth rests on the hypothesis that there are no qualitative differences between the *processes* of revolutionary science and of normal science, between work of high creativity and journeyman work. I shall not claim that the case can be proven conclusively. My main evidence will be data indicating that the processes that show up in relatively simple and humdrum forms of human problem solving are also the ones that show up when great scientists try to describe how they do their work. How convincing the evidence is can better be judged at the end of the chapter.

Let us return, then, to the problem-solving theory proposed in the last chapter and confront that theory with the recorded phenomena of scientific discovery.

The problem-solving theory asserted that thinking is an organization of elementary information processes, organized hierarchically and executed serially. In overall organization, the processes exhibit large amounts of highly selective trial-and-error search using rules of thumb, or heuristics, as bases for their selectivity. Among the prominent heuristic schemes are means-end analysis, planning and abstraction, factorization, and satisficing. Our task is to show how a system with these characteristics can behave like a scientist.

## 1. SELECTIVE TRIAL-AND-ERROR SEARCH

The prominence of selective trial-and-error processes in accounts of scientific discovery makes an extended discussion of this phenomenon unnecessary.[2] Examples of such accounts that come immediately to mind, out of a multitude that could be cited, are Hanson's analyis of the development of Kepler's theories (*Patterns of Discovery*, pp. 73–84), and Wertheimer's report of his conversations with Einstein on the theory of special relativity (*Productive Thinking*, Chapter 10).

Wertheimer's book is particularly interesting in this connection, because he can be regarded as a hostile witness. As a Gestaltist he maintains the greatest skepticism about the processes, like trial-and-error, postulated by associationists to account for problem solving. In fact, he almost never uses the phrase 'trial and error' without prefixing the adjective 'blind'. His chapter certainly provides no evidence that Einstein engaged in 'random' search. It does provide ample evidence that he made many attempts at solutions that failed — that a great deal of *selective* trial and error took place over the decade or more during which Einstein struggled with the problem of the velocity of light.

Hadamard (*The Psychology of Invention in the Mathematical Field*, p. 48) has expressed the point metaphorically: "It is well known that good hunting cartridges are those which have a proper scattering. If this scattering is too wide, it is useless to aim; but if it is too narrow, you have too many chances to miss your game by a line. I see quite similar circumstances in our subject."

The theory and empirical explorations described above call for precisely this kind of mixture of search and aim. Except where an algorithm is available — that is, in areas that are already well structured, hence well behind the frontiers of discovery — some amount of trial and error is essential. On the other hand, the sizes of the problem spaces encountered even in relatively simple laboratory tasks show that without powerful heuristics, principles of selectivity, the search could only rarely reach its object.

The theory has a further implication. Evidences of trial and error should be most prominent in those areas of problem solving where the heuristics are least powerful, least adequate to narrow down the problem space. Hence, the paths leading to discoveries we would call creative might be expected to provide even more visible evidences of trial and error than those leading to relatively routine discoveries. We have no quantitative evidence to test this prediction. Moreover, it rests implicitly on a somewhat doubtful *ceteris paribus* assumption: that the heuristics of persons who make creative discoveries are no more powerful than those of their contemporaries who do not.

Let us examine the question more closely. One characteristic of a discovery that marks it as creative is its unexpectedness. To say that it is 'surprising' or 'unexpected' is to say that it would not readily be chanced upon. But chanced upon by whom? Presumably by scientists working at the time of the discovery. Since it was, by definition, chanced upon or found by the actual discoverer, we must conclude (1) that he was lucky, (2) that he searched longer and harder than his contemporaries, or (3) that he had more powerful selective heuristics than they did. The most plausible hypothesis is that all three conditions are generally met, in varying proportions. Of these three conditions conducive to discovery, the first, luck, implies nothing about the amount of trial and error, or its selectivity.[3] To the extent that the second condition, persistence, is present, trial-and-error search should be prominently visible. If the third condition, superior heuristics, is chiefly responsible for the discovery, no more trial-and-error search will be present than would appear normal in cases of less creative activity.

The evidences of a high degree of persistence in pursuing fundamental problems are numerous in the biographies of creative scientists. Persistence does not always mean continual conscious preoccupation with the problem, or orderly, organized pursuit, but concern with the problem over a considerable period of years, indicated by recurrent attention to it. One could conjecture that while the biographies of 'journeyman' scientists might reveal persistent attention to a problem *area* over comparable periods of time, the activity would more likely than in the case of highly creative scientists represent attacks upon, and solutions of, a whole series of relatively well-structured problems within the general area (e.g., determinations of structures of a number of molecules, or of the parameters of a system under a range of experimental conditions). However, the data on this point remain to be gathered.

A good deal less conjectural is the hypothesis that superior problem solvers in a particular area have more powerful heuristics and that they will produce adequate solutions with less search, or better solutions with equivalent search as compared with less competent persons. A. de Groot, for example, compared the searches of grandmasters and ordinary chess players for a good move in a middle-game position. Both classes of players searched for about the same length of time (which was partly an artifact of the laboratory situation), and examined approximately the same number of branches of the game tree. In fact, it was impossible to distinguish, from the statistics of the search, between the grandmasters and the ordinary players. They were easily distinguished by one datum, however: In the particular position examined, all five grandmasters attained better solutions to the problem (chose moves that could be shown to be objectively better) than any of the solutions attained by the ordinary players. While the grandmasters did not engage in more search than the others, their superior selective heuristics allowed them to search more significant and relevant parts of the game tree.[4]

Whence do the superior heuristics, the secret weapons, of the creative scientist come? Frequently, they derive from his possession of a superior technique of observation or of representation. Examples of the former are commonplace: Leeuwenhoek and his microscope, Galileo and his telescope, Lawrence and his cyclotron, and so on. God is on the side of the highest resolutions. The classic example of the interaction between apparatus for symbolizing or representation and scientific discovery is the relation of the calculus to the birth and growth of Newtonian mechanics. One might ask how the creative scientist comes to possess superior techniques. The answer would again be in terms of luck, persistence, and superior heuristics. The answer is not really circular, for it is quite legitimate, in dynamic systems, to explain chickens by the hatching of eggs, and eggs by the laying processes of chickens.

The theory of problem solving set forth in these two chapters itself provides an example of apparatus and representation as sources of heuristic. The idea that problem solving is a process of selective trial and error is an old one. The idea remained vague and largely untested until a formalism became available (list-processing language for computers) that was powerful enough to state the theory formally and precisely and until an instrument became available (the digital computer) that was powerful enough to draw out the implications and predictions of the theory for human problem-solving behavior. The scientists who have been active in developing and testing this theory were all in one way or another – sometimes in very 'accidental' ways – thrown into contact with computers soon after these intruments were invented.


## 2. INCUBATION AND UNCONSCIOUS PROCESSES IN DISCOVERY

The phenomena of incubation and sudden illumination have held immense fascination for those who have written on scientific discovery. Poincaré's experience on boarding the bus at Coutances takes its place in the annals of illumination along with Proust's madeleine dipped in tea:

Just at this time I left Caen, where I was then living, to go on a geological excursion under the auspices of the school of mines. The changes of travel made me forget my mathematical work. Having reached Coutances, we entered an omnibus to go some place or other. At the moment when I put my foot on the step the idea came to me, without anything in my former thoughts seeming to have paved the way for it, that the transformations I had used to define the Fuchsian functions were identical with those of non-Euclidean geometry.[5]

Hadamard places particular emphasis on the role of the unconscious in mathematical invention. While he proposes no specific theory of the processes that go on during incubation, he argues strongly that these are active processes and not merely a forgetting of material generated during conscious work that is inhibiting the problem solution.

The theory of problem solving proposed in the last chapter does not assign any special role to the unconscious – or, for that matter, to the conscious. It assumes, implicity, that the information processes that occur without consciousness of them are of the same kinds as the processes of which the thinker is aware. It assumes, further, that the organization of the totality of processes, conscious and unconscious, is fundamentally serial rather than parallel in time.

Our examination of the phenomena of incubation and illumination and their explanation will proceed in several stages. First, I shall describe briefly the phenomena themselves. Second, I shall consider the question of why the phenomena should be regarded as surprising and in what sense they require special explanation. Finally, the information-processing theory of problem solving will be applied to provide an explanation of the main features of incubation and illumination.

The phenomena themselves are relatively simple, and their occurrence is well documented. In the case of many important scientific discoveries (we do not know in what proportion of all cases), the discoverer reports three main stages in the progress of his inquiry. The first stage, which Hadamard calls 'preparation,' involves conscious, prolonged investigation that is more or less unsuccessful in solving, or sometimes even satisfactorily framing, the problem. Ultimately, frustration becomes intense, and the problem is dropped from conscious attention. Some time later, often suddenly and with little or no warning (as in the instance reported by Poincaré), or immediately upon awakening from sleep, the central idea for the solution presents itself to the conscious mind, only the details remaining to be worked out. The period between this illumination and the preceding preparation is the incubation period.

While there is little question about the phenomena, they provide no clues as to what goes on during incubation. In the absence of a full-fledged theory of problem solving, one can fill that period with almost any imaginable activity. Illumination is a vivid experience for the person who experiences it, because he is given no hint as to what occasioned the problem solution. Worse, since the incubation processes apparently go on independently of his conscious efforts to solve the problem (and best after these efforts have ceased), the experience gives him few cues as to what he should do when he next encounters a difficult problem – other than to 'sleep on it'. He must wait until the god decides to seize him.

We can see readily why the phenomenon should be puzzling and surprising to the illuminatee. The solution to a problem that has resisted his hardest efforts suddenly, and without further work, reveals itself to his conscious mind. The notions of continuity in space and time are intrinsic to most of our ideas of causation, and illumination appears to violate this continuity. One must say 'appears' because, of course, the laws are only violated in the way they are violated when a magician produces a rabbit from a hat. When we watch the magician, we do not cease to believe in the spatial and temporal continity of causation, but only in our ability to observe the connections. The same distinction applies to illumination.

If illumination is surprising to a scientist who experiences it, it is less easy to see why it should surprise a psychologist.[6] It is commonplace that many, if not most, of the processes of the central nervous system are inaccessible to consciousness. The subconscious plays a major role in modern theories of motivation, emotion, and psychopathology. There is no a priori reason, then, to assign the problem-solving processes to the conscious rather than the unconscious. From the phenomenal evidence, they in fact belong to both.

I have been using the terms 'conscious' and 'unconscious' (or 'subconscious' – for present purposes, no distinction is made between unconscious and subconscious) to distinguish between what a person is aware of and can report, and what he is not aware of and cannot report. The reports of illumination contain numerous instances that occurred immediately on awakening, but also numerous others that occurred when the discoverer had been awake for some time. Hence, 'unconscious' is a more comprehensive term than 'asleep'. For the sake of parsimony, we shall assume that unconscious processes of the same kinds can occur both in the sleeping and waking states.

It has sometimes been argued that the evidence for unconscious processes is evidence that the information processing in the brain is parallel rather than serial. This argument only has force, of course, for unconscious processes that occur in the waking state when, presumably, they are operating in parallel with the conscious processes and are capable (viz., the Poincaré episode) of interrupting the latter. One can show, however, that a serial system is capable (through a 'time-sharing' organization of its processing) of behaving in the observed manner, and the explanation I shall propose for illumination is compatible with either a serial or a parallel organization of cognitive processing.

With these preliminaries out of the way, let us return to incubation and illumination. I should like to describe two mechanisms currently employed in the information-processing theories that appear to go a long way toward accounting for these phenomena. The first of these mechanisms is called *familiarization*, the second is called *selective forgetting*. The familiarization mechanism emerged in the course of constructing a theory of human rote memory, the forgetting mechanism in the course of trying to discover why the organization of the first theorem-proving program, the Logic Theorist, was more effective in solving problems than the organization of early versions of the General Problem Solver. Neither mechanism was devised, then, with incubation and illumination in mind; they were introduced into the theory to meet other requirements imposed by the data on problem solving.

## 2.1. Familiarization

Thinking processes make use of certain means in the central nervous system for holding symbols in short-term or 'immediate' memory. Little is known of the neurophysiological substrate of immediate memory, but a good deal is known about its phenomenal characteristics. Most important, the number of symbols that can be stored in immediate memory is severely limited – in George Miller's words, 'seven, plus or minus two'. But a 'symbol' can serve as the name for anything that can be recognized as familiar and that has information associated with it in permanent memory. Thus '*a*' is a symbol; so is 'Lincoln's Gettysburg Address'. For most native speakers of English 'criminal lawyer' is a symbol, but for a person just learning the language, the phrase may constitute a pair of symbols denoting a lawyer with certain antisocial tendencies.

The important facts are (1) that only about seven symbols can be held and manipulated in immediate memory at one time and (2) that anything can become a symbol through repeated exposure to it, or familiarization. Familiarization involves storing in *permanent* memory information that allows the symbol to be recognized and a single symbol or 'name' to be substituted for it.

Since immediate memory can only hold a few symbols at a time, complex structures can only be acquired by gradually building them up from substructures which are formed, in turn, from still smaller substructures. As each substructure is learned and stored in permanent memory, the symbol that serves as its 'name' internally can be used in immediate memory as a single chunk when combining it with other substructures. Thus, a total structure of unlimited size can be assembled without the need for holding more than a few symbols in immediate memory at any given moment. Lincoln's Gettysburg Address is memorized by assembling phrases out of words (which are already familiar units), sentences out of phrases, paragraphs out of sentences, and so on.

Familiarization processes, for reconciling the limits of immediate memory with the needs for storing information structures of unlimited size and complexity in permanent memory, are incorporated in the information-processing theory of memorization called EPAM (Elementary Perceiver and Memorizer), a program that has successfully accounted for a wide range of laboratory data on human memorizing.[7] We will assume here that these same processes go on during complex problem solving, so that in later stages of problem solving complex units are available that existed only as disconnected particulars at an earlier stage.

In proving mathematical theorems it is common first to introduce and prove some subsidiary theorems, or lemmas, which then enter as premises in the proof of the final theorem. The lemma serves to sum up a whole segment of the proof so that the name of the lemma can be used as premise in place of that segment. It should not be assumed that all or most familiarization is as deliberate or conscious as this use of lemmas by mathematicians, but the processes are analogical and perform the same function.

## 2.2. Selective Forgetting

A second mechanism to be found in information-processing theories of problem solving that is essential to our proposed explanation of incubation and illumination involves more rapid forgetting of some memory contents than of others. The selective forgetting rests, in turn, on the distinction between forms of short-term and long-term memory.

In the typical organization of a problem-solving program, the solution efforts are guided and controlled by a hierarchy or 'tree' of goals and subgoals. Thus, the subject starts out with the goal of solving the original problem. In trying to reach this goal, he generates a subgoal that will take him part of the way (if it is achieved) and addresses himself to that subgoal. If the subgoal is achieved, he may then return to the now-modified original goal. If difficulties arise in achieving the subgoal, sub-subgoals may be erected to deal with them.

The operation of such a process requires the goal hierarchy to be held in memory. If a subgoal is achieved, it can be forgotten, but the tree of unattained goals must be retained. In human problem solvers this retention is not always perfect, of course. When part of the structure is lost, the subject says, 'Where am I?' or 'Now why was I trying to get that result?' and may have to go over some of the same ground to get back into context – i.e., to locate himself in that part of the tree that has been retained in memory. If we were designing such a system, instead of probing the one that human beings possess, we would specify that the goal tree be held in some kind of temporary memory, since it is a dynamic structure, whose function is to guide search, and it is not needed (or certainly not all of it) when the problem solution has been found. Our hypothesis is that human beings are also constructed in this way – that the goal tree is held in a relatively short-term memory.

During the course of problem solving, a second memory structure is being built up. First of all, new complexes are being familiarized, so that they can be handled by the processing system as units. In addition, the problem solver is noticing various features of the problem environment and is storing some of these in memory. If he is studying a chess position, for example, in the course of his explorations he may notice that a particular piece is undefended or that another piece is pinned against the queen.

This kind of information is perceived while the problem solver is addressing himself to particular subgoals. What use is made of it at the time it is noted depends on what subgoal is directing attention at that moment. But some of this information is also transferred to more permanent forms of memory and is associated with the problem environment – in this example, with the chess position. This information about the environment is used, in turn, in the processes that erect new subgoals and that work toward subgoal achievement. Hence, over the longer run, this information influences the growth of the subgoal tree. To have a short name for it (since it is now a familiar unit for us!), I will call the information about the task environment that is noticed in the course of problem solution and fixated in permanent (or relatively long-term) memory the 'blackboard'.

The course of problem solving, then, involves continuous interaction between goal tree and blackboard.[8] In the course of pursuing goals, information is added to the blackboard. This information, in turn, helps to determine what new goals and subgoals will be set up. During periods of persistent activity, the problem solver will always be working in local goal contexts, and information added to the blackboard will be used, in the short run, only if it is relevant in those contexts.

What happens, now, if the problem solver removes himself from the task for a time? Information he has been holding in relatively short-term memory will begin to disappear, and to disappear more rapidly than information in long-term memory. But we have hypothesized that the goal tree is held in short-term memory, the blackboard in long-term memory. Hence, when the problem solver next takes up the task, many or most of the finer twigs and branches of the goal tree will have disappeared. He will begin again, with one of the higher level goals, to reconstruct that tree – but now with the help of a very different set of information, on the blackboard, than he had the first time he went down the tree.

In general, we would expect the problem solver, in his renewed examination of the problem, to follow a quite different path than he did originally. Since his blackboard now has better information about the problem environment than it did the first time, he has better cues to find the correct path. Under these circumstances (and remembering the tremendous differences a few hints can produce in problem solution), solutions may appear quickly that had previously eluded him in protracted search.

There is almost no direct evidence at the present time for the validity of this explanation of incubation and illumination. (I have been able, intro-spectively, to account for my most recent illumination experiences quite simply in these terms, but perhaps my introspections are compromised as witnesses.) It invokes, however, only mechanisms that have already been incorporated in problem-solving theories. It does leave one aspect of the phenomena unaccounted for – it does not explain how the problem that the problem solver has temporarily (consciously) abandoned is put back on the agenda by unconscious processes. It does, however, account for the suddenness of solution without calling on the subconscious to perform elaborate processes, or processes different from those it and the conscious perform in the normal course of problem-solving activity. Nor does it postulate that the unconscious is capable of random searches through immense problem spaces for the solution.

It is difficult, in brief compass, to give an actual example of the tree-blackboard scheme in operation, but a schematized hypothetical example will show in general how the mechanism operates. Suppose that we assign 'values' to nodes on the goal tree, the values representing estimates of the reward that could be achieved by searching further from the corresponding nodes. The purpose of the search is to find a node with a value of at least 20 – such a node represents a solution of the problem (Figure 1).

A reasonable search rule, starting from any given node, would be to search next from the subbranch with the highest value. Thus, if the problem solver were at node $G$ he would pick up branch $J$, with value 12, next, then the subbranch $P$ (value 15) of that branch, the sub-subbranch $Q$ (value 8), and so on.

Suppose that, in addition, each time a new node was generated, its name and value were added to a list on a blackboard, and that as soon as the subnodes of that node had been generated, the name and value of the node was erased. The blackboard would then contain, at any moment, the names and values of all nodes that had been generated but had not yet been explored. A possible search rule, different from the one previously men-tioned, would be always to pick for next exploration the node on the blackboard with the highest value.

Using the first search rule, the search of this particular hypothetical tree would proceed: $A$-$B$-$E$-$G$-$J$-$P$-$Q$-... Using the second search rule, the search of the tree would proceed: $A$-$B$-$E$-$C$-$F$-$I$-$M$, reaching the solution. For, the branch $C$ with value 11, generated at the same time as $B$, but not immediately investigated, would be selected from the blackboard in preference to the subgoal $G$, with value only 9, of goal $E$.

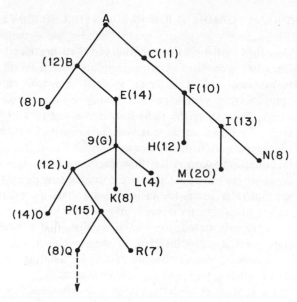

Fig. 1.

Now our theory of incubation and illumination derives from the hypothesis that during continued attention to a problem, search tends to be context-determined and to follow something like the first rule. During incubation, the tree disappears, leaving the blackboard, and when search resumes, it begins on the basis of the second rule.

Experiments with programs for discovering mating combinations in chess have shown that very different exploration trees are generated in game situations by the two rules, and that the second rule usually finds the mating combinations with far less search than the first. It would be easy, then, to reproduce incubation and illumination phenomena with these programs – by starting a search with a program using the first rule, but maintaining a blackboard, then at some point switching for a short time to the second rule.

As was mentioned earlier, the same point is demonstrated by comparison of the problem-solving power of the Logic Theorist with the power of early versions of the General Problem Solver. Without going into detail, it can simply be stated that the Logic Theorist used a form of the tree-and-blackboard scheme, while search in the General Problem Solver was always determined in the local context of current goals.[9]

### 3. PROBLEM FORMULATION IN SCIENTIFIC DISCOVERY

The theories described in the previous section postulate organized systems of processes which, when a problem of an appropriate kind is posed, will go to work on that problem and attempt to solve it. Scientific development involves not only solving problems, but posing them as well. In some discussions of creativity, asking the right questions is regarded as the crucial creative act; answering questions, in this view, is a relatively routine activity once the questions have been properly posed.

The view that question asking rather than question answering is the critical part of the creative process would be hard to defend in its extreme form. Perhaps it even illustrates itself, for in implying a sharp boundary between question asking and question answering, it may be posing the wrong question. If the issue were properly stated, we would see, first, that reformulation of questions – more generally, modification of representations – is one of the problem-solving processes; second, that the task of formulating a problem can itself be posed as a problem to a problem-solving system.

In exploring the relation of question asking to question answering, Thomas Kuhn's distinction between normal and revolutionary science becomes relevant. Normal science, he argues, does not have to pose its own questions. These questions have already been formulated for it by previous scientific revolutions. The textbooks and classics of science, incorporating the revolution, served "for a time implicitly to define the legitimate problems and methods of a research field for succeeding generations of practitioners." They can do this for two reasons: "Their achievement [is] sufficiently unprecedented to attract an enduring group of adherents away from competing modes of scientific activity. Simultaneously, it [is] sufficiently open-ended to leave all sorts of problems for the redefined group of practitioners to resolve.

Kuhn refers to achievements that share these two characteristics as 'paradigms', and he defines normal science as scientific activity within the framework of received paradigms, revolutionary science as scientific activity that establishes new paradigms.[10] Within Kuhn's theory, it is easy to state who poses the problems for investigators engaged in normal science: Their problems come from the paradigms themselves. We must either define 'creativity' so that it does not imply question asking as well as question answering, or we must conclude that creativity is not involved in normal science. The choice is one of definition.[11]

Is it necessary to adduce entirely new mechanisms to account for problem formulation in revolutionary science? Kuhn argues that it is not, for the paradigms of any given revolution arise out of the normal science of the previous period. Normal science, in Kuhn's account, leads to the discovery of anomalies, of facts that are difficult or impossible to reconcile with the accepted paradigms. The new problem then — the problem to which the prospective revolutionists address themselves — is to modify the paradigm, or replace it with another that is consistent with the facts, including the new anomalous ones.

In sum, we do not need a separate theory of problem formulation. A problem-solving system of the kind we have been considering — capable of generating subproblems from an initial problem, and capable of testing the adequacy of its solutions by generating new data about the environment — such a system will continue indefinitely to create new problems for itself. Problem formulation in science is to be understood by looking at the continuity of the whole stream of scientific endeavor.

A theory of scientific discovery adequate to explain revolutionary as well as normal science must account not only for the origins of problems, but for the origins of representations, of paradigms, as well. I do not underestimate the importance of this topic, but I shall not undertake to deal with it at any length here. In a previous paper, my colleagues A. Newell and J. C. Shaw, and I have made some general observations about it to which I refer the reader.[12] I shall add just a few more comments.

New representations, like new problems, do not spring from the brow of Zeus, but emerge by gradual — and very slow — stages. The caution stated in the opening pages of this chapter may be recalled: We must not overestimate the capacity of the human mind to invent new representations. The number of such inventions in human history has been very small.

Problem solvers use representations of the spatial relations of objects (engineering drawings are a relatively sophisticated and formalized example). They use representations of the abstract relations of objects (as, for example, in flow charts, genealogical charts, and chemical formulae). They use representations of programs (for example, systems of differential equations, computer programs). One can list a small number of other basic forms of representation and a somewhat larger number of specialized formats within each of these basic forms. The list is not long, and it is hard to find items for it whose history does not go back beyond the Christian era. (The *program* is probably the most recently developed broad form of representation, but it must not be forgotton that a recipe is a program, as is an algorithm like Eratosthenes' sieve. The differential equation represents a highly important subclass within this broad class of representations.)

Thus, our general answer to the question, 'Where do representations come from?' is the same as our answer to the question, 'Where do problems come from?' Representations arise by modification and development of previous representations as problems arise by modification and development of previous problems. A system that is to explain human problem solving and scientific discovery does not need to incorporate a highly powerful mechanism for inventing completely novel representations. If it did contain such a mechanism, it would be a poor theory, for it would predict far more novelty than occurs.

## 4. CONCLUSION

Theories are now available that incorporate mechanisms sufficient to account for some of the principal phenomena of problem solving in at least certain relatively well-structured situations. The aim of this chapter has been to ask how much these theories need to be modified or extended in order to account for problem solving in science. The general tenor of the argument has been that problem solving in science, like problem solving in the psychological laboratory, is a tedious, painstaking process of selective trial and error. Our knowledge of it does not suggest the presence of completely unknown processes far more powerful than those that have been observed in the laboratory.

Several kinds of objections can be raised, and have been, against this 'minimalist' theory. One objection is that it does not account for striking phenomena like incubation and illumination. To meet this objection, a mechanism has been proposed that is believed sufficient to produce exactly these kinds of phenomena.

Another objection is that the theory only explains how problems are solved that have already been stated and for which there exist well-defined representations. This objection has not been answered in detail, but an answer has been sketched in terms of the broader social environment within which scientific work takes place. Most scientific activity goes on within the framework of established paradigms. Even in revolutionary science, which creates those paradigms, the problems and representations are rooted in the past; they are not created out of whole cloth.

We are still very far from a complete understanding of the whole structure of the psychological processes involved in making scientific discoveries. But perhaps our analysis makes somewhat more plausible the hypothesis that at the core of this structure is the same kind of selective trial-and-error search that has already been shown to constitute the basis for human problem-solving activity in the psychological laboratory.

## NOTES

*The preparation of this chapter has been aided by research grants from the Carnegie Corporation and the National Institutes of Health (MH-07722-01). Most of the ideas in it have been developed in collaboration with my colleague Allen Newell. See his 'Some Problems of Basic Organization in Problem-Solving Programs', in *Self-Organizing Systems*, ed. by Yovits, Jacobi, and Goldstein (New York: Spartan Press, 1962).

[1] Obviously, I am not immune to this tendency.

[2] For further discussion, see the previous chapter and A. Newell, J. C. Shaw, and H. A: Simon, 'The Processes of Creative Thinking', in *Contemporary Approaches to Creative Thinking,* ed. by Gruber, Terrell, and Wertheimer (New York: Atherton Press, 1962).

[3] There are numerous anecdotes, some true, some fictitious, about the role of luck in invention. It is clear, however, that chance events played a role in: discovering vulcanization of rubber, the sweetening power of saccharine, developers in photography, and many other discoveries. See Joseph Rossman, *The Psychology of the Inventor* (Washington: The Inventors Publishing Co., 1931), Chapter 7.

[4] A. de Groot, *Thought and Choice in Chess* (Amsterdam: Mouton, 1965).

[5] Henri Poincaré, *Mathematical Creation*, reprinted in *The World of Mathematics,* ed. by James R. Newman, IV, 2041–50.

[6] Mary Henle begins her essay on 'The Birth and Death of Ideas', with the sentence, "Perhaps the most astonishing thing about creative thinking is that creative thinkers can tell us so little about it" (in *Contemporary Approaches to Creative Thinking,* Chapter 1). Why astonishing? Would we say: "Perhaps the most astonishing thing about neurotic behavior is that persons suffering from neuroses can tell us so little about it?" Why would we expect, a priori, self-consciousness to be more characteristic of the one than of the other?

[7] For an introduction to EPAM see E. A. Feigenbaum, 'The Simulation of Verbal Learning Behavior', pp. 297–309 in *Computers and Thought,* ed. by Feigenbaum and Feldman (New York: McGraw-Hill, 1964).

[8] The role of goal tree and blackboard in the organization of problem solving have been discussed by Allen Newell, in 'Some Problems of Basic Organization'.

[9] See A. Newell, J. C. Shaw, and H. A. Simon, 'Empirical Explorations of the Logic Theory Machine'; A. Newell and H. A. Simon, 'GPS, A Program that Simulates Human Thought', in Feigenbaum and Feldman (eds.), pp. 109–33, 279–93; and A. Newell and H. A. Simon, *Human Problem Solving* (Englewood Cliffs, N.J.: Prentice-Hall, 1972).

[10] Kuhn, pp. 10–12.

[11] The account elides some important details. Generating subgoals from a more general goal is a form of question asking also, which is a part both of normal science and of our problem-solving theories. Since this process has already been considered, our only present concern is with problems whose generation cannot be explained in this way.

[12] 'The Processes of Creative Thinking', pp. 98–104.

# THE STRUCTURE OF ILL-STRUCTURED PROBLEMS† *

Certain concepts are defined mainly as residuals – in terms of what they are not. Thus a UFO is an aerial phenomenon not explainable in terms of known laws and objects; and ESP is communication between persons, without evidence of the transmission of signals of any kind.

In just the same way, 'ill structured problem' (ISP) is a residual concept. An ISP is usually defined as a problem whose structure lacks definition in some respect. A problem is an ISP if it is not a WSP (well structured problem).

Residual categories are tenacious: it is extremely difficult, or even impossible, to prove that they are empty. The scope of a residual category can be narrowed progressively by explaining previously unexplained phenomena; it cannot be extinguished as long as a single phenomenon remains unexplained.

In this paper I wish to discuss the relation between ISPs and WSPs with the aim of asking whether problems regarded as ill structured are inaccessible to the problem solving systems of artificial intelligence in ways that those regarded as well structured are not. My aim will not be to restrict the class of problems we regard as ISPs – in fact I shall argue that many kinds of problems often treated as well structured are better regarded as ill structured. Instead, I will try to show that there is no real boundary between WSPs and ISPs, and no reason to think that new and hitherto unknown types of problem solving processes are needed to enable artificial intelligence systems to solve problems that are ill structured.

Some years ago, Walter Reitman provided the first extensive discussion of ISPs (which he called 'ill defined problems'; see [10, 11] ). More recently, the topic has been developed in a somewhat different vein by Allen Newell [6], who emphasized the relation between problem structure and problem-solving methods. Newell characterized the domain of ISPs as the domain in which only weak problem-solving methods were available.

In this account, I continue the discussion begun by Reitman (and on which I earlier made some preliminary remarks in [14, Section 5, pp.

† [*Artificial Intelligence* **4**, 181–201 (1973)].

274–76]). I shall try to give a positive characterization of some problem domains, that have usually been regarded as ill structured, rescuing them from their residual status; and then I shall ask whether the methods used in contemporary artificial intelligence systems are adequate for attacking problems in these domains. I shall not prejudge whether the methods applicable to these problems are weak or strong, but shall leave that to be decided after the fact.

The first section sets forth a set of strong requirements that it is sometimes asserted a task must meet in order to qualify as a WSP. Each of these requirements is examined, in order to characterize the kinds of ISPs that fail to satisfy it. The meaning of the requirements, and their relation to the power of the available problem solving systems, is then explored further by considering some specific examples of WSPs and ISPs. Finally, this exploration provides the basis for a description of problem solving systems that are adapted to attacking problems in the domains usually regarded as ill structured.

## 1. WELL STRUCTURED PROBLEMS

For reasons that will become clear as we proceed, it is impossible to construct a formal definition of 'well structured problem'. Instead, we must be content simply to set forth a list of requirements that have been proposed at one time or another as criteria a problem must satisfy in order to be regarded as well structured. A further element of indefiniteness and relativity arises from the fact that the criteria are not absolute, but generally express a relation between characteristics of a problem domain, on the one hand, and the characteristics and power of an implicit or explicit problem solving mechanism, on the other.

With these caveats, we will say that a problem may be regarded as well structured to the extent that it has some or all of the following characteristics:

1. There is a definite criterion for testing any proposed solution, and a mechanizable process for applying the criterion.

2. There is at least one problem space in which can be represented the initial problem state, the goal state, and all other states that may be reached, *or considered*, in the course of attempting a solution of the problem.

3. Attainable state changes (legal moves) can be represented in a problem space, as transitions from given states to the states directly attainable from them. But considerable moves, whether legal or not, can also be

represented — that is, all transitions from one considerable state to another.

4. Any knowledge that the problem solver can acquire about the problem can be represented in one or more problem spaces.

5. If the actual problem involves acting upon the external world, then the definition of state changes and of the effects upon the state of applying any operator reflect with complete accuracy in one or more problem spaces the laws (laws of nature) that govern the external world.

6. All of these conditions hold in the strong sense that the basic processes postulated require only practicable amounts of computation, and the information postulated is effectively available to the processes — i.e., available with the help of only practicable amounts of search.

As I have warned, these criteria are not entirely definite. Moreover, phrases like 'practicable amounts of computation' are defined only relatively to the computational power (and patience) of a problem solving system. But this vagueness and relativity simply reflect, as I shall try to show, the continuum of degrees of definiteness between the well structured and ill structured ends of the problem spectrum, and the dependence of definiteness upon the power of the problem solving techniques that are available.

### 1.1. The General Problem Solver

If a problem has been formulated in such a way that it can be given to a program like the General Problem Solver (GPS), can we say that it is a WSP? Before GPS can go to work on a problem, it requires:

(1) a description of the solution state, or a test to determine if that state has been reached;

(2) a set of terms for describing and characterizing the initial state, goal state and intermediate states;

(3) a set of operators to change one state into another, together with conditions for the applicability of these operators;

(4) a set of differences, and tests to detect the presence of these differences between pairs of states;

(5) a table of connections associating with each difference one or more operators that is relevant to reducing or removing that difference.

The first three requirements for putting a problem in a form suitable for GPS correspond closely to the first three characteristics of a WSP. The fourth and fifth requirements for putting a problem in a form suitable for GPS correspond closely to the fourth characteristic of a WSP. Since GPS operates on the formally presented problem, and not on an external real world, the fifth requirement for a WSP appears irrelevant to GPS.

In our description of the conditions for GPS's aplicability, it is implicit that the sixth requirement for WSPs is also satisfied, for the operators and tests mentioned above can all presumably be executed with reasonable amounts of computation. This does *not* imply, of course, that any problem presented to GPS within the defined domain can be solved with only reasonable amounts of computation. Many problems may not be solvable at all. Of those that are solvable in principle, many may require immense numbers of applications of operators and tests for their solution, so that the total amount of computation required may be impractical.

Thus, it would appear at first blush that all problems that can be put in proper form for GPS can be regarded as WPSs. But what problem domains satisfy these, or similar, requirements? Let us examine a couple of possible examples.

### 1.2. Is Theorem Proving a WSP?

Consider what would appear to be an extreme example of a WSP: discovering the proof of a theorem in formal logic. Condition 1 for a WSP will be satisfied if we have a mechanical proof checker. Condition 2 might be regarded as satisfied by identifying the problem space with the space of objects that can be described in terms of wffs. However, we should note that limiting the problem solver in this way excludes it from even considering expressions that are not wffs.

The same reservation must be made with respect to Condition 3: definitions of the axioms, the rules of inference, and the processes for applying the latter determine the legal moves and attainable state changes; but the problem solver may wish to consider inferences without determining in advance that they meet all the conditions of 'legality' — e.g., working backwards from unproved wffs. Hence the set of considerable moves is not determined uniquely by the set of legal moves.

Satisfying Condition 4 is even more problematic. There is no difficulty as long as we restrict ourselves to the object language of the logic under consideration. But we have no reason to exclude metalinguistic knowledge, knowledge expressed in a model space, or even analogical or metaphorical knowledge. A human theorem prover, using a metalanguage, may prove a theorem that is not provable in the object language; or may use a truth table as a model for solving a problem in the propositional calculus; or may use the proof of one theorem as an analogical guide to the proof of another that seems, in some respect, to be similar to the first.

Of course, there is nothing magical here in the problem solver being human. Mechanical systems can be, and have been, given the same kinds of capabilities. (For an example of the use of metalinguistic techniques in theorem proving, see [9]; for the use of analogies, see [3]. What some notions of well-structuredness require, however, is that these capabilities be defined in advance, and that we do not allow the problem solver to introduce new resources that "occur" to him in the course of his solution efforts. If this condition is imposed, a problem that admits restructuring through the introduction of such new resources would be an ill structured problem.

A problem that is not solvable with reasonable amounts of computation when all knowledge must be expressed in terms of the original problem space may be easily solvable if the solver is allowed to (or has the wits to) use knowledge in another space. It follows that, under a literal interpretation of Condition 4, problems of discovering proofs in formal logic are not, for all problem solvers, well structured.[1]

Condition 5 is always satisfied in theorem proving since there is no external 'real world' to be concerned about. Condition 6 is usually satisfied, as far as the basic processes are concerned. Nevertheless, because of the enormous spaces to be searched, contemporary mechanical theorem provers, confronted with difficult theorems, usually fail to find proofs. It is sometimes said that they could only succeed if endowed with ingenuity; but ingenuity, whatever it is, generally requires violating Condition 4 — moving out into the broader world of ISPs.

### 1.3. Is Chess Playing a WSP?

Next to theorem proving, the world of games would appear to offer the best examples of well-structuredness. All of the reservations, however, that applied to the well-structuredness of theorem proving apply to game playing as well. In addition, new reservations arise with respect to Condition 1 — the solution criterion — and Condition 5 — the correspondence between the inner world of thought and the outer world of action on real chess boards. Let us consider these two matters in more detail.

In both cases the difficulty stems from the immense gap between computability *in principle* and practical computability in problem spaces as large as those of games like chess. In principle, the concept of 'best move' is well defined; but in practice, this concept has to be replaced by, say, maximizing some approximate evaluation function. When a chess playing program has found (if it does) the move that maximizes this function, it can still be far from finding the move that will win the game of chess — as the modest ability of the best contemporary programs testifies.

In terms of Condition 5, it is not hard to define the WSP of playing an approximate kind of 'chess', where 'winning' means maximizing the postulated evaluation function. But the values of moves as calculated by the approximate evaluation function are simply a means for predicting the actual consequences of the moves in the real game 'outside'. Feedback in terms of the expected or unexpected moves of the opponent and the expected or unexpected board situations arising from those moves calls for new calculations by the problem solver to make use of the new information that emerges.

The ill-structuredness, by the usual criteria, of chess playing becomes fully evident when we consider the play of an entire game, and do not confine our view to just a single move. The move in the real game is distinguished from moves in dynamic analysis by its irrevocability — it has real consequences that cannot be undone, and that are frequently different from the consequences that were anticipated. Playing a game of chess — viewing this activity as solving a single problem — involves continually redefining what the problem is. Even if we regard chess playing as a WSP in the small (i.e., during the course of considering a single move), by most criteria it must be regarded as an ISP in the large, i.e., over the course of the game).

## 1.4. Summary: The Elusiveness of Structure

As our two examples show, definiteness of problem structure is largely an illusion that arises when we systematically confound the idealized problem that is presented to an idealized (and unlimitedly powerful) problem solver with the actual problem that is to be attacked by a problem solver with limited (even if large) computational capacities. If formal completeness and decidability are rare properties in the world of complex formal systems, effective definability is equally rare in the real world of large problems.

In general, the problems presented to problem solvers by the world are best regarded as ISPs. They become WSPs only in the process of being prepared for the problem solvers. It is not exaggerating much to say that there are no WSPs, only ISPs that have been formalized for problem solvers.

A standard posture in artificial intelligence work, and in theorizing in this field, has been to consider only the idealized problems, and to leave the quality of the approximation, and the processes for formulating that approximation to informal discussion outside the scopes both of the theory and of the problem solving programs. This is a defensible strategy, common to many fields of intellectual inquiry; but it encourages allegations that the 'real' problem solving activity occurs while providing a problem with structure, and not after the problem has been formulated as a WSP. As Newell and I have observed elsewhere [7, p. 850, footnote 20] these allegations are refuted simply by observing that "if [they] were correct, and tasks from the same environment were presented sequentially to a subject, only the first of them would present him with a problem, since he would not need to determine a new problem space and program for the subsequent tasks". Nevertheless, there is merit to the claim that much problem solving effort is directed at structuring problems, and only a fraction of it at solving problems once they are structured.

## 2. ILL-STRUCTURED PROBLEMS

Perhaps something is to be learned by turning the question around. We have generally asked how problems can be provided with sufficient structure so that problem solvers like GPS can go to work on them. We may ask instead how problem solvers of familiar kinds can go to work even on problems that are, in important respects, ill structured. Since the problem domains that have been most explored with mechanical techniques fail in several ways to satisfy the requirements for WSPs, perhaps we have exaggerated the essentiality of definite structure for the applicability and efficacy of these techniques. Perhaps the tricks that thave worked in relatively well structured domains can be extended to other domains that lie far toward the ISP end of the spectrum.

To explore this possibility, we will again examine several examples. Each example will illustrate some specific facet (or several facets) of ill-structuredness. Analysis of these facets will provide us with a positive characterization of ISPs, rescuing them from the status of a residual category. With this positive characterization in hand, we will be in a better position to set forth the capabilities a problem solving system must have in order to be able to attack problems that are initially ill structured in one or more ways.

### 2.1. Designing a House

It will generally be agreed that the work of an architect — in designing a house, say — presents tasks that lie well toward the ill structured end of the problem continuum. Of course this is only true if the architect is trying to be 'creative' — if he does not begin the task by taking off his shelf one of a set of standard house designs that he keeps there.

The design task (with this proviso) is ill structured in a number of respects.

There is initially no definite criterion to test a proposed solution, much less a mechanizeable process to apply the criterion. The problem space is not defined in any meaningful way, for a definition would have to encompass all kinds of structures the architect might at some point consider (e.g., a geodesic dome, a truss roof, arches, an A-frame, cantilevers, and so on and on), all considerable materials (wood, metal, plexiglass, ice — before you object, I must remind you it's been done — reinforced concrete, camel's hides, field stone, Vermont marble, New Hampshire granite, synthetic rubber, . . . ), all design processes and organizations of design processes (start with floor plans, start with list of functional needs, start with facade, . . . ).

The hopelessness of even trying to sketch the congeries of elements that might have to be included in the specification of a problem space proves the greater hopelessness of defining in reasonable compass a problem space that could not, at any time during the problem solving process, find its boundaries breached by the intrusion of new alternatives. The second, third, and fourth characteristics of a WSP appear, therefore, to be absent from the house design problem.

The fifth characteristic is also lacking. One thing an architect often does is to make renderings or models of the projected structure. He does this partly because these productions predict, more accurately than other means, properties that the real-world structure will possess if it is actually built. Viewing a model, the architect can detect relations among components of the design that were not available to him directly from his plans. Of course, even the renderings and models fall far short of predicing the actual characteristics of the real building, or the way in which the laws of nature will operate upon it and affect it. Hence, while Frank Lloyd Wright was not greatly disturbed by a leaking roof, it can hardly be supposed that he designed his roofs to leak, which they often did. Nor was the action of New York's atmosphere on the surface of the Seagram Building, and its consequent change of color, predicted. Doors stick, foundations settle, partitions transmit noise, and sometimes even happy accidents (examples of these are harder to come by) conspire to make the building as it actually exists and is used something different from the building of the plans.

Finally, even if we were to argue that the problem space can really be defined — since anything the architect thinks of must somehow be generated from, or dredged from, his resources of memory or his reference library — some of this information only shows up in late stages of the design process after large amounts of search; and some of it shows up when it does, almost accidentally. Hence, the problem is even less well defined when considered from the standpoint of what is actually known at any point in time than when considered from the standpoint of what is knowable, eventually and in principle.

All of this would seem to make designing a house a very different matter from using GPS to solve the missionaries and cannibals puzzle, or from discovering the proof of a theorem in the predicate calculus. It surely is different, but I shall try in the next paragraphs to show that understanding what the architect does goes far toward bridging the gulf between these problem domains. In this I shall be following quite closely the path first blazed by Walter Reitman [11, Chapter 8] in his analysis of the thinking-aloud protocol of a composer writing a fugue. It should not, of course, appear surprising that a house-designing process would have much in common with a process of musical composition. Showing that they do have much in common is critical to the attempt here to provide a positive characterization of the processes for solving ISPs.

## 2.2. The Architect's Processes

Reitman uses the term 'constraints' quite broadly to refer to any or all of the elements that enter into a definition of a problem. He observes [11, p. 169] :

One of the interesting features of many of the problem instances . . . is that even though they generally would be considered complex, they include very few constraints as given. Composing a fugue is a good example. Here the main initial constraint, and it is an open constraint at that [i.e., one that is incompletely specified], is that the end product be a fugue. All other constraints are in a sense supplementary, generated from one transformation of the problem to the next.

Similarly, the architect begins with the sole problem of designing a house. The client has presumably told him something of his needs, in terms of family size or number of rooms, and his budget (which the architect will multiply by 1.5 or 2 before accepting it as a constraint). Additional specification will be obtained from the dialogue between architect and client, but the totality of that dialogue will still leave the design goals quite incompletely specified. The more distinguished the architect, the less expectation that the client should provide the constraints.

*2.2.1. Evaluating the specifications.* We can imagine a design process that proceeds according to the following general scheme. Taking the initial goals and constraints, the architect begins to derive some global specifications from them — perhaps the square footage or cubic footage of the house among them. But the task itself, 'designing a house', evokes from his long-term memory a list of other attributes that will have to be specified at an early stage of the design: characteristics of the lot on which the house is to be built, its general style, whether it is to be on a single level or multi-storied, type of frame, types of structural materials and of sheathing materials, and so on. The task will also evoke from memory some over-all organization, or executive program, for the design process itself.

Neither the guiding organization nor the attributes evoked from memory need at any time during the process provide a complete procedure nor complete information for designing a house. As a matter of fact, the entire procedure could conceivably be organized as a system of productions, in which the elements already evoked from memory and the aspects of the design already arrived at up to any given point, would serve as the stimuli to evoke the next set of elements.

Whether organized as a system of productions or as a system of subroutine calls, the evocation of relevant information and subgoals from long-term memory can be sequential. As Reitman says of the fugue [11, p. 169] :

Just as 'sentence' transforms to 'subject plus predicate', and 'subject' may transform to 'article plus noun phrase' . . . , so 'fugue' may be thought of as transforming to 'exposition plus development plus conclusion', 'exposition' to 'thematic material plus countermaterial', and 'thematic material' to 'motive plus development of motive'.

Applying the same linguistic metaphor to house design, 'house' might transform to 'general floor plan plus structure', 'structure' to 'support plus roofing plus sheathing plus utilities', 'utilities' to 'plumbing plus heating system plus electrical system', and so on.

The requirements that any of these components should meet can also be evoked at appropriate times in the design process, and need not be specified in advance. Consideration of the heating system can evoke from the architect's long-term memory (or the appropriate reference handbooks) that the system should be designed to maintain a temperature of $70°$, that the minimum outside temperature to be expected is $-5°$, that the heat transmission coefficient of the proposed sheathing is kBTU per hour per square foot per degree of temperature differential, and so on.

Design alternatives can also be evoked in component-by-component fashion. The subgoal of designing the heating system may lead the architect to consider various fuels and various distribution systems. Again, the source of these generators of alternatives is to be found in his long-term memory and reference facilities (including his access to specialists for helping design some of the component systems).

The whole design, then, begins to acquire structure by being decomposed into various problems of component design, and by evoking, as the design progresses, all kinds of requirements to be applied in testing the design of its components. During any given short period of time, the architect will find himself working on a problem which, perhaps beginning in an ill structured state, soon converts itself through evocation from memory into a well structured problem. We can make here the same comment we made about playing a chess game: the problem is well structured in the small, but ill structured in the large.

*2.2.2 Coordination of the design.* Now some obvious difficulties can arise from solving problems in this manner. Interrelations among the various well structured subproblems are likely to be neglected or underemphasized. Solutions to particular subproblems are apt to be disturbed or undone at a later stage when new aspects are attended to, and the considerations leading to the original solutions forgotten or not noticed. In fact, such unwanted side effects accompany all design processes that are as complex as the architectural one we are considering. As a result, while the final product may satisfy all the requirements that are evoked when that final product is tested, it may violate some of the requirements that were imposed (and temporarily satisfied) at an earlier stage of the design. The architect may or may not be aware of the violation. Some other appropiate design criteria may simply remain dormant, never having been evoked during the design process.

The danger of inconsistencies and lacunae of these kinds is mitigated to some extent by that part of the architect's skill that is imbedded in the over-all organization of his program for design. Part of his professional training and subsequent learning is directed to organizing the process in such a way that the major interactions among components will be taken care of. Certain ways of dividing the whole task into parts will do less violence to those interactions than other ways of dividing it – a good procedure will divide the task into components that are as nearly 'self-contained' as possible [1]. Early stages of the design can also establish global parameters which then become constraints operating on each of the components to which they are relevant. Thus general decisions about 'style' can impose constraints on the stylistic decisions about particular portions of the house.

Much of the coordination of the various well structured design subtasks is implicit – built into the organization of the whole process. To the extent that this is so, the local design activities are guaranteed to mesh into a reasonable over-all structure. This means that the final product may be very much influenced by the order in which the design steps are taken up. As a result, differences in style between different designs can result as readily from the organization of the design process as from explicit decisions of the architect to specify one style or another. If the process calls for designing the facade before the floor plan, different kinds of designs will emerge than if the process calls for specifying the room arrangements before the facade [13].

*2.2.3. The over-all design process.* The design process sketched above can be composed from a combination of a GPS, which at any given moment finds itself working on some well structured subproblem, with a retrieval system, which continually modifies the problem space by evoking from long-term memory new constraints, new subgoals, and new generators for design alternatives. We can also view this retrieval system as a recognition system that attends to features in the current problem space and in external memory (e.g., models and drawings), and, recognizing features as familiar, evokes relevant information from memory which it adds to the problem space (or substitutes for other information currently in the problem space). The retrieval system, then, is capable of interrupting the ongoing processes of the problem solving system. A schematic flow diagram for a system with these characteristics is shown in Figure 1.

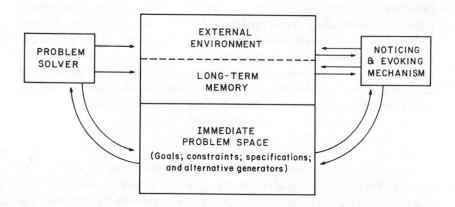

Fig. 1.   Schematic diagram of a system for ill structured problems. It shows the alternation between a problem solver working on a well structured problem, and a recognition system continually modifying the problem space.

One might ask why the system is organized in this fashion — with
alternation between problem solving in a (locally) well structured problem
space and modification of the problem space through retrieval of new
information from long-term memory. The answer revolves around the
basically serial character of the problem solving system. The problem solving
processes are capable, typically, of taking a few arguments as inputs and
producing a small number of symbol structures as outputs. There is no way in
which a large amount of information can be brought to bear upon these
processes locally — that is, over a short period of processing. If a large
long-term memory is associated with a serial processor of this kind, then most
of the contents of long-term memory will be irrelevant during any brief
interval of processing.

Consider the alternative, of bringing all of the potentially relevant
information in long-term memory together once and for all at the outset, to
provide a well structured problem space that does not change during the
course of the problem solving effort. One must ask 'bringing it together
where?' Presumably it could all be assembled in some designated part of
long-term memory. But to what purpose? Retrieval processes would still be
necessary for the serial problem solving processes to discover the inputs they
needed at the time they needed them. To the outside observer, the continuing
shift in attention from one part of the assembled task information to another
would still look like a series of transformations of the problem space.

In the organization described in Figure 1, there is no need for this initial
definition of the problem space and task structure. All of the necessary
definitory information is potentially available, but distributed through
long-term memory. It is retrieved through two mechanisms: first, the normal
subroutine structure, which enables processes to call subprocesses and to pass
input and output information from one to another; second, the evoking
mechanism, which recognizes when certain information has become relevant,
and proceeds to retrieve that information from long-term memory.

## 2.3. Design as an Organization Process

If this description of how an ill structured problem of design can be handled
seems at all fanciful, its realism can be supported by comparing it with the
description of complex design processes that take place in organizations. Let
me quote at length the process, described by Sir Oswyn Murray some fifty
years ago, of designing and producing a new battleship [5, pp. 216–217] :

We start with the First Sea Lord and his Assistant Chief of Naval Staff laying down in general terms the features that they desire to see embodied in the new design — the speed, the radius of action, the offensive qualities, the armour protection. Thereupon the Directory of Naval Construction, acting under and in consultation with the Controller, formulates provisional schemes outlining the kind of ship desired together with forecasts of the size and cost involved by the different arrangements. To do this he and his officers must have a good general knowledge — in itself only attainable by close relations with those in charge of these matters — of the latest developments and ideas in regard to a great range of subjects — gunnery, torpedo, engineering, armour, fire-control, navigation, signalling, accommodation, and so on — in order to be reasonably sure that the provision included in his schemes is likely to satisfy the experts in all these subjects when the time for active cooperation arrives.

With these alternative schemes before them, the Sea Lords agree on the general lines of the new ship, which done, the actual preparation of the actual designs begins. The dimensions and shape of the ship are drawn out approximately by the naval constructors. Then the Engineer-in-Chief and his Department are called in to agree upon the arrangement of the propelling machinery, the positions of shafts, propellers, bunkers, funnels, etc., and at the same time the cooperation of the Director of Naval Ordnance is required to settle the positions of the guns with their barbettes, and magazines and shell rooms and the means of supplying ammunition to the guns in action.

An understanding between these three main departments enables further progress to be made. The cooperation of the Director of Torpedoes and the Director of Electrical Engineering is now called for to settle the arrangements for torpedo armament, electric generating machinery, electric lighting, etc. So the design progresses and is elaborated from the lower portions upwards, and presently the Director of Naval Construction is able to consult the Director of Naval Equipment as to the proposed arrangements in regard to the sizes and towage of the motor boats, steamboats, rowing and sailing boats to be carried, as well as of the anchors and cables; the Director of the Signal Department as to the wireless telegraphy arrangements; the Director of Navigation as to the arrangements for navigating the ship, and so on. In this way the scheme goes on growing in a tentative manner, its progress always being dependent on the efficiency of different parts, until ultimately a more or less complete whole is arrived at in the shape of drawings and specifications provisionally embodying all the agreements. This really is the most difficult and interesting stage, for generally it becomes apparent at this point that requirements overlap, and that the best possible cannot be achieved in regard to numbers of points within the limit set to the contractors. These difficulties are cleared up by discussion at round-table conferences, where the compromises which will least impair the value of the ship are agreed upon, and the completed design is then finally submitted for the Board's approval. Some fourteen departments are concerned in the settlement of the final detailed arrangements.

The main particular in which this account differs from our description of the architectural process is in the more elaborate provision, in the ship design process, for coordinating the numerous criteria of design that are evoked during the process, and preventing criteria, once evoked, from being overlooked in the latter stages of the process. In the ship design process too the 'evoking' takes on an organizational form — it involves consulting the relevant specialists. The long-term memory here is literally a distributed memory, divided among the various groups of experts who are involved at one or another stage of the design process.

What is striking about Sir Oswyn's account is how well structured each part of the design process appears. We can visualize each group of experts, provided with the overall specifications, sitting down with their specific subproblem of designing a particular system, and finding that subproblem to be a relatively well structured task. Of course the more complex subproblems may themselves be in numerous ways ill structured until further subdivided into components (cf. the descriptions of the role of the Engineer-in-Chief and of the Director of Naval Ordnance).

Wherever complex designs are produced by organizations, and where, as a consequence, the design process must be partially externalized and formalized, we find descriptions of that process not unlike this description of ship design. An initial stage of laying down general (and tentative) specifications is followed by stages in which experts are called up ('evoked') to introduce new design criteria and component designs to satisfy them. At a later stage, there is attention to inconsistencies of the component designs, and a search for modifications that will continue to meet most of the criteria, or decisions to sacrifice certain criteria in favor of others. Each small phase of the activity appears to be quite well structured, but the overall process meets none of the criteria we set down for WSPs.

## 2.4. An Intelligent Robot

A different aspect of structure comes to the forefront when we consider the design of an intelligent robot capable of locomoting and solving problems in a real external environment. The robot's planning and problem solving must be carried out in terms of some internal representation of the external environment. But this internal representation will be inexact for at least two reasons: First, it must abstract from much (or most) of the detail of the actual physical environment. (It surely cannot represent the individual molecules and their interactions, and it must almost always ignore details that are much grosser and more important than those at the molecular level.) Second, the internal representation includes a representation of the changes that will be produced in the external environment by various actions upon it. But for this prediction of the effects of operators to be exact would require an exact knowledge of the laws of nature that govern the effects of real actions upon a real environment.

The robot, therefore, will continually be confronted with new information from the environment: features of the environment which have become relevant to its behavior but are omitted from, or distorted in, its internal representation of that environment; and changes in the environment as a consequence of its behavior that are different from the changes that were predicted by the planning and problem solving processes.

But this external information can be used by the robot in exactly the way that information evoked from long-term memory was used by the architect. The problem representation can be revised continually to take account of the information − of the real situation − so that the problem solver is faced at each moment with a well structured problem, but one that changes from moment to moment.[2]

If the continuing alteration of the problem representation is short-term and reversible, we generally call it 'adaptation' or 'feedback', if the alteration is more or less permanent (e.g., revising the 'laws of nature'), we refer to it as 'learning'. Thus the robot modifies its problem representation temporarily by attending in turn to selected features of the environment; it modifies it more permanently by changing its conceptions of the structure of the external environment or the laws that govern it.

## 2.5. *Chess Playing as an ISP*

We can now return to the task environment of chess, and reinterpret our earlier comments − that in some repects chess appears to resemble an ISP rather than a WSP. To make the point still sharper, we consider a (over-simplified) chess program that has three principal components:

(1) a set of productions,
(2) an evaluator,
(3) an updating process.

The set of productions serves as a move generator. Each production consists of a condition part and an action part; the condition part tests for the presence of some configuration of pieces or other features in a chess position; the action part evokes a move that should be considered when the condition with which it is associated is present. Such a set of productions can also be viewed as an indexed memory, or discrimination and recognition net. When the presence of a condition is recognized by the net, the corresponding action is accessed in long-term memory. By the operation of this system of productions, each chess position evokes a set of moves that should be considered in that position.

The second component of the chess program is an evaluator that takes a move and a position as input and (recursively) makes a dynamic evaluation of that move. We will assume — without specifying exact mechanisms — that the dynamic evaluation converges. The evaluator produces a search tree that constitutes its prediction of the consequences that might follow on any given move.

The third component of the chess program is the updating routine. After a move has been made and the opponent has replied, the updater brings the position on the board up to date by recording the moves, prunes the analysis tree, and turns control over again to the discrimination net.

Consider now a problem space consisting of the set of features recognizable by the productions, together with the moves associated with those features. Consider the subspace consisting of the features actually evoked by a given position, together with the moves associated with this smaller set of features. If we regard the latter, and smaller, space as the effective problem space for the program (since its processing during a limited period of time will be governed only by the productions actually evoked during that time), then the effective problem space will undergo continuing change throughout the course of the game, moving from one subspace to another of the large space defined by the entire contents of long-term memory. The problem faced by the chess program will appear just as ill structured as the architect's problem or the robot's problem — and for exactly the same reasons.

## 2.6. Serial Processors and ISPs

Our analysis has led us to see that any problem solving process will appear ill structured if the problem solver is a machine that has access to a very large long-term memory (an effectively infinite memory) of potentially relevant information, and/or access to a very large external memory that provides information about the actual real-world consequences of problem-solving actions. 'Large' is defined relative to the amount of information that can direct or affect the behaviour of the processor over any short period of time; while 'potentially relevant' means that any small part of this information may be evoked at some time during the problem solving process by recognition of some feature in the current problem state (the information available *directly* to the processor).

If we refer back to the original definition of WSP, we see that the present view of the boundary between WSPs and ISPs derives from our insistence that notions of computability in principle be replaced by notions of practicable computability in the definition of WSP. But this shift in boundary has highly important consequences. It implies that, from the standpoint of the problem solver, any problem with a large base of potentially relevant knowledge may appear to be an ill structured problem; and that the problem solver can be effective in dealing with it only if it has capabilities for dealing with ISPs. Conversely, it suggests that there may be nothing other than the size of the knowledge base to distinguish ISPs from WSPs, and that general problem solving mechanisms that have shown themselves to be efficacious for handling large, albeit *apparently* well structured domains should be extendable to ill structured domains without any need for introducing qualitatively new components.

However well structured the problem space in which a problem solver operates, if it is to be capable of modifying that space as problem solving progresses, it must possess means for assimilating the information it acquires from long-term memory, from problem instructions, and from the external environment. The next section discusses briefly the nature of the capabilities of these kinds that are required.

## 3. ASSIMILATING NEW INFORMATION

When the problem space remains unchanged throughout the problem solving process, the assimilation of new information by the problem solving system offers no particular difficulties. Any information that can be used belongs to one of the forms of information that are specified in the definition of the problem space. In fact, the only new information that can be acquired is information descriptive of new states that are reached in the course of the problem solving search.

When the problem space is subject to modification during problem solving, provision must be made for accepting and assimilating information from one or more of three sources: information evoked from long-term memory, information contained in problem instructions or additions and modifications to instructions, and information obtained through sensory channels from the external world.

### 3.1. Information from Long-Term Memory

Information evoked by the production—recognition system from long-term memory should not create particular difficulties of assimilation. The forms in which such information is stored, the processes for retrieving it and incorporating it in the redefined problem space are all part of the problem solving system, broadly construed.

This does not mean that we have had much actual experience in constructing and using such semantic information stores. Perhaps, when we come to have such experience, difficulties will emerge that cannot now be anticipated. Nevertheless, the designer of the problem solving system controls the format in which information is to be stored in long-term memory. The storage scheme can put the information into a relatively simple, general, and homogeneous format (e.g., a network of description list structures — commonly referred to as a colored directed graph); and the system can be provided with relatively simple, general, and homogeneous processes for searching for information and retrieving it from the store. Interfacing with an environment whose design is under our control (memory search) is always several orders of magnitude easier than interfacing with a given external environment (perception).

### 3.2. Information from Instructions

Tasks presented to a problem solver through natural language instructions pose the difficult initial problem of understanding the instructions, that is, of generating from them a well structured (or ill structured) statement of the problem. A general discussion of understanding natural language would take us far afield from our main concerns here, and must be omitted from the present paper. The reader is referred to Simon [14], Siklóssy and Simon [12], chapters by Bobrow and Raphael in [4], and Winograd [15]

Hayes and Simon [2] have recently constructed a system that reads problem instructions in natural language, and constructs from them a problem representation in the form of input appropriate for a problem solving system like GPS. Their program carries out the major steps in translating relatively simple ISPs into WSPs.

### 3.3. Information about the External World

An ability to assimilate information about the external world — either information about the effects of the problem solver's actions, or information about autonomous changes in that world, or both — is the earmark of those problem solvers we have called 'robots'. Here we are concerned with the problem solver's perceptual or pattern recognizing capabilities — another topic that falls outside the scope of the present paper. The outer limits on acquisition of such information are defined by the primitive sensory discriminations of which the problem solver is capable, but in the short run, the higher level concepts already developed and stored may pose the most severe problems of assimilating new information.

In the cases both of information from instructions and information about the external world, the acquisition process involves a continual interaction between the incoming raw data and programs and data already stored in the problem solver. This interaction is both a vital aid to, and a limitation upon, the understanding process. It is an aid because it fits the new information to formats and structures that are already available, and adapts it to processes for manipulating those structures. It is a limitation, because it tends to mold all new information to the paradigms that are already available. The problem solver never perceives the *Ding an sich*, but only the external stimulus filtered through its own preconceptions. Hence the acquistion process exercises a strong influence in the direction of conserving existing problem formulations. The world as perceived is better structured than the raw world outside.

## 4. IMPLICATIONS FOR ARTIFICIAL INTELLIGENCE

Molière's hero discovered that he had been speaking prose all his life without knowing it. Our analysis here implies that throughout the history of artificial intelligence, computer problem solving programs have, also unknowingly, been handling many aspects of problem solving that are usually regarded as ill structured. Several examples of programs now fifteen years old can be cited.

The early NSS chess program [8] contained a number of independent move generators, each associated with a particular subgoal (development, center control, King safety, etc.). A move generator was activated by the presence in the chess position of features relevant to the goal in question. When evoked, the generator proposed one or more moves for advancing the goal in question. These moves were evaluated by dynamic analysis which again was sensitive to features noticed in new positions as they arose during the analysis. Hence the over-all organization of the program was quite close to that of the hypothetical program we described earlier.

The proposals for using a planning method in the General Problem Solver can also be interpreted as a way of handling problems that are not completely well structured. Planning was done by abstracting from the detail of a problem space, and carrying out preliminary problem solving in the abstracted (and consequently simpler) space. But the plan then had to be tested by trying to carry it out in the original problem space. The detail of the plan was thereby elaborated and its feasibility tested. The relation between the abstract planning space and the original problem space was quite analogous to the relation we have discussed between an internal problem space of a robot and the external real world in which the robot performs.

What has been absent from (or at least not prominent in) schemes like these is a very large long-term memory of potentially evocable information that can be used to bring about repeated modifications in the problem space. The recent growth of interest in semantics, in the design and construction of semantic nets, in the intepretation of instructions, and in interfacing robots with the external world are all movements in the direction of enriching our arsenal of artificial intelligence methods along the dimensions that will become increasingly important as we move toward more comprehensive schemes for handling ill structured problem solving. Our analysis gives us reason to be optimistic that progress will not require us to introduce mechanisms that are qualitatively different from the ones already introduced in artificial intelligence schemes – mechanisms with which we have already had some limited experience.

The boundary between well structured and ill structured problem solving is indeed a vague and fluid boundary. There appears to be no reason to suppose that concepts as yet uninvented and unknown stand between us and the fuller exploration of those problem domains that are most obviously and visibly ill structured.

## NOTES

*This research was supported in part by Research Grant MH-07722 from the National Institute of Mental Health and in part by the Advanced Research Projects Agency of the Office of the Secretary of Defense (F44620-70-C-0107) which is monitored by the Air Force Office of Scientific Research. I am grateful to Dr. Aaron Sloman and Prof. Saul Amarel for helpful comments on an earlier draft of this paper.
[1] Notice that we are not appealing here to formal undecidability or incompleteness. Our concern throughout is with effective or practicable solvability using reasonable amounts of computation. Problems may be (and often are) unsolvable in this practical sense even in domains that are logically complete and decidable.
[2] 'Robots' that operate on synthesized worlds represented inside the computer, like the well-known system of T. Winograd, are not robots in the sense in which I am using the term here; for they do not face the issue that is critical to a robot when dealing with a real external environment – the issue of continually revising its internal representation of the problem situation to conform to the facts of the world. Thus the information given PLANNER, the problem solving component of Winograd's system, is a complete and accurate characterization of the toy world of blocks that the system manipulates. The accuracy of the information guarantees in turn that any theorem proved by PLANNER will be true of the block world.

## REFERENCES

[1]  Alexander, C., *Notes on the Synthesis of Form* (Cambridge, Mass.: Harvard Univ. Press, 1964).

[2]  Hayes, J. R. and Simon, H. A., 'Understanding Written Problem Instructions', *Knowledge and Cognition*, L. W. Gregg (ed.), (New York: Halsted-Wiley, 1974).

[3]  Kling, R. D., 'A Paradigm for Reasoning by Analogy', *Proc. 2nd Intern. Joint Conf. on Artificial Intelligence* (London: British Computer Society, 1971) pp. 568–585.

[4]  Minsky, M. (ed.), *Semantic Information Processing* (Cambridge, Mass.: M.I.T. Press, 1969).

[5]  Murray, Sir Oswyn A. R., 'The Administration of a Fighting Service', *J. Public Admin.* 1, 216–217 (July 1923).

[6]  Newell, A., 'Heuristic Programming: Ill Structured Problems', *Progress in Operations Research,* Vol. 3, J. Aronofsky (ed.), (New York: Wiley, 1969) pp. 360–414.

[7]  Newell, A. and Simon, H. A., *Human Problem Solving* (Englewood Cliffs, N.J.: Prentice-Hall, 1972).

[8]  Newell, A., Shaw, J. C., and Simon, H. A., 'Chess-Playing Programs and the Problem of Complexity', *IBM J. Res. Develop.* 2, 320–335 (1958).

[9]  Pitrat, J., 'Réalisation des programmes de démonstration des théorèmes utilisant des méthodes heuristiques', Doctoral Thesis, Faculty of Sci., Univ. of Paris, 1966.

[10]  Reitman, W. R., 'Heuristic Decision Procedures, Open Constraints, and the Structure of Ill-Defined Problems', *Human Judgments and Optimality,* M. W. Shelley and G. L. Bryan (eds.), (New York: Wiley, 1964) pp. 282–315.

[11]  Reitman, W. R., *Cognition and Thought* (New York: Wiley, 1965).

[12]  Siklóssy, L. and Simon, H. A., 'Some Semantic Methods for Language Processing', *Representation and Meaning,* H. A. Simon and L. Siklóssy (eds.) (Englewood Cliffs, N.J.: Prentice-Hall, 1972).

[13]  Simon, H. A., 'Style in Design', *Proc. 2nd Ann. Environ. Design Res. Assoc. Conf.,* 1–10, October 1970, J. Archea and C. Eastman (eds.) (Pittsburgh, Pa.: Carnegie-Mellon Univ., 1971).

[14]  Simon, H. A., 'The Heuristic Compiler', *Representation and Meaning,* H. A. Simon and L. Siklóssy (eds.) (Englewood Cliffs, N.J.: Prentice-Hall, 1972).

[15]  Winograd, T., 'Understanding Natural Language', *Cognitive Psychol.* 3, (1) 1–191 (1973).

# DOES SCIENTIFIC DISCOVERY HAVE A LOGIC?†*

It is unusual for an author, less than one-tenth of the way through his work, to disclaim the existence of the subject matter that the title of his treatise announces. Yet that is exactly what Karl Popper does in his classic, *The Logic of Scientific Discovery,* [4], announcing in no uncertain terms on p. 31 that scientific discovery has no logic. The disclaimer is so remarkable that it deserves to be quoted at length:

> I said above that the work of the scientist consists in putting forward and testing theories.
> The initial stage, the act of conceiving or inventing a theory, seems to me neither to call for logical analysis nor to be susceptible of it. The question how it happens that a new idea occurs to a man – whether it is a musical theme, a dramatic conflict, or a scientific theory – may be of great interest to empirical psychology; but it is irrelevant to the logical analysis of scientific knowledge. The latter is concerned not with *questions of fact* (Kant's *quid facti?*), but only with questions of *justification or validity* (Kant's *quid juris?*) . . . .
> Accordingly, I shall distinguish sharply between the process of conceiving a new idea, and the methods and results of examining it logically. As to the task of the logic of knowledge – in contradistinction to the psychology of knowledge – I shall proceed on the assumption that it consists solely in investigating the methods employed in those systematic tests to which every new idea must be subjected if it is to be seriously entertained . . . .
> . . . . my view of the matter, for what it is worth, is that there is no such thing as a logical method of having new ideas, or a logical reconstruction of this process. My view may be expressed by saying that every discovery contains 'an irrational element', or 'a creative intuition', in Bergson's sense. In a similar way, Einstein speaks of the 'search for those highly universal laws . . . from which a picture of the world can be obtained by pure deduction. There is no logical path', he says, 'leading to these . . . laws. They can only be reached by intuition, based upon something like an intellectual love (*'Einfühlung'*) of the objects of experience'. ([4], pp. 31–32)

This mystical view towards discovery, while shared by most of the world, including most of its creative scientists and artists, has not gone without challenge. Peirce coined the term 'retroduction' as a label for the systematic processes leading to discovery; while Norwood Hanson, in his *Patterns of Discovery*, revived that term and gave us a careful account of the retroductive

† [*Philosophy of Science* **40**, 471–480 (1973)].

path that led Kepler to the elliptical orbits of the planets. It is instructive to confront Popper's view, just quoted, with Hanson's:

H-D [hypothetico-deductive] accounts all agree that physical laws explain data, but they obscure the initial connexion between data and laws; indeed, they suggest that the fundamental inference is from higher-order hypotheses to observation statements. This may be a way of setting out one's reasons for accepting an hypothesis after it is got, or for making a prediction, but it is not a way of setting out reasons for proposing or for trying an hypothesis in the first place. Yet the initial suggestion of an hypothesis is very often a reasonable affair. It is not so often affected by intuition, insight, hunches, or other imponderables as biographers or scientists suggest. Disciples of the H-D account often dismiss the dawning of an hypothesis as being of psychological interest only, or else claim it to be the province solely of genius and not of logic. They are wrong. If establishing an hypothesis through its predictions has a logic, so has the conceiving of an hypothesis. ([2], p. 71)

Hanson made his case for retroduction by examining historical examples of scientific discovery. He did not propose an explicit formal theory of the retroductive process, nor did he draw any sharp line between psychology and logic. Indeed, his analysis places great emphasis upon perceptual processes, upon the discovery of pattern – a pun upon the title of his book that, I am sure, had occurred to him. For this reason, it is easy for persons of an H-D persuasion to judge Hanson's work superficially as a contribution only to psychology and not to the logic of science. In this, they are wrong also.

It is the aim of this paper to clarify the nature of retroduction, and to explain in what sense one can speak of a 'logic of discovery' or 'logic of retroduction.' Like Hanson, I shall proceed from examples of retroductive processes, but examples that are less impressive than his. Their modesty as instances of discovery will be compensated by their transparency in revealing underlying process. The argument of Popper and of the others who agree with his position is, after all, a general argument. If "There is no such thing as a logical method of having new ideas", then there is no such thing as a logical method of having small new ideas.[1]

## 1. WHAT IS A LOGIC OF METHOD?

At the outset it is important to make clear what might be meant by the term 'logic' in this context. I suppose no one any longer imagines that there exists a process for deriving scientific laws deductively (much less, for validating them) either from particular facts or from any other kinds of prevalidated premises. Nor is that what Popper means by 'logical analysis' in the passage quoted at the beginning of this paper. The distinction Popper draws is between psychology and logic – between a description of how people actually behave (e.g. judge, reason), and a prescription of norms of valid behavior (e.g. judging soundly, reasoning correctly and rigorously).

We commonly call a process 'logical' when it satisfies norms we have established for it; and these norms derive from our concern that the process be efficacious or efficient for accomplishing the purpose for which it was established. A logic of scientific method, then, is a set of normative standards for judging the processes used to discover or test scientific theories, or the formal structure of the theories themselves (Simon [6], p. 443). The use of the term 'logic' suggests that the norms can be derived from the goals of the scientific activity. That is to say, a normative theory rests on contingent propostions like: 'If process $X$ is to be efficacious for attaining goal $Y$, then it should have properties $A, B, C$'.

It is in this sense that we can speak of the 'logic' of a chess strategy. The game of chess has a goal: to checkmate the opponent's King. The chessplayer uses a strategy to discovery and evaluate moves directed toward that goal. Books on chess contain normative statements about these discovery and evaluation processes – e.g.. "In a position where the player has greater mobility than his opponent, he should examine moves that attack the position of the opponent's King directly." The validity of this normative statement rests on a premise like: "Where one player has the greater mobility, direct attacks on the postion of the opponent's King are frequently the best paths toward checkmating the opponent."

To generalize, suppose that we have a goal, $G$, a set of processes, $p \in P$, and a set of conditions, $c \in C$. The conditions can be attributed to processes, so that $c(p)$ is a function from $C \times P$ to the truth-values T and F. If, now, $\forall c(G \supset c)$, then we can regard $C$ as a set of norms for $P$ with respect to $G$. That is to say, if attainment of the goal, $G$, implies that the conditions, $C$, be satisfied, then we should employ a process, $p$, that satisfies $C$ (i.e. such that $\forall c(c(p) = T)$).

If $G$ is the goal of discovering valid scientific laws, and $P$ is a class of discovery processes, then $C$ provides a normative theory of scientific discovery. If $G$ is the goal of testing the validity of proposed laws, and $P$ is a class of test processes, then $C$ provides a normative theory of testing laws. The premises, $G \supset c$, may themselves have either a logical or an empirical basis. In the game of tic-tac-toe, a move that puts a second cross at the intersection of two unblocked arrays, each of which has one cross already, is a winning move. A normative theory of tic-tac-toe would recommend strategies that make such a move when possible, and condemn strategies that do not. The correctness of this condition can be deduced rigorously from the rules of tic-tac-toe. On the other hand, the norm of chess strategy mentioned earlier – that attacks on the King should be considered when superior mobility has been achieved – is an empirical rule based on the cumulated experiences of chess players. No formal deduction of this norm from the rules alone of chess is known.

Notice that we have formulated matters so that the use of a rcommended strategy does not guarantee the achievement of the goal. We wrote $G \supset c$ and not $c \supset G$. In order to achieve the goal (e.g. to discover a scientific law), it is recommended that we use processes that satisfy the condition, $c$; it is not implied that using such processes will necessarily lead to discovery of a law. Hence, we have not smuggled an induction axiom into our formulation.

We have seen that the norms can have either a logical or an empirical basis. Perhaps the presence of an empirical component in norms has encouraged the notion that certain processes cannot be subject to 'logical analysis' but only to description. But if the phrase 'logical analysis' is interpreted broadly, then, as we have just seen, one can undertake normative logical analysis of any goal-directed process. And if the phrase 'logical analysis' is interpreted narrowly, in order to exclude deductions from empirically based premises, then the dichotomy between logical analysis and description is a false one. For in this case, we must consider three possibilities, not two: (1) description, (2) normative analysis not dependent on empirical premises, and (3) normative analysis dependent on empirical premises. In any event, we see that we must reject Popper's assertion that the "question how it happens that a new idea occurs to a man . . . may be of great interest to empirical psychology; but it is irrelevant to the logical analysis of scientific knowledge" ([4], p. 31). The genuine normative questions about the efficacy of processes of scientific discovery cannot be dismissed in this way.

## 2. LAW DISCOVERY: AN EXAMPLE

We might ask how the premature dismissal of the possibility of a normative theory of discovery occurred. I suspect, but only suspect, that it occurred because the possibility of such a theory was supposed, erroneously, to depend on the solution of the problem of induction. The discovery process runs from particular facts to general laws that are somehow induced from them; the process of testing discoveries runs from the laws to predictions of particular facts deduced from them. Hence, ordinary, garden-variety deductive logic provides the formal foundation for a normative theory of law testing (in particular, of law falsification); while a normative theory of law discovery has been thought to require a quite different inductive logic as its foundation.

If this were the case, the normative theory of discovery would then share the difficulties of the inductive logic on which it rested. And if there is anything we can reach agreement upon with respect to inductive logic, it is that any particular proposed system of inductive logic (unless it is our own system) is defective. In the light of the innumerable, unsuccessful attempts to untie the Gordian knot of induction, we shall be well advised to cut it — to construct a normative theory for evaluating discovery processes that does not demand a deductive justification for the products of induction. I should now like to explain exactly how this can be done, beginning with a concrete example.

Consider the following sequence of letters:

ABMCDMEFMGHMIJMKLM
                            MNMOPMQRMSTMUVMWXMYZMABMC . . .

If we examine the sequence, we soon detect that it is patterned; that is to say, it is redundant, and can consequently be described more parsimoniously by defining the pattern than by exhibiting the sequence itself. In particular, it can be described as a sequence of triads. The first two letters of each triad progress through the alphabet, the third letter is an 'M'. Given an appropriate notation for patterns, we can represent the general triad of the sequence by some such pattern as:

$$n(\alpha)n(\alpha)s(\beta); \alpha = Z, \beta = M,$$

where '$n(\alpha)$' means replacing a symbol by the symbol next to it on the alphabet, $\alpha$; '$s(\beta)$' means repeating the same symbol as $\beta$; while the expressions '$\alpha = Z$' and '$\beta = M$' set the initial values on the alphabets, at Z and M, respectively. (The alphabets are assumed 'circular,' so that A follows Z.)

Are we really certain that (1) is the law of the sequence? Yes, for we can apply it to the sequence and see that it matches the letters that actually appear there. But what about the continuation of the sequence — the omitted letters indicated by dots? The expression (1) predicts that the extrapolation will begin with DMEFM, and so on; and there is no guarantee that it will in fact continue in this particular way. To provide a logical justification for the extrapolation, we need to appeal to some principle of the uniformity of nature, or some other premise of induction. We appear not to have avoided at all the troublesome problem of induction.

However, the difficulty with which we are confronted here is illusory. It does not arise at all in connection with discovering a pattern – recoding parsimoniously the portion of the sequence that was presented explicitly. It arises only if we wish to predict and test whether this same pattern will contine to govern the sequence when it is extrapolated. Law discovery means only finding pattern in the data that have been observed; whether the pattern will continue to hold for new data that are observed subsequently will be decided in the course of testing the law, not discovering it.

We will banish the problem of induction from our discussion of law discovery once and for all by defining:

> A *law-discovery process* is a process for recoding, in parsimonious fashion, sets of empirical data.

> A *normative theory of scientific discovery* is a set of criteria for evaluating law-discovery processes.

## 3. EFFICIENT AND INEFFICIENT LAW-DISCOVERY PROCESSES

We have seen that the discovery process has nothing to do with the usual problem of justifiying inductions, because the adequacy of the pattern to describe the sequence actually presented (as distinguished from its extrapolation) can be settled in purely finitary terms. There is no doubt at all that the particular pattern, (1), describes accurately the sequence of letters that was exhibited above. Of course no claim is made that this description is unique, or even that it is the most parsimonious possible.

But we have not explained how we discovered the pattern. To explain the discovery, do we have to postulate an 'irrational element' or a 'creative intuition?' Or, on the contrary, can we give a descriptive account of how people make such discoveries, and a normative account of relatively efficient ways of making them? If we can do the latter, then we will have constructed a logic of discovery – at least for simple situations like the one of the example.

Let us suppose that we have a pattern discovery process possessing means for representing the relations of *same* and *next*, so that it can compose formulas like '$n(\alpha)n(\alpha)s(\beta)$'. Then it can discover the pattern in a sequence by generating such formulas in some order – starting, say, with the simplest and generating progressively longer ones – testing each until it finds one that fits the actual sequence. In another context, Allen Newell and I have called such a generative process a 'British Museum Algorithm' (BMA) to honor the monkeys who were alleged to have used it to reproduce the volumes in the British Museum. For the simple case before us, the algorithm might actually succeed in a reasonable time. For example, it might generate a sequence of patterns like: s($\alpha$), n($\alpha$), s($\alpha$)s($\beta$), n($\alpha$)n($\beta$), s($\alpha$)n($\alpha$), s($\alpha$)n($\beta$), and so on. The pattern n($\alpha$)n($\alpha$)s($\beta$) would then occur among the first fifty or so generated.

It is easy, however, to construct a pattern discovery process that is far more efficient than the British Museum Algorithm. By drawing upon information that is explicit in the sequence presented, the algorithm can construct a suitable pattern directly, with little or no trial and error. It begins by scanning the sequence, and noting occurrences of the relations of *same* and *next* between symbols that are not too far separated. In the case before us, it would find that every third symbol in the sequence is an 'M'. From this fact it would conjecture that the sequence has a period of three symbols. It would then notice that the second symbol in each triad terminated by an 'M' is the successor in the alphabet of the first symbol, and that the first symbol is the successor in the alphabet of the second symbol of the previous triad. This information is sufficient to define the pattern 'n($\alpha$)n($\alpha$)s($\beta$)'. Finally, the initial conditions, $\alpha = Z$ and $\beta = M$, can be determined directly by matching with the appropriate symbols in the sequence.

If we are interested in reducing the amount of trial-and-error search required to find the formula that describes the sequence, then we will prefer this second algorithm (which we will call a Heuristic Search Algorithm – HSA) to the British Museum Algorithm. The BMA tries alternatives systematically until it finds one that works; the HSA extracts information from the sequence in order to generate directly an alternative that will work. The difference between the two algorithms is exactly parallel to the difference between solving an algebraic equation by trying possible solutions in some systematic order, and solving it by eliminating constants from the left side, next eliminating variables from the right side, and then dividing through by the coefficient of the variable.

The normative theory of discovery processes can be viewed as a branch of the theory of computational complexity. Given a class of computational problems, we wish to discover algorithms that are most efficient on average; or, if we cannot find the most efficient, at least to discover some that make good use of the information available in the problem situation. In the case of symbolic sequences like the example, this information consists in the periodic recurrence of certain symbols, or the periodic recurrence of *successor* relations between neighboring symbols drawn from the same ordered set.

It is not hard to write computer programs that will detect relations of these kinds, and conduct heuristic searches for pattern in an orderly and efficient way. Several such programs have, in fact, been written and tested with success on such materials as the Thurstone Letter Series Completion Test. The programs are vastly more efficient than would be a BMA-like program for the same task. (See [5] and [8].)

If there is a pattern in the sequence, of one of the kinds that the program is capable of detecting, it will be detected, and usually with a relatively small amount of search. Of course, failure to detect a pattern does not guarantee that one does not exist — a pattern, say, employing relations that are not within the program's competence. Given a particular class of potential patterns, however, some programs will regularly find patterns in this class much more rapidly and efficiently than will other programs. The normative theory of discovery is concerned with characterizing these efficient programs.

Moreover, the particular class of patterns we have been discussing in the example is not as specialized as might appear at first blush. The relation of *successor* in an ordered set (with the circularity convention mentioned above) defines a cyclic group on the set. This is just the capability we need to detect groups of symmetries; and most of the patterns we succeed in extracting from nature appear to be representable in terms of such groups. Consider, for example, the Periodic Law of Mendeleev. Discovering this law involves arranging the elements by the successor relation with respect to atomic weight, and then noting the periodic repetition of certain chemical properties (e.g. valence) in this list. Other examples of pattern discovery in science are discussed in Simon, [6].

## 4. CONCEPT ATTAINMENT: A SECOND EXAMPLE

The notion of informational efficiency of law-discovery processes can also be illustrated with an example drawn from the domain of concept attainment. In the standard psychological concept-attainment task, a sequence of stimuli is presented, some of which are positive instances of a concept and others negative instances. The goal is to discover the concept — that is, a criterion that will allow the positive instances to be distinguished from the negative instances.

Suppose that the stimuli vary in color, size, and shape. Suppose further that only simple concepts — a particular value on a particular dimension — are admitted. Thus, the concept in a given case might be 'circles'. A relatively inefficient process would examine the instances in sequence after selecting an initial hypothesis. If the hypothesis led to a wrong classification in any single case, it would be rejected and a new hypothesis tried. A much more efficient process would examine the instances in sequence and eliminate from further consideration the whole set of concepts inconsistent with each successive instance. In general, the number of instances the latter process would have to examine before selecting a concept that was consistent with the entire set would vary with the logarithm of the number of possible hypotheses. For the former process, it would vary linearly with the number of possible hypotheses. Clearly the expected number of trials needed to find the correct hypothesis is smaller with the more sophisticated process. Again, we can construct a normative theory that evaluates the relative power and sophistication of different discovery processes in this domain.

## 5. REPLY TO AN OBJECTION

A perceptive reader of an earlier draft of this paper observed that in arguing for the possibility of a logic of discovery I have used examples that prejudice the case in my favor. The examples envisage situations in which the range of alternatives can be delimited in advance (the sorts of patterns at issue, the range of possible hypotheses, or the like). These examples do not prove at all that outside the range of limited and 'artificial' problems one can, in science, define the processes of genuine innovation that redefine the range of alternatives that can be envisaged.

This objection rests on the commonly drawn distinction between well-structured problems, which are amenable to orderly analysis, and ill-structured problems, which are the exclusive domain of creativity. It is reminiscent also of the Kuhnian distinction between normal and revolutionary science. The objection depends for its force upon these distinctions being qualitative, and not merely matters of degree.

The simplest reply to the objection is to admit it, but to observe that it does not invalidate the thesis of this paper. As I observed in the introduction, those who have argued against the possibility of a logic of discovery have drawn no such distinction between 'normal' and 'revolutionary' discoveries. If a logic of discovery can be constructed for even one small realm — and my examples show that it can for several — then their arguments must be faulty. If they wish now to argue against the possibility only of a logic of revolutionary discovery, they will have to find new arguments that apply to this realm alone.

But I am not persuaded that even this much ground must be yielded to the objectors. The notion of 'delimiting in advance' the range of hypotheses to be considered is not at all a clear concept. We know that all that is required to generate an infinite number of elements from a finite set of primitives is some kind of recursively applicable rule of generation. Thus, *modus ponens* applied to a small finite set of axioms may suffice to generate an infinity of theorems; and an extremely simple phrase-structure or transformational grammer can spawn an infinite number of grammatical sentences. Have we any genuine reason to deny that 'revolutionary' hypotheses are the products of this kind of generation of much from little?

It was pointed out earlier that Mendeleev's Periodic Table does not involve a notion of pattern more complex than that required to handle patterned letter sequences. To be sure, Mendeleev had to conjecture that atomic weight was the attribute according to which the elements should be ordered. But it should be observed that he made his discovery just a few years after the notion of atomic weight had been clarified, its central importance had been accepted, and the atomic weights of most of the known elements had been determined. The space of possible (or plausible) patterns in which Mendeleev was searching was perhaps of rather modest size. And, indeed, at least a half dozen of Mendeleev's contemporaries had noticed the pattern independently of him, although they had not exploited it as systematically or vigorously as he did.

Before we accept the hypothesis, therefore, that 'revolutionary science' is not subject to laws of effective search we would do well to await more microscopic studies than have generally been made to date of the histories of revolutionary discoveries. The case of Mendeleev may prove to be not at all exceptional. At present, one can argue this only as a possiblity. But as long as it is a possiblity, we must receive with skepticism arguments that would seek to prove the 'impossibility' of a logic of scientific discovery – even revolutionary discovery.

### 6. CONCLUSION

The simple examples cited in this paper show that one can construct a normative theory – a 'logic', if you will – of discovery processes. The greater efficacy of one process compared with another in discovering laws need not be attributed to chance, irrationality, or creative intuition. Rather, it is a matter of which process is the more capable of detecting the pattern information contained in the data, and using this information to recode the data in more parsimonious form.

At present, in the field of artificial intelligence, there exist the beginnings of a normative theory of problem solving – a theory of the design of effective problem-solving algorithms. (See, for example, Nilsson [3], and Simon [7].) The normative theory of pattern-discovery is less far advanced, partly because fewer successful examples have been constructed of powerful pattern discovery programs. Our analysis suggests, however, that this difference in stage of development is rather to be viewed as an historical accident than as an indication of some fundamental qualitative difference in the requirements for normative theory in these two domains.

The fact that a process can extract pattern from finite data sets says nothing about the predictive power of the patterns so extracted for new observations. As we move from pattern detection to prediction, we move from the theory of discovery processes to the theory of processes for testing laws. To explain why the patterns we extract from observations frequently lead to correct predictions (when they do) requires us to face again the problem of induction, and perhaps to make some hypothesis about the uniformity of nature. But that hypothesis is neither required for, nor relevant to, the theory of discovery processes. The latter theory does not assert that data are patterned. Rather, it shows how pattern is to be detected if it is there. This is not a descriptive or psychological matter, it is normative and logical. By separating the question of pattern detection from the question of prediction, we can construct a true normative theory of discovery – a logic of discovery.

## NOTES

*This research has been supported by a Public Health Service Grant from the National Institute of Mental Health, and by the Advanced Research Projects Agency of the Office of the Secretary of Defense, which is monitored by the Air Force Office of Scientific Research. I am indebted to Nicholas Rescher for valuable comments on an earlier draft of this paper.
[1] For another essay taking essentially the same view as this one toward the possibility of a logic of discovery, and considering at length the philosophical objections to this view, see Buchanan, [1].

## REFERENCES

[1] Buchanan, B. G., *Logics of Scientific Discovery*, A. I. Memo 47 (Computer Science Department, Stanford University, 1966).
[2] Hanson, N. R., *Patterns of Discovery* (Cambridge: Cambridge University Press, 1958).
[3] Nilsson, N. J., *Problem-Solving Methods in Artificial Intelligence* (New York: McGraw-Hill, 1971).
[4] Popper, K. R., *The Logic of Scientific Discovery* (London: Hutchinson and Company, 1959).

[5] Simon, H. A. and Kotovsky, K., 'Human Acquisition of Concepts for Serial Patterns', *Psychological Review* 70, 534–546 (1963).

[6] Simon, H. A., 'On Judging the Plausibility of Theories', in *Logic, Methodology and Philosophy of Science,* Vol. III. Edited by B. Van Rootselar and J. F. Staal (Amsterdam: North-Holland Publishing Company, 1968), (reprinted as Chapter 1.4 in this volume).

[7] Simon, H. A., 'The Theory of Problem Solving', *Information Processing* 71 (1972). (reprinted as Chapter 4.3 in this volume).

[8] Simon, H. A. and Lea, G., 'Problem Solving and Rule Induction: a Unified View', in *Knowledge and Cognition,* edited by L. W. Gregg, (New York: Halsted-Wiley, 1974).

# DISCUSSION: THE *MENO* PARADOX†

An argument of Michael Polanyi ([3], pp. 21–24) for the necessity of 'tacit knowledge', based upon the paradox of the *Meno* is refuted correctly by Michael Bradie [1] who observes that the paradox, in Polanyi's version, rests on the false premise that "if you know what you are looking for, there is no problem". Bradie's refutation is based on an example, but he does not explain how the example works or why Polanyi's premise is generally fallacious. It is the purpose of this note to describe some classes of conditions under which Polanyi's premise will be false. I have given the argument less formally elsewhere ([4] and [5]), but will try to make it more precise here.

Polanyi's thesis ([3], p. 4) is that "we can know more than we can tell". In part, he supports the thesis by citing empirical phenomena that appear to imply the existence of tacit knowledge: that we can recognize faces without knowing how we do it ([3], pp. 4–7); that a human subject, in psychological experiments, can acquire certain conditioned responses without awareness of the stimulus that is being conditioned ([3], pp. 7–10); that we can only understand the behavior of another person by an unanalyzed empathetic process ([3], pp. 16–17); that when we attend repeatedly to the pronunciation of a word (i.e., to the tacit knowledge whereby we recognize it), it loses its meaning ([3], p. 18). He follows these examples by a general argument ([3], pp. 20–21): "in order that we may formalize the relations that constitute a comprehensive entity ... this entity ... must be first identified informally by tacit knowing." Finally ([3], pp. 21–23), he argues that "the *Meno* shows conclusively that if all knowledge is explicit, i.e., capable of being clearly stated, then we cannot know a problem or look for its solution. And the *Meno* also shows, therefore, that if problems nevertheless exist, and discoveries can be made by solving them, we can know things, and important things, that we cannot tell."

Thus, the *Meno* paradox provides only one of several arguments on which Polanyi rests his thesis of the need for tacit knowledge, but one on which he places great emphasis. This note is limited to showing the invalidity of this particular argument, and does not address itself to the general question of

† [*Philosophy of Science* **43**, 147–151 (1976)].

whether or not Polanyi's thesis is valid. The *Meno* paradox, based as it is upon Plato's theory of knowledge as recollection, has sufficient historical and philosophical interest to merit treatment in its own right.

Consider a formal system $S$ of the usual kind (see Mendelson [2] for details): it contains a countable set of symbols, finite sequences of which are called *expressions;* a subset $F$ of the expressions are called *well-formed-formulas* (wffs) of $S$, and a set of the $F$'s are called *axioms.* There is a finite set $R$ of relations among $F$'s called *rules of inference.* If there are $j$ wffs that stand in the relation $R_j$ to a wff $C$, where $R_j$ is one of the rules of inference, then $C$ is a *direct consequence* of these $j$ wffs. A *proof* in $S$ is a sequence of wffs, each of whose members is either an axiom of $S$ or a direct consequence of some of the preceding wffs by virtue of the rules of inference. A *theorem* $T$ of $S$ is a wff such that there is a proof in $S$ whose final member is $T$.

We suppose further that there is an effective procedure to determine whether a given expression in $S$ is a wff; that there is an effective procedure to determine whether a given wff is an axiom; and that there is an effective procedure for determining whether a given wff, $C$, is a direct consequence of some other given set of wffs.

A *problem* can now be posed for the system $S$ by generating a wff, call it $P$, and setting the task of determining whether $P$ is a theorem of $S$. Now $P$ is a theorem of $S$ if and only if $P$ is the final member of some proof of $S$. Hence, we know exactly what we are looking for: we are looking for a sequence of wffs such that each member is a direct consequence of some previous members and $P$ is the final member. Moreover, the effective procedures available to us enable us to determine whether any object presented to us is such a sequence.

Notice that our ability to know what we are looking for does *not* depend upon our having an effective procedure for finding it: we need only an effective procedure for *testing* candidates. Of course, even if the former procedure exists, so that the system $S$ is decidable, actually finding a proof may be a non-trivial task. Hence, we can define theorem-proving problems, without tacit knowledge, in both decidable and non-decidable systems.

Since not all problems are problems of proving theorems, we wish to generalize our result. Consider a system containing wffs, as before, together with two distinct effective procedures for generating certain subsets of wffs. Call the subsets $A$ and $B$. Now we can generate a member of $A$, and set the problem of determining whether it is also a member of $B$. Again, we know exactly what we are looking for: a sequence of members of $B$ whose final member is the desired member of $A$. We can give to each member of $A$ a name: the letter 'A' prefixed to the number designating the order in which it will be generated by the first effective procedure. Similarly we can give to each member of $B$ a name formed by prefixing 'B' to the corresponding order number for the second effective procedure. Now we can state problems of the form: find a B-name for the wff whose A-name is $An$, where $n$ is a definite number.

The particular form of naming proposed in the previous paragraph is not important to our scheme. What we require are two generators, each of which generates some set of objects that can be referred to by definite names, together with an effective procedure that, when given an object from each of the two sets, decides whether they are the same object or different objects. For example, the first generator could generate numbers named as successors of zero (e.g., $0''''''''$), while the second generator could generate numbers named by their prime factors expressed in decimal notation (e.g., $2^2 \times 3$). A simple procedure could then make the judgments of equality by recoding the former numbers decimally, performing the multiplications indicated for the latter, and comparing the recoded results for identity.

Finally, let us reexamine the example that Bradie used to refute Polanyi's premise. Bradie considers a mathematician who seeks to refute Goldbach's conjecture (that every even number is representable as the sum of two primes) by finding a counterexample: i.e., an even number that is not the sum of two primes. Any number can be named (uniquely) in decimal notation. Alternatively, it can be named (possibly non-uniquely) as a sum of two other numbers. An addition operator provides an effective procedure for determining whether a given number, named in the former fashion, is identical with a number named in the latter. Thus, the addition operator will decide that $(5 + 5)$ is identical with 10; but that $(3 + 5)$ is not identical with 9. Now the mathematician sets up an effective procedure for generating the even numbers, and another effective procedure for generating all pairs of prime numbers whose sum is less than some $n$. With these procedures he can now define the problem of looking for a refutation of Goldbach's conjecture: find a number $k$ generated by the first procedure that does not belong to the numbers generated by the second procedure for $n = k$. Thus we see that Bradie's example fits our general scheme for defining problem solutions prior to finding them.

## REFERENCES

[1]  Bradie, M., 'Polanyi on the Meno Paradox', *Philosophy of Science* 41, 203 (1974).
[2]  Mendelson, E., *Introduction to Mathematical Logic* (Princeton, New Jersey: D. Van Nostrand, 1964).

[3] Polanyi, M., *The Tacit Dimension* (Garden City, New York: Doubleday & Co 1967).

[4] Simon, H. A., 'The Logic of Heuristic Decision Making', in *The Logic of Decision and Action*, ed. by N. Rescher (Pittsburgh, Pennsylvania: University of Pittsburgh Press 1967) (reprinted as Chapter 3.2 in this volume).

[5] Simon, H. A., 'The Architecture of Complexity', *Proceedings of the American Philosophical Society* **106**, 467–482 (1962). See also Chapter 4.4 in this volume.

# FORMALIZING
# SCIENTIFIC THEORIES

The research reported in this section began with a modest inquiry into the axioms of·classical mechanics, which then drew me into more and more fundamental questions of the nature of definitions in empirical theories, and finally into a general inquiry into the status of theoretical terms. The path of investigation was full of surprises for me, and I hope that these chapters, which appear here in the order of their original publication, will capture a bit of the suspense of the long adventure they represented for me.

## 1. THE AXIOMATIZATION OF MECHANICS

Until I rediscovered recently my embryonic thesis outline of 1937 (see General Introduction), I had alway supposed that the topic of Chapter 6.1, which sets the central question for all of the papers of this section, had found its way onto my agenda more or less by accident. In the mid-1940's, I attended a course in theoretical mechanics offered by my colleague Eli Sternberg at the Illinois Institute of Technology. As I consulted textbooks in the field, I became less and less satisfied with the definitions of mass that I found in them. Some introduced mass as 'quantity of matter'. Others used the Second Law of Motion as a definition: 'mass equals force divided by acceleration'. A few drew upon Mach's definition in terms of mutual accelerations. The loose and vague axiomatic foundations of these texts stood in glaring contrast to the mathematical rigor of their subsequent derivations. When further search failed to reveal even a single treatment of the axioms of mechanics subsequent to Mach's that met reasonable standards of clarity (I did not encounter Pendse's papers until my own was written), I constructed the axiomatization of Chapter 6.1.

Part I of Chapter 6.1 sets forth the grounds of my unhappiness even with Mach's attempts to define mass, and also explains why I chose the arena of celestial mechanics for my definition. Specifically, it seemed to me that a definition must be suspect unless it took account of *all* the interactions among the components of the system to which it was applied. That kind of isolation could not be guaranteed for terrestrial phenomena.

A second guiding consideration in constructing the axiomatization was that it should show how the numerical values of the defined terms could be estimated from empirical observations. In celestial mechanics, the only observables are the time paths of stars and planets relative to an arbitrary reference system. Concepts were to be defined by expressing them in terms of these observed time paths – and, moreover, in such a way that their values would be invariant under admissible transformations of the reference system. These are, of course, requirements of identifiability, but that term had not even been invented when I wrote my paper, and the connection with the identification problem did not occur to me until I became involved in the work that led to Chapter 2.1 a few years later.

Six years after the publication of the paper of Chapter 6.1, McKinsey, Sugar and Suppes[1] produced an alternative axiomatization, strikingly different from mine in motivation and formulation, and constituting one important step of progress and two of retrogress. The progress was in the formalism used: 'system of Newtonian mechanics' was defined as a set-theoretic predicate. The retrogress was in ignoring all the issues of identifiability that I had raised, and handled, in my paper. In some of my subsequent work (see especially Chapter 6.5), I have tried to capture the virtues of both the McKinsey-Sugar-Suppes approach and my own by employing a set-theoretic predicate, but without losing sight of the questions of identifiability. In *The Logical Structure of Mathematical Physics*,[2] Sneed has employed a definition of 'momentum particle mechanics' that is essentially identical with the set-theoretic predicate for a Newtonian system of particle mechanics defined in Chapter 6.5. Although Sneed's discussion (pp. 131–153) of the identifiability of mass and force is somewhat inconclusive, his conclusions appear to be in essential agreement with Chapters 6.1. through 6.5.

## 2. DEFINABILITY AND IDENTIFIABILITY

In their 1953 paper, McKinsey *et al.*, raised a technical objection to the definition of mass in Chapter 6.1. By application of the method of Padoa, they showed that the alleged definition does not meet the conditions for definability proposed by Tarski. One could respond to their objection in either of two ways: (1) by accepting the conclusion that mass is a primitive term, or (2) by concluding that Tarski's concept of definability is not the appropriate one for use in axiomatizing empirical theories. For reasons that are set forth in Chapter 6.3, I chose the second alternative and undertook to find a slightly weakened notion of definability that would fit the axiomatization of Chapter 6.1. My initial candidates were 'generic definability' and 'definability almost everywhere', both explained in Chapter 6.3. Montague, in a rather savage review of that chapter,[3] demonstrated that 'generic definability' was far too weak for its intended purpose. The concept of definability almost everywhere, which appears closer to the mark, is treated more formally in the brief Chapter 6.4. In Section 3.4 of Chapter 6.5, I return to this topic again, and propose there a concept of 'general definability', which appears to serve the purpose for which I had earlier intended 'generic definability', but does not suffer from the logical deficiencies of the latter concept. My present views on this topic are still represented accurately by Chapter 6.5.

## 3. THE STATUS OF THEORETICAL TERMS

The difficulties of incorporating technically adequate definitions of theoretical terms like 'mass' and 'force' in axiomatizations of classical mechanics raise the general question of the meaningfulness of such terms when definition is impossible. Many years ago Ramsey had pointed out that the testability of a theory containing undefined theoretical terms would not be endangered if these terms were *eliminable* – that is, if all the empirical claims of the theory could be expressed without them. Ramsey apparently believed that all theoretical terms would be eliminable from any properly formulated scientific theory, but that not all need be definable. Sneed, however, produced examples of simple systems containing non-eliminable terms.

Chapter 6.6, which I wrote with Guy Groen, argues that Sneed's examples of non-eliminable theoretical terms are, in a certain precise sense, pathological. Only theories, we propose, are to be admitted that satisfy certain conditions of testability – namely, that are finitely and irrevocably testable (FIT). We show that theoretical terms are always eliminable from theories that meet these conditions.

Tuomela[4] and others have raised the objection that the FITness conditions are too strong – that they exclude systems that we would want to regard as proper theories. There are examples from the theory of fundamental measurement – for instance, some axiomatizations of conjoint measurement – that are not finitely and irrevocably testable. However, in these cases alternative axiomatizations are known that are FIT, and there are reasons for believing that such alternatives will always be available. This claim is discussed briefly in Chapter 6.7, but making it precise and proving it is work for the future.

The largest part of Chapter 6.7 is devoted to weaving together the main themes of Sections 2 and 6, pertaining to definability, eliminability, and identifiability of theoretical terms, and to showing the relation of these notions to the concept of meaningfulness. Making use of Hintikka's definition of depth of information, the chapter shows that theoretical terms, even if eliminable, may serve to reduce the maximum depth of sentences in an axiom system. A final section of the chapter returns to the topic of mechanisms, first introduced in Section 2, deriving from it a possible answer to Sneed's call for "a rationale for the practice of exploiting values of theoretical functions obtained in one application of [a] theory to draw conclusions about other applications of the theory."

## NOTES

[1] 'Axiomatic Foundations of Classical Particle Mechanics', *Journal of Rational Mechanics and Analysis* 2, 253–72 (1953).
[2] Dordrecht: Reidel, 1971.
[3] *Journal of Symbolic Logic* 25, 355–6 (1960).
[4] *Theoretical Concepts* (New York: Springer-Verlag, 1973).

# THE AXIOMS OF NEWTONIAN MECHANICS†

Although the laws of Newtonian mechanics are now acknowledged to be only approximately correct, classical mechanics is still the tool used by all save the nuclear physicists and the astronomers. No apology should be needed, therefore, for an investigation of the axioms of Newtonian mechanics. The fact that these axioms are not in exact accord with physical experience does not in any way imply that they cannot be stated clearly, precisely, operationally, and without internal contradiction. It is the aim of this paper to develop an axiom system that meets these standards.

There was widespread interest among physicists of the last half of the nineteenth century in the axiomatization of mechanics. Analysis of Newton's formulation in the *Principia* led to two lines of activity: first, the clarification of the concepts of 'mass' and 'force', and second, the elucidation of 'absolute' and 'relative' time, space, and motion. The latter line of investigation attracted the most interest, and was involved in the discovery of the special theory of relativity. This discovery, in turn, diverted attention almost completely from the axiomatization of classical mechanics. It is only very recently that any new attempts appear to have been made to further examine Newtonian mass and force.[1]

Perhaps the most important product of the nineteenth century's studies in axiomatics, so far as mass and force are concerned, is Ernst Mach's reformulation of the laws of motion.[2] The most careful statements of the axioms to be found in modern textbooks follow closely those of Mach. Hence, the present paper will begin with a re-examination of Mach's formulation and then proceed to a modified statement which, it is hoped, amends Mach at those points where he falls short of modern standards of 'operationalism'.

## 1. MACH'S STATEMENT OF THE LAWS OF MOTION

As already suggested, the laws of motion can be treated in two parts. First, rules can be stated for motion relative to a given reference system. Second,

†[*The Philosophical Magazine, Ser.* 7, 38, 888–905 (1947)].

rules can be stated for the selection of an appropriate reference system. (It will appear presently that these two parts are not entirely independent.)

With respect to the first part, Mach's principal contribution was to transform Newton's laws into kinematic definitions of force and mass. The first and second laws he treated not as physical hypotheses, but as definitions of force; and the third law follows as a consequence of his definitions of mass and force. All that remained of physical hypothesis as distinguished from definition in his version of Newton's system were the assumptions that:

(a) the mass ratios of two bodies A and B (say $m_{A/B}$) remain constant over time, and

(b) the mass ratios of bodies are transitive, i.e. $m_{A/C} = m_{A/B} \cdot m_{B/C}$.

For purposes of reference we give here Mach's definitions and hypotheses as stated in 'The Science of Mechanics':[3]

a. *Experimental Proposition*. Bodies set opposite each other induce in each other, under certain circumstances to be specified by experimental physics, contrary accelerations in the direction of their line of junction. (The principle of inertia is included in this.)

b. *Definition*. The mass-ratio of any two bodies is the negative inverse ratio of the mutually induced accelerations of those bodies.

c. *Experimental Proposition*. The mass-ratios of bodies are independent of the character of the physical states (of the bodies) that condition the mutual accelerations produced, be those states electrical, magnetic, or what not; and they remain, moreover, the same, whether they are mediately or immediately arrived at.

d. *Experimental Proposition*. The accelerations which any number of bodies A, B, C,... induce in a body K, are independent of each other. (The principle of the parallelogram of forces follows immediately from this.)

e. *Definition*. Moving force is the product of the mass-value of a body into the acceleration induced in that body.

This statement certainly represents a substantial advance in clarity over Newton's formulation. One point deserves special notice: the definition of mass is purely inertial, that is, it makes no reference to the gravitational or other special forces acting on the system. In this respect its viewpoint differs rather fundamentally from that of general relativity theory.[4]

In spite of their virtues, the laws stated by Mach raise some disturbing questions. First, in his definition of mass, Mach speaks of one body 'inducing' an acceleration in another. It is not clear what 'inducing' means. Two bodies are placed close to one another. Perhaps they are magnetized, or electrified, or even connected by a spring. It is observed that these bodies undergo certain accelerations (relative to some reference system). Are these the 'mutually induced accelerations' of which Mach speaks? How do we know that the accelerations produced are not due to the presence of other bodies in the environment of the two under consideration? Since the accelerations, and hence the mass ratio, depend upon the reference frame chosen, how do we select the 'correct' reference frame?

A solution of these difficulties might take one of several paths.

1. It might be possible to 'isolate' the two particles in question, so that the influences of other bodies are eliminated. Even if it be admitted that a mental experiment of this kind can be performed (and this is directly contrary to Mach's insistence that the existence of the world *as given* cannot be ignored or wished away in the statement of physical laws), it is hard to see how this ideal experiment could lead to the determination of mass in actual cases. In the solar system, for example, there are given not two bodies but several dozen, all members of an inter-related system. Moreover, it is not clear what 'isolation' means here, or how it could be assumed that spatial isolation implies dynamic isolation.

2. It might be admitted that two bodies cannot be isolated from the rest of the world, but asserted instead that two bodies can be placed in identical force fields, so far as environmental bodies are concerned, so that their accelerations can be analysed into 'external' and 'mutually induced' components. This would still not be satisfactory, as shown by Filon, unless the external force-field were at right angles to the line joining the two bodies. Moreover, this approach already involves a circularity, because the forces are only defined when the masses are known, and what is worse, the concept of a *component force* as distinguished from that of a *resultant force* (or moving force, as Mach calls it), has not even been introduced.

3. It might be possible to deduce from the accelerations of a *set* of bodies a unique set of component accelerations which could be used to determine the mass ratios. This really does not avoid the previous difficulties, for it is necessary to assume that the bodies of the given set are not accelerated by 'external' forces or are all accelerated equally, and this is an additional assumption involving also the notion of component force together with the parallelogram law. Even if these difficulties are overcome, it is necessary to show that the masses are uniquely determined by this procedure.

A second difficulty, closely related to the foregoing one, is that Mach does not indicate the connection between the static force that is measured by a spring dynamometer, and the moving force defined by Newton's second law. The removal of this difficulty, too, requires the introduction of the concept of component force.

A third difficulty is that the formulation assumes the mass-ratios are independent of the reference system chosen to determine them, or at least that there is an independent criterion for choosing the proper reference system.[5] If it turns out that mass-ratios are not independent of the reference system, then it is inadmissible to refer the motions of a set of bodies to a reference system whose choice depends upon the masses; unless the masses of the bodies are already known, or are simultaneously determined.

A final general objection to Mach's statement, which includes the difficulties raised already, is the presence, in (a), of the vague phrase 'under certain circumstances to be specified by experimental physics'. The circumstances here referred to must certainly include a specification of the conditions under which two bodies or a system of bodies may be considered 'isolated', as well as a specification of the reference system. But it needs also to be clarified whether there are circumstances in addition to these two that must be specified before (a) and (b) can be employed.

The remainder of this paper will be devoted to the exposition of an axiom system which, it is believed, meets these difficulties. In Section 2 the concept of mass will be introduced. The problem of isolation will be avoided (or postponed) by following the third of the possible lines of action outlined above: defining mass for sets, rather than pairs, of bodies. It will be shown that the concept of mass need not involve the idea of component accelerations or forces. In Section 3 and 4 a solution will be offered for the problem of selecting a unique reference system. In Section 5 the notion of component force will be introduced, and a method set forth for connecting the operations used to measure dynamic forces with the operations used to measure static forces.

## 2. THE DEFINITION OF MASS

DEFINITION 1.    A motion, $(\pi)$, is a finite point-set, $\{P_i\}$, $(i = 1, \ldots, n)$, on which is defined, for $a \leqslant t \leqslant b$, a regular vector function

$$\bar{r}_i(t) = \bar{r}_i[x_i(t), y_i(t), z_i(t)].$$

Here $x, y, z$ and $t$ are real numbers, and $x, y, z$ are single-valued functions of $t$.

DEFINITION 2.    The vector $\bar{r}_i(t)$ is called the position of $P_i$ at $t$ in the motion $(\pi)$.

DEFINITION 3.    If there exists a set of scalars $\{m_i\}$, $m_i \neq 0$, $(i = 1, \ldots, n)$, constant with respect to $t$, such that

(a) $$\sum_{i=1}^{n} m_i \ddot{\bar{r}}_i(t) \equiv 0.$$

(b) $$\sum_{i=1}^{n} m_i \ddot{\bar{r}}_i(t) \times \bar{r}_i(t) \equiv 0, \tag{1}$$

both identically in $t$, than the set $\{P_i\}$, together with the associated vectors $\{\bar{r}_i(t)\}$ and scalars $\{m_i\}$ is called an *isolated motion*, $[\pi]$.

*Comment.*    Equations (1) are equivalent to the statement that the system of external forces acting upon the $\{P_i\}$ is statically equivalent to zero. It is preferable, however, to avoid this mode of expression at the present stage, since the notion of force has not yet been introduced. It may also be mentioned that, once force is defined, equations (1) follow from the third law of motion. Only so much of the third law as is contained in (1) is needed in the present exposition.

Equations (1), deduced from the third law in its usual form, were used to calculate mass by Pendse (1939), on a suggestion from E. A. Milne. Pendse, however, employed Mach's definition of mass instead of basing his definition directly upon Equations (1).

DEFINITION 4.    The element $P_i$, together with the functions $\bar{r}_i$ and $m_i$ defined on it, is called a *mass point* or *particle* in $[\pi]$.

DEFINITION 5.    The scalar $m_i$ is called the *mass* of $P_i$ in $[\pi]$. The set of $\{m_i\}$ can be considered a scalar function defined on the point-set $\{P_i\}$.

*Comment.*    From Definition 3 it is seen that a necessary condition for the existence of the $\{m_i\}$ is that the set of functions $\ddot{\bar{r}}_i(t)$ be linearly dependent, and similarly the set $\ddot{\bar{r}}_i(t) \times \bar{r}_i(t)$. This is not sufficient, however, since we also require that all the $m_i$ differ from zero. In any event the existence of $\{m_i\}$ for a given $(\pi)$ is by no means trivial. The question of the uniqueness of the $\{m_i\}$ for a given $(\pi)$ is settled by Theorems I and II.

THEOREM I.    A necessary and sufficient condition that the $\{m_i\}$ of an isolated motion $[\pi]$ be unique within a factor of proportionality is that there exist no proper subset, $(\pi')$, of the motion $(\pi)$ for which a set $\{m_i'\}$ of Definition 3 can be found.

*Proof.* For convenience we introduce the notation

$$\phi_{\rho i}(t) \qquad (\rho = 1, \ldots, 6),$$

where

$$\phi_{1i}(t) = \ddot{x}_i(t); \quad \phi_{2i}(t) = \ddot{y}_i(t); \quad \phi_{3i}(t) = \ddot{z}_i(t);$$
$$\phi_{4i}(t) = (\ddot{y}_i(t)z_i(t) - \ddot{z}_i(t)y_i(t));$$
$$\phi_{5i}(t) = (\ddot{z}_i(t)x_i(t) - \ddot{x}_i(t)z_i(t));$$
$$\phi_{6i}(t) = (\ddot{x}_i(t)y_i(t) - \ddot{y}_i(t)x_i(t)).$$

Then the conditions (a) and (b) of Definition 3 may be written

$$\sum_{i=1}^{n} (m_i)\phi_{\rho i}(t) \equiv 0, \qquad (\rho = 1, \ldots, 6). \tag{2}$$

Ad Sufficiency. – Since $[\pi]$ is an isolated motion, we have

$$\sum_{i=1}^{n} m_i \phi_{\rho i}(t) \equiv 0, \qquad (\rho = 1, \ldots, 6).$$

Suppose the $\{m_i\}$ not unique. Then there exists a set $\{m_i'\}$, $m_i' \neq 0$ for all $i$, such that the $\{m_i'\}$ are not proportional to the $\{m_i\}$. Multiply the $\{m_i'\}$ by $\lambda = m_1/m_1'$ so that $m_i'' = \lambda m_i'$. Then $m_1 = m_1''$, and:

$$\sum_{i=2}^{n} (m_i - m_i'')\phi_{\rho i}(t) = 0, \qquad (\rho = 1, \ldots, 6). \tag{3}$$

Now define $\mu_i = m_i - m_i''$ $(i = 2, \ldots, n)$. Not all the $\mu_i$ vanish, otherwise the $\{m_i'\}$ would be proportional to the $\{m_i\}$. Then the set of those $\mu_i$ for which $\mu_i \neq 0$ are masses for the corresponding $(\pi')$, for

$$\Sigma \mu_i \phi_{\rho i}(t) \equiv 0, \qquad (\rho = 1, \ldots, 6), \tag{4}$$

where the sum is taken over all $i$ for which $\mu_i \neq 0$.

Ad Necessity. – Suppose, *per contra*, there is a proper subset $\{P_i'\}$ of $\{P_i\}$, on which is defined an isolated motion $[\pi']$, with masses $\{\mu_i\}$, $(i = 1, \ldots, k)$. We have:

$$\sum_{i=1}^{k} \mu_i \phi_{\rho i}(t) = 0, \qquad (\rho = 1, \ldots, 6). \tag{5}$$

Also, by hypothesis:

$$\sum_{i=1}^{n} m_i \phi_{\rho i}(t) = 0, \qquad (\rho = 1, \ldots, 6). \tag{6}$$

Define $\lambda_i = |m_i/\mu_i|$. Select any non-zero constant, $\lambda$, such that $\lambda \neq \lambda_i (i = 1, \ldots, k)$. This is always possible since $\{\lambda_i\}$ is a finite set. Define $m_i' = m_i + \lambda\mu_i$ for $i = 1, \ldots, k$, and $m_i' = m_i$ for $i = k+1, \ldots, n$. Then $m_i' \neq 0 \, (i = 1, \ldots, n)$, and

$$\sum_{i=1}^{n} m_i' \phi_{\rho i}(t) = \sum_{i=1}^{k} \lambda\mu_i \phi_{\rho i}(t) + \sum_{i=1}^{n} m_i \phi_{\rho i}(t) = 0,$$

$$(\rho = 1, \ldots, 6),$$

since each of the two terms on the right-hand side is zero by hypothesis. Then $\{m_i'\}$ together with $(\pi)$, $(i = 1, \ldots, n)$, define an isolated motion distinct from that defined by the $\{m_i\}$. But this is contrary to the hypothesis that the $\{m_i\}$ are unique.

DEFINITION 6.    An isolated motion which determines the $\{m_i\}$ uniquely, within a factor of proportionality, will be called *holomorphic*.

THEOREM II.    Let $(\pi)$ be a motion of the set $\{P_i\}$. Let

$$[\pi_\alpha], [\pi_\beta], \ldots, [\pi_\omega]$$

be all the holomorphic motions which exist for subsets of the $\{P_i\}$, say $\{P_i^\alpha\}$, $\{P_i^\beta\}$, etc., respectively. These subsets need not be disjoint. Let $\{\mu_i^\alpha\}$, $\{\mu_i^\beta\}$, etc., be the (unique) masses of the holomorphic motions. Then a necessary and sufficient condition that $\{m_i\}$, $(i = 1, \ldots, n)$, together with $(\pi)$ define an isolated motion is that

$$m_i = \sum_{k=\alpha}^{\omega} \lambda_k \mu_i^k, \quad \text{and} \quad m_i \neq 0 \, (i = 1, \ldots, n), \tag{7}$$

where the $\lambda$'s are arbitrary constants associated with the several sets, and where we take $\mu_i^k = 0$ whenever $P_i$ is not a member of the set $\{P_i^k\}$.

Ad Sufficiency. — By hypothesis,

$$\sum_{P_i \text{ in } \{P_i^k\}} \lambda_k \mu_i^k \phi_{\rho i} = 0, \quad (\rho = 1, \ldots, 6; k = \alpha, \ldots, \omega). \tag{8}$$

The summation here is for all the $P_i$ that are members of the particular subset $\{P_i^k\}$ of $\{P_i\}$. Since we have defined $\mu_i^k = 0$ for those $P_i$ that are not members of $\{P_i^k\}$, we may write this more simply

$$\sum_{i=1}^{n} \lambda_k \mu_i^k \phi_{\rho i} = 0, \quad (\rho = 1, \ldots, 6; k = \alpha, \ldots, \omega). \tag{9}$$

From our definition of the $\{m_i\}$, we have

$$\sum_{i=1}^{n} m_i \phi_{\rho i} = \sum_{i=1}^{n} \sum_{k=\alpha}^{\omega} \lambda_k \mu_i^k \phi_{\rho i},$$

or

$$\sum_{i=1}^{n} m_i \phi_{\rho i} = \sum_{k=\alpha}^{\omega} \sum_{i=1}^{n} \lambda_k \mu_i^k \phi_{\rho i} \equiv 0, \quad (\rho = 1, \ldots, 6). \tag{10}$$

Ad Necessity. – Suppose, *per contra*, there is a set $\{m_i\}$ satisfying definition 3, for which (7) does not hold. Select a set of representative points, $\Gamma$, as follows:

(a) choose any $P_i$ belonging to certain of the subsets $\{P_i^k\}$;

(b) Select a second representative belonging to at least one of the subsets to which the first representative does not belong;

(c) continue this process until each subset contains at least one representative.

Let the set complementary to $\Gamma$ be designated $\Omega$. Now select $\lambda$'s for each of the subsets $\{P_i^k\}$, $(k = \alpha, \ldots, \omega)$, such that, for each $P_i$ in $\Gamma$,

$$m_i = \sum_{k=\alpha}^{\omega} \lambda_k \mu_i^k, \quad (i \text{ in } \Gamma), \tag{11}$$

where we take $\mu_i^k = 0$ when $P_i$ is not a member of the set $\{P_i^k\}$. Such a set of $\lambda$'s always exists, and can be found as follows: – number the $P_i$ in $\Gamma$ from 1 to $\Gamma$ in the order in which they were selected. Consider the first representative. $\lambda$'s can always be found to satisfy $m_1 = \sum_{k=\alpha}^{\omega} \lambda_k \mu_1^k$ for given values of $m_1$ and $\mu_1^k$. Now in the second equation of (11) there will appear at least one $\lambda$ that did not appear in the first. Hence, by choosing an appropriate value for this $\lambda$ (or these $\lambda$'s), the second equation can be satisfied. This process is continued until $\Gamma$ is exhausted. Now, for all members of $\{P_i\}$ take

$$m_i' = m_i - \sum_{k=\alpha}^{\omega} \lambda_k \mu_i^k, \quad (i = 1, \ldots, n). \tag{12}$$

Then $m_i' = 0$ for all the points in $\Gamma$, but there must exist at least one $P_i$ in $\Omega$ for which $m_i' \neq 0$, otherwise (7) is satisfied, contrary to hypothesis. Let $\theta$ be the subset of $\Omega$ for which $m_i' \neq 0$ ($P_i$ in $\theta$). Then the $\{m_i'\}$ define an isolated motion on the $\{P_i^\theta\}$ for we have

$$\sum_{P_i \text{ in } \{P_i^\theta\}} m_i' \phi_{\rho i} = 0, \quad (\rho = 1, \ldots, 6). \tag{13}$$

Call this isolated motion $[\pi_\theta]$. Then $[\pi_\theta]$ either is holomorphic or contains a holomorphic motion. But $\Gamma$, which by hypothesis contains a representative of each set on which a holomorphic motion is defined, contains no member of $\{P_i^\theta\}$. But this is a contradiction; thus proving the necessity of the condition in our theorem.

*Comment.* That the $\{m_i\}$ of Definition 3 are not necessarily unique was stated by Pendse (1939), who also gave an example of non-uniqueness.

DEFINITION 7.    A motion is *disjunct* if $\ddot{r}_i(t) \equiv 0$, $(i = 1, \ldots, n)$. It is clear that a disjunct motion is isolated and that any arbitrary set of scalars $\{m_i\}$ are masses for the $\{P_i\}$.

*Comment.*    From some standpoints it might appear preferable to admit only positive $m_i$ in Definition 3. This would complicate Theorems I and II, however. To show this, call an isolated motion 'proper' if the $m_i$ are all positive. Then it can easily be shown that Theorem I becomes:

THEOREM I.    A necessary and sufficient condition that the $\{m_i\}$ of a proper isolated motion $[\pi]$ be unique within a factor of proportionality is that there exist no proper subset $(k')$ of the motion $(\pi)$ on which an isolated motion (proper or improper) can be defined.

The sufficiency follows exactly as before. To prove the necessity note that the multiplier $\lambda$ in the proof of Theorem I can be chosen sufficiently small that $m_i > \lambda \mu_i$, and hence $m_i' > 0$ $(i = 1, \ldots, n)$.

It seems preferable, therefore, to permit the $m_i$ to be either positive or negative, and to introduce the fact that they are all of the same sign as a separate physical hypothesis. (See Physical Hypothesis II below.) Finally, it may be observed that from Theorem I it follows that the masses of a system of disjunct particles (e.g. the fixed stars) cannot be determined by inertial means.

### 3. DEPENDENCE OF MASS ON THE REFERENCE SYSTEM

The definitions given above permit the determination of the masses of an isolated motion — uniquely if the motion is holomorphic — relative to a given reference system. It is necessary to examine next whether the same values would be derived for the masses if another reference system were used. Preliminary to this, the physical operations which are assumed in postulating a reference system must be discussed briefly.

The class of reference systems that is admitted in the present discussion is defined by the following limitations on the admissible transformations:

(a) The space coordinates transform independently of the time coordinates, and conversely, the time coordinates independently of the space coordinates.

(b) Only distance-preserving space transformations are admitted.

(c) Only monotonic-increasing time transformations are admitted.

In physical terms, these limitations mean (i) that the unit of length is the distance between two marks on a rigid bar, whose length, therefore, is defined to be independent of its motion; and (ii) that there exists absolute simultaneity of events, and a unique direction of time's arrow.

In this section it will be assumed that $t$ is given i.e., that the observer possesses a clock independent of the motions he is observing. Hence only transformations of the space coordinates will be considered. Time transformations, and the construction of a dynamic clock, will be discussed in Section 4.

That a set $\{m_i\}$ of masses is not invariant with transformations of the reference system is shown by the following theorem:

THEOREM III.    Let $(\pi)$ be any motion of a set $\{P_i\}$, and let $\{\alpha_i\}$ be an arbitrary set of numbers in one-to-one correspondence with the $\{P_i\}$. Then there exists a transformation of the reference system which carries $(\pi)$ into a new motion, $(\pi'')$, such that $(\pi'')$ is an isolated motion, $[\pi'']$ with $m_i = \alpha_i (i = 1, \ldots, n)$.

*Proof.* The transformation is carried out in two steps. First $\bar{r}_i$ in reference system $A$ is translated into $\bar{r}_i'$ in $B$ with the origin of $B$ in $A$ taken at the 'centre of mass' — using the $\alpha_i$ as 'masses' — of the system. The $\bar{r}_i'$ satisfy Equations (1a). Next, the $\bar{r}_i'$ in $B$ are rotated into $\bar{r}_i''$ in $C$ such that Equations (1b) are satisfied. The first transformation gives three equations for the origin of the system $C$, the second, three equations for its rotation relative to the system $A$. Both the origin and the angle of rotation will, of course, be functions of $t$. Then

$$\bar{r}_i' = \bar{r}_i - \bar{r}_0 \ (i = 1, \ldots, n),$$

where

$$r_0 = \sum_{i=1}^{n} \alpha_i \bar{r}_i \Big/ \sum_{i=1}^{n} \alpha_i.$$

It follows that

$$\sum_{i=1}^{n} \alpha_i \bar{r}_i' \equiv 0. \tag{14}$$

Now rotate $B$ into $C$. Let $\bar{i}, \bar{j}, \bar{k}$ be unit vectors along the coordinate axes in $C$. Denote by $\dot{\bar{r}}_i'$ and $\ddot{\bar{r}}_i'$ the first and second time derivatives of $\bar{r}_i'$ in $B$, and by $\dot{\bar{r}}_i''$ and $\ddot{\bar{r}}_i''$ the corresponding derivatives of $\bar{r}_i''$ in $C$. We have then:

$$\bar{r}_i' = \bar{r}_i'' = x\bar{i} + y\bar{j} + z\bar{k}. \tag{15}$$

Now let

$$\bar{\omega} = (\dot{\bar{j}} \cdot \bar{k})\bar{i} + (\dot{\bar{k}} \cdot \bar{i})\bar{j} + (\dot{\bar{i}} \cdot \bar{j})\bar{k}, \tag{16}$$

(all derivatives in $B$), so that

$$\bar{\omega} \times \bar{i} = \dot{\bar{i}}, \text{ etc.}; \quad \bar{\omega} \times \dot{\bar{i}} + \dot{\bar{\omega}} \times \bar{i} = \ddot{\bar{i}}, \text{ etc.} \tag{17}$$

Then we find

$$\dot{\bar{r}}_i' = \dot{\bar{r}}_i'' + \bar{\omega} \times \bar{r}_i', \tag{18}$$

and

$$\ddot{\bar{r}}_i' = \ddot{\bar{r}}_i'' + 2\bar{\omega} \times \dot{\bar{r}}_i' - \bar{\omega} \times (\bar{\omega} \times \bar{r}_i') + \dot{\bar{\omega}} \times \bar{r}_i'. \tag{19}$$

Then, a necessary and sufficient condition that $\sum_{i=1}^{n} \alpha_i \ddot{\bar{r}}_i'' \times \bar{r}_i'' = 0$ is that

$$\sum_{i=1}^{n} \alpha_i \ddot{\bar{r}}_i \times \bar{r}_i' = 2 \sum_{i=1}^{n} \alpha_i \{\bar{\omega} \times \dot{\bar{r}}_i'\} \times \bar{r}_i' - \sum_{i=1}^{n} \alpha_i \{\bar{\omega} \times (\bar{\omega} \times \bar{r}_i')\} \times \bar{r}_i'$$

$$+ \sum_{i=1}^{n} \alpha_i \{\dot{\bar{\omega}} \times \bar{r}_i'\} \times \bar{r}_i'. \tag{20}$$

This is a system of three differential equations of the first degree in the components of $\bar{\omega}$ and will in general uniquely determine $\bar{\omega} = \bar{\omega}(t)$, within a constant of integration $\bar{\omega}_0 = \bar{\omega}(t_0)$. Hence, if we take $m_i = \alpha_i$ ($i = 1, \ldots, n$), the $\{m_i\}$ form an isolated motion with the $\{\bar{r}_i''\}$.

*Comment.* Theorem III was proved for a very special case

(one-dimensional motion of two particles) by Pendse (1939). A general proof
has been given by Appell.

There has appeared here a relativity not of time and distance with respect
to the motion of the observer, but of mass with respect to the motion of the
reference frame. Any arbitrary set of scalars can be assigned to any arbitrary
set of bodies and, if an appropriate reference frame be chosen, these bodies
will behave like an isolated set of particles with the arbitrary scalars as their
masses. Hence, some unique reference frame must be adopted if mass is to
have physical meaning. Moreover, this reference system must be chosen on
the basis of purely kinematic criteria, since any reference to mass would
involve a circularity.

DEFINITION 8.    A transformation of the spatial reference system is
*Galilean* if it leaves the $\ddot{\vec{r}}_i$ $(i = 1, \ldots, n)$ unchanged. A class of reference
systems is Galilean if any member of the class can be obtained from any other
member by a Galilean transformation.

*Comment.*    It is easily shown that the class of Galilean transformations
of a given reference system is the class of uniform translations. Hence, if a
motion is isolated (or disjunct) in a particular system, it remains isolated (or
disjunct) under Galilean transformations. Since these transformations admit
an inverse, the condition that the transformation be Galilean is both
necessary and sufficient to the invariance of isolation or disjunction of the
system.

*Physical Hypothesis I.*    There exists a Galilean class of reference systems
with respect to which the motion of the fixed stars (excepting double stars) is
a disjunct motion.

DEFINITION 9.    Masses determined with respect to a reference system, of
Physical Hypothesis I are called *Newtonian inertial masses* (N. i. masses), and
the reference system itself is called a *Newtonian* system.

*Physical Hypothesis II.*    N. i. masses can always be chosen for any set of
particles so as all to be positive.

*Comment.*    The masses of Definition 9 are the masses of classical physics.
Although the definition does not make any specific assumption as to the
forces to which the particles are subject – hence may fairly be called
'inertial' – it should be pointed out that the specification of the reference
system does imply certain general properties of the force system. In taking
the motion of the fixed stars as disjunct, it follows, using the Second Law as
the definition of resultant force, that each fixed star is free from resultant

force. The plausibility of this assumption lies in the 'isolation' of the fixed stars, i.e., in the idea that at 'great distances' forces are 'small'. What is asserted then, is that spatial 'isolation' implies dynamic isolation in the sense of Definition 3.

To a certain extent, then, our definition of mass is a departure from Mach's programme which involved (1) the determination of mass without reference to a force system, and (2) the *verification* of a special force law like that of gravitation. Since Mach himself pointed out that the masses and forces could be determined only relatively to the given reference system, his own formulation does not avoid this difficulty.

On the other hand, the procedure adopted here for the determination of mass appears preferable to a method that requires particular specification of the force system, (e.g., assumption of the law of gravitation). Such methods have been proposed as early as 1887 by Muirhead, and as recently as 1939 by Narlikar. The method followed here permits independent verification of any postulated force law to a greater extent than if postulation of that law were also required for the determination of mass.

It should be noted further that the possibility of the separate determination of the force law and of mass hinges on the possibility of postulating a system of disjunct motions. If these did not exist, at least to a sufficient approximation, the procedure of Muirhead would be the only admissible one. The fixed stars are unaccelerated (within the limits of observation) because gravitational accelerations are minute at the great distances involved, and because of the relatively random distribution of the stars in space.

Since motions are in fact determined with respect to an empirical reference system, it is useful to have a theorem on the existence of a transformation that will carry the system into a Newtonian one.

THEOREM IV.    Given a motion $(\pi)$, a necessary and sufficient condition that there exist a transformation of the spatial coordinates carrying $(\pi)$ into a disjunct motion $(\pi')$ is that there exist an $\overline{\omega}$ such that:

$$\ddot{\overline{r}}_i' = 2\overline{\omega} \times \dot{\overline{r}}_i' - \overline{\omega} \times (\overline{\omega} \times \overline{r}_i') + \dot{\overline{\omega}} \times \overline{r}_i', \quad (i = 1, \ldots, n), \quad (21)$$

where $\overline{r}_i'$ is the position of $P_i$ in a coordinate system $B$, with origin at one of the $P_i$.

*Proof.*    From Equation (19), Equations (21) are equivalent to $\ddot{\overline{r}}_i'' = 0$ $(i = 1, \ldots, n)$, where $\overline{r}_i''$ is the position of $P_i$ in the coordinate system $C$ obtained from $B$ by the rotation $\overline{\omega}$. Hence the proof is immediate.

*Comment.* Since, in general, a unique $\bar{\omega}$ can be found satisfying any one of the Equations (21), a coordinate system in which the motion of two points is disjunct always exists. For more than two points, $\bar{\omega}$ will exist only for a special class of motions. Necessary or sufficient conditions for the existence of such a transformation may be stated in many forms. Mach, for example, noted that if the motion of two particles is disjunct,

$$\ddot{r}_{12} = (a^2 - \dot{r}_{12}^2)/r_{12}, \tag{22}$$

where $r_{12}$, the scalar distance between the two particles, is invariant with respect to coordinate transformations.

## 4. SPECIFICATION OF A DYNAMIC CLOCK

It is possible that the observer is provided with an independent clock, e.g., the frequency of the yellow sodium band from a light source at rest relative to him. On the other hand, it is equally possible to employ a kinematic clock, that is, to base time measurement on the motion of one or more of the bodies in the system considered.

Suppose that a reference system and a clock exist with respect to which a certain motion is disjunct. Then, for any permissible transformation of $t$, the motion of each particle is still rectilinear, though its speed is possibly variable. For any such motion, we must have:

$$\ddot{\bar{r}}_i'' \times \dot{\bar{r}}_i'' = 0, \quad (i = 1, \ldots, n), \tag{23}$$

where $\bar{r}_i''$ is the position of $P_i$ in the desired coordinate system, $C$. Hence, by a procedure analogous to the proof of Theorem IV, we find:

THEOREM V. A necessary condition for the existence of a coordinate and time transformation that carries the motion into a disjunct one is that there exist an $\bar{\omega}$ such that

$$\{r_i' - 2(\bar{\omega} \times \dot{\bar{r}}_i') + \bar{\omega} \times (\bar{\omega} \times \bar{r}_i') - \dot{\bar{\omega}} \times r_i'\} \times (\dot{\bar{r}}_i' - \bar{\omega} \times \bar{r}_i') \equiv 0,$$
$$(i = 1, \ldots, n), \quad (24)$$

where $\bar{r}_i'$ is obtained from $\bar{r}_i$ as in Theorem IV, by translating the origin to one of the points of the set.

*Proof.* We prove Theorem V by noting that if such a coordinate and time transformation exists, then a coordinate transformation alone must exist carrying the given motion into one in which the path of each point is rectilinear, i.e., for which (23) holds. But (18) and (19) hold for all rotations. Hence, cross-multiplying (19) by $r''_i$, using (23) to eliminate one term, and then using (18) to eliminate $\vec{r}''_i$, we obtain (24).

*Comment.* Again, $\bar{\omega}$ is in general uniquely determined, except for the constants of integration, by any one of the Equations (24). Now consider a particular point, $P_k$, and determine $\bar{\omega}$ so that (23) is satisfied. Then the path of $P_k$ is rectilinear in the system $C$, and $r_k = f(t)$, where $r_k$ is the scalar distance of $P_k$ from some arbitrary origin on its path. Suppose $f(t)$ is a monotonic function of $t$. Now define $t' = \phi(t)$ as an implicit function of $t$ by the equation

$$\frac{d^2 r_k}{dt^2} \left( \frac{dt}{dt'} \right)^2 + \frac{dr_k}{dt} \frac{d^2 t}{dt'^2} = 0. \tag{25}$$

Since the left-hand side of (25) is identically equal to $d^2 r_k / dt^2$ it follows that $P_i$ is unaccelerated with respect to $t'$. In general, $t'$ will be unique up to two constants of integration — an arbitrary origin and a scale factor. Now transforming all the $\vec{r}''_i(t)$ into $\vec{r}''_i(t')$, the following theorem results immediately:

THEOREM VI.   A necessary and sufficient condition that a space and time transformation exist carrying a motion into a disjunct one is that there exist an $\bar{\omega}$ satisfying (24), and a $t'(t)$ such that

$$\frac{d^2 r_i}{dt'^2} = 0, \quad (i = 1, \ldots, n). \tag{26}$$

*Comment.* For alternative approaches to this problem the reader is referred to the papers by Thomson (1884), Lange (1885 and 1902), Petzoldt (1908), and Anding.

The comment following Physical Hypothesis II is also *a propos* here, namely, that unless a disjunct system exists, a dynamical measurement of time can only be made simultaneously with the measurement of mass and force, i.e., along the lines proposed by Muirhead.

Before proceeding to the discussion of force, a third physical hypothesis may be stated:

*Physical Hypothesis III.*   In a Newtonian reference system the motion of the bodies of the solar system is an isolated motion.

*Comment.* This hypothesis discloses the possibility in principle of determining the masses of particles in the solar system without use of the law of gravitation. Whether the masses so determined are unique depends on the empirical question of whether the solar system is holomorphic. It would appear that Filon was wrong in his assertion that mass can be operationally defined only in terms of weight.

## 5. RESULTANT AND COMPONENT FORCE

Thus far, the formal development has not required the concept of force. This concept will now be introduced, thus permitting the specification of various component accelerations determined by component forces. Then, and only then, will it become possible to speak unambiguously of accelerations 'induced' in one body by another. Hence, the present section will connect the definition of mass proposed in Definition 3, above, with Mach's definition.[6]

DEFINITION 10.    The vector $\bar{F}_i(t)$, defined by

$$\bar{F}_i(t) = m_i \ddot{\bar{r}}_i(t), \tag{27}$$

is called the *resultant force* on $P_i$ at $t$ in the isolated motion $[\pi]$.

DEFINITION 11.    Let $\bar{u}_{ij}$ be the unit vector with direction $\overrightarrow{P_i P_j}$. Let $\{\bar{f}_{ij}\}$ $(i, j = 1, \ldots, n; i \neq j)$, be a system of $n(n-1)$ vectors such that

(a)        $\bar{f}_{ij} = \alpha_{ij} \bar{u}_{ij};$        (b)    $\alpha_{ij} = \alpha_{ji},$        $(i, j = 1, \ldots, n),$

$$\tag{28}$$

where the $\alpha_{ij}$ are scalars; and

(c)        $\displaystyle\sum_{j=1}^{n} \bar{f}_{ij} = \bar{F}_i,$    $(i = 1, \ldots, n).$        $\tag{29}$

Then the $\{\bar{f}_{ij}\}$ are called a system of *component forces* of the resultant force system $\{\bar{F}_i\}$.

*Comment.* There are $n(n-1)/2$ distinct scalars, $\alpha_{ij}$, and only $(3n-6)$ independent scalar Equations (29) (Six degrees of freedom are lost in satisfying the requirements of Definition 3.) Hence the component forces (and consequently Mach's 'mutually induced accelerations') are not uniquely determined when $n > 4$ – a fact pointed out by Pendse (1937). The usefulness of Definition 3 lies in the fact that it permits the determination of mass in spite of this indeterminacy of the component accelerations.

DEFINITION 12.    Let an isolated motion $[\pi]$ be defined on the points $\{P_i\}$ $(i = 1, \ldots, n)$. Designate by $\{P_i'\}$ $(i = 1, \ldots, m)$ a certain subset of the $\{P_i\}$. Let $\{\bar{f}_{ij}\}$ be a system of component forces in $[\pi]$. Then the $\{\bar{f}_{ij}'\}$, where $\bar{f}_{ij}' = \bar{f}_{ij}$ $(i,j = 1, \ldots, m)$ is called an internal force system for the $\{P_i'\}$, while $F_i^E = \Sigma_{i=m+1}^n \bar{f}_{ij}$ $(i = 1, \ldots, m)$ is called an external force system for the $\{P_i'\}$

DEFINITION 13.    $\bar{F}_i^I = \Sigma_{j=1}^m \bar{f}_{ij}$ is called the *total internal force* at $P_i$. The $\bar{f}_{ij}$ may be called the components of the $\bar{F}_i^I$.

*Comment.*    As before, the $\bar{f}_{ij}'$ have

$$m(m - 1)/2 - (3m - 6) = (m^2 - 7m + 12)/2$$

degrees of freedom, hence are not uniquely determined if $m > 4$. To obtain a unique internal force system, even when the $\bar{F}_i^I$ are known, we must introduce additional restrictions on the $\bar{f}_{ij}'$.

DEFINITION 14.    Any relation of the form

$$\phi_k(f_{12}', f_{13}', \ldots, f_{1m}';\ f_{23}', f_{24}', \ldots, f_{(m-1)m}';$$
$$\bar{r}_1, \ldots, \bar{r}_m;\ \dot{\bar{r}}_1, \ldots, \dot{\bar{r}}_m) \equiv 0 \quad (30)$$

is a *constraint* on the $\{\bar{f}_{ij}\}$.

DEFINITION 15.    Given a set $\{\bar{F}_i^I\}$ $(i = 1, \ldots, m)$ of total internal forces and a set $\{\phi_k\}$ $(k = 1, \ldots, \sigma)$, of constraints; if there exists a *unique* set of components $\{\bar{f}_{ij}'\}$ of the $\bar{F}_i^I$ which satisfy the constraints, the set $\{\bar{f}_{ij}\}$ are called the *proper component forces of the* $\bar{F}_i^I$ under the constraints $\{\phi_k\}$.

*Comment.*    The programme proposed here for the calculation of proper component forces requires that (1) the motions of the particles be observed, (2) the $\{\bar{F}_i^I\}$ be known, and (3) a sufficient number of constraints be placed on the $\{\bar{f}_{ij}'\}$ to determine them uniquely. In the analysis of a statically determinate structure, for example, certain 'active' external forces (the forces of gravity on the structure and its load) are given. From these, and from the fact that the structure does not move, 'reactive' external forces are calculated, and it is then possible to determine the total internal force at each point. The constraints required on the $\{\bar{f}_{ij}'\}$ then consist of the assumptions that $\bar{f}_{ij}' = 0$ whenever $P_i$ and $P_j$ are not connected by a member of the structure.

In other applications, however, the order of procedure is different. In astronomy, the proper component forces may be calculated directly from a knowledge of the instantaneous configuration and the assumption of the law of gravitation. If, then, the paths of the particles are also known, the system is 'over-determined' — there are more than enough relations to specify the proper component forces — and it is an empirical question whether the observed paths are consistent with the law of gravitation.

In one important respect, proper component forces have a very different epistemological status from masses. If an isolated motion be observed, then under favourable circumstances (i.e., if the motion is holomorphic) the masses can be calculated directly. On the other hand, provided the number of particles is sufficiently large, a unique system of component forces can never be calculated directly from the motion. It is necessary to assume for the system some additional constraints — usually in the form of particular force laws. If these constraints are just sufficient to determine the component forces uniquely, then their empirical correctness cannot be tested. If, however, they over-determine the component forces, their consistency with the observed motion becomes an empirical question. It is important to note that the empirical test can never prove that the force law in question is the only one which could have produced the observed motion, for this would be equivalent to asserting that the force law can be uniquely deduced from the observed motion.

if the number of particles is sufficiently small, then this difficulty is no longer present. For example, if two astronomical bodies form an isolated system, *and if it is assumed that they are subject to no external forces*, then the inverse square law can be deduced from their motion.

Since the forces measured by a spring dynamometer are proper component forces, it is clear that the equivalence of the static and dynamic measurements of force can be derived from observations only if appropriate assumptions are made as to the force laws that are operating on the structure under consideration. If there is a sufficient number of givens: motions of the particles, external forces on the particles, etc., to uniquely determine the proper component forces, then the correspondence of static and dynamic force can be tested by inserting a spring dynamometer into the structure. This statement may be rephrased in the following physical hypothesis:

*Physical Hypothesis IV:*

1. Calibrate a spring dynamometer by suspending known weights from it and resting weights on it, in the earth's gravitational field.

2. Consider a system of particles subject to forces in which some of these forces, at least, consist of forces of tension and compression in solid members.

3. Insert the spring dynamometer in place of one of the solid members.

4. Suppose there are a sufficient number of givens (motions of the particles, force laws, etc.) to determine uniquely the proper component forces corresponding to the solid members.

5. Then the reading on the spring dynamometer will be equal to the proper component force in its member under the given conditions.

*Comment.* Two or three examples may be given of particular structures that permit a test of Physical Hypothesis IV.

A. Consider a just-rigid truss of weightless members with masses concentrated at their junction points, and subject to (a) gravitational force, and (b) reactive forces that prevent the structure's motion. Assume the forces sufficiently small that the distances between points can be considered invariant. Replace one of the members with a spring dynamometer, equating its total length to the length of the member before replacement. The reading on the spring dynamometer will then equal the proper component force in the member in question.

B. Consider a system of particles to which known external forces are applied. Let each pair of particles be connected by a calibrated elastic member obeying Hooke's law, with known modulus of elasticity. Let the system be at rest and in equilibrium. Then the proper component forces will be proportional to the elongations or contractions of the members.

C. It is not necessary, of course, that the system be at rest. Let a particle be attached to a fixed point by a light elastic member, calibrated as in B. Let a rotation of the particle be produced by the application of known external forces. Then, if the fixed point be considered a particle of infinite mass, the proper component force between the two particles will be proportional to the elongation produced in the elastic member.

## 6. CONCLUSION

The preceding exposition shows that the determination of mass depends upon the specification of an inertial reference system, but not upon the specification of a particular force law. The statement of the equivalence of static and dynamic force does require, however, independent knowledge of the force law. The latter can only be tested to a limited extent – its sufficiency to produce the observed motion can be tested, but not its necessity. This is true even if the reference system is taken as given.

In conclusion it may be useful to point out several unsolved problems.

First, the present paper uses the particle model exclusively. New problems, particularly with respect to the uniqueness of masses and of component forces, would certainly arise in a continuum model.

Second, it was suggested in the opening paragraphs that Newtonian mass is fundamental to the mechanics of special relativity as well as to classical mechanics. The connection between these two needs to be made precise, so that the concepts of special relativity theory may be given a firm operational base.

## 7. ACKNOWLEDGEMENTS

Prof. Eli Sternberg has given me very great help and encouragement at every stage of this project. Prof. L. R. Wilcox read the manuscript and offered valuable suggestions.

## NOTES

[1] See the bibliography appended to this paper, and particularly the papers by C. G. Pendse.
[2] Mach, p. 304.
[3] *Op. cit.*
[4] *Cf.* Narlikar for a formulation from the standpoint of general relativity. Since, in general relativity theory, gravitational force is simply the curvature in space associated with mass, and since the motions from which mass is determined occur in this curved space, the natural procedure is to define operations that determine mass and gravitational force simultaneously.
[5] The latter assumption is most consistent with Mach's viewpoint. See Mach, pp. 281–283.
[6] On this point see the paper by Requard.

## REFERENCES

Anding, E., 'Koordinaten und Zeit', *Encyklopädie der Mathematischen Wissenschaften*, vi, Section 2, Part 1: 2–9, (Leipzig, 1901–1908).
Appell, P., 'Sur la notion d'axes fixes et de mouvement absolu', *Comptes rendus*, clxvi, 513–516 (1918).
Filon, L. N. G., 'Mass and Force in Newtonian Mechanics', *Mathematical Gazette*, xxii, 9–16 (1938).
Lange, L., Über der wissenschaftliche Fassung der Galileischen Beharrungsgezetzes', *Wundt's Philosophischen Studien*, ii, 266–297, 539–545 (1885).
Lange, L., 'Das Inertialsystem vor dem Forum der Naturforschung', *ibid.* xx, 1–63 (1902).
Le Roux, J., 'Les systemes de reference a gravitation apparente', *Comptes rendus*, clxxxviii, 1376–1378 (1929).
Mach, Ernst, 'The Science of Mechanics', (5th English edition) (La Salle: Open Court Publishing Co., 1942).

Muirhead, F., 'The Laws of Motion', *Phil. Mag. (5)*, xxiii, 472–489 (1887).

Narlikar, V. V., 'The Concept and Determination of Mass in Newtonian Mechanics', *Phil. Mag. (7)*, xxvii, 33–36 (1939).

Pendse, C. G., 'A Note on Definition and Determination of Mass in Newtonian Mechanics', *Phil. Mag. (7)*, xxiv, 1012–1022 (1937).

Pendse, C. G., 'A Further Note . . .', *ibid. (7)*, xxvii, 51–61 (1939).

Pendse, C. G., 'On Mass and Force in Newtonian Mechanics', *ibid. (7)*, xxix, 477–484 (1940).

Petzoldt, J., 'Die Gebiete der absoluten und der relativen Bewegung', *Ostwald's Annalen der Naturphilosophie*, vii, 29–62 (1908).

Requard, F., 'Ein Vorschlag zur Revision des Kraftbegriffes der Makromechanik', *Zeitschrift für Physik*, xciv, 544–548 (1935).

Voss, A., 'Die Prinzipien der rationellen Mechanik', *Encyklopädie der Mathematischen Wissenschaften*, iv, Section 1, Part 1: 30–41, 46–55, (Leipzig, 1901–1908).

For additional references see Anding, Mach, Pendse (1940), and Voss.

# DISCUSSION: THE AXIOMATIZATION OF CLASSICAL MECHANICS†

The purpose of this note is to examine a recent axiomatization of classical particle mechanics, and its relation to an alternative axiomatization I had earlier proposed.[1] A comparison of the two proposals casts some interesting light on the problems of operationalism in classical celestial mechanics.

## 1. COMPARISON OF THE TWO AXIOMATIZATIONS

The basic differences between the two proposals arise from the nature of the undefined terms. Both systems take the *set of particles, time*, and *position* as primitive notions. Both systems assume that there exists a set of particles having continuous, twice-differentiable paths over some time interval. In addition, CPM takes *mass* and *force* as primitive notions, and assumes that with each particle there is associated a mass and a set of forces such that Newton's Second Law is satisfied (Axiom P6). A system with these properties is called in CPM 'a system of particle mechanics'. If, in addition, the set of forces in the system satisfies Newton's Third Law, the system is called in CPM 'Newtonian'.

In NM *mass* is defined. If a set of numbers, $(m_i)$, can be found (its existence is not assumed), such that the system of particles preserves its total momentum and angular momentum when these numbers, $(m_i)$, are interpreted as the $m_i$ that appear in the usual definitions of momentum and angular momentum, then the $m_i$ are defined as the *masses* of the particles, and the motion of the system is defined as *isolated*. Finally Newton's Second Law is used to define the resultant force on each particle. Hence, the 'isolated motion' of NM is a 'Newtonian system' of CPM and *vice versa*.

The 'forces' of CPM are the 'component forces' of NM. In the latter only 'balanced' forces in the sense of CPM are considered, since only isolated systems are under discussion. In NM, the component forces are *defined* as

†[*Philosophy of Science* 21, 340–343 (1954)].

numbers having certain properties. In general, their existence is guaranteed, but not their uniqueness. With respect to masses, the reverse holds: given the paths of the particles and the frame of reference, the masses in NM are, in general, unique if they exist. ('In general' is meant in the sense that a matrix 'in general' is not singular.)


## 2. SYNTACTICAL AND SEMANTICAL ASPECTS OF AXIOM SYSTEMS

These brief comments may provide the reader with a guide to the similarities and differences between the two axiomatizations. But what is their significance? What distinguishes the two axiomatizations at a more fundamental level is the difference in purpose — and the difference in purpose reveals itself in the selection of undefined primitives. The authors of CPM state that: 'Our sole aim has been to present an old subject in a mathematically rigorous way.' My aim in NM was to present an old subject in a mathematically rigorous and *operationally meaningful* way.

The implicit canons of axiomatization underlying NM are: (1) that there should be a sharp demarcation among sentences that are (a) definitions, (b) mathematically provable theorems derivable from the definitions taken together with the axioms of logic and mathematics, and (c) physical hypotheses; (2) that the undefined primitive terms of the system should correspond to *observables* in some operationally meaningful sense of that term; (3) that for all other terms introduced by definition, the conditions of existence and uniqueness should be settled.

*The viewpoint taken in NM is that in the axiomatization of a piece of physical theory we are concerned not only with the formal and analytic aspects of the axiom system, but equally with the semantical relations between the system and the phenomena it purports to denote.* In NM the analytic portion of the system consists solely of undefined terms, definitions, and theorems. There are no axioms[2] other than those of mathematics and logic. The physical portion of the system consists of (1) semantical statements as to how the numbers corresponding to primitives are to be (physically) measured, and (2) physical hypotheses asserting that certain physical systems satisfy the conditions of certain of the definitions when these definitions are interpreted materially: e.g., 'There exists a Galilean class of reference systems with respect to which the motion of the fixed stars is disjunct.' 'Galilean reference systems' and 'disjunct' have previously been defined in the formal system by means of the primitive notions.

### 3. OPERATIONAL INDEPENDENCE OF THE LAWS OF MOTION AND OF GRAVITATION

The physical model that the axiomatization of NM denotes is the model of classical celestial mechanics. The observables are the positions of astronomical bodies. Masses and forces are not directly observable, and hence it becomes important to determine under what conditions the magnitudes of masses and forces can be inferred uniquely from the observations. *To be specific: from observations of the sun and planets is it possible: (a) to determine their relative masses without hypothesizing the inverse square law or some equivalent law of force; (b) to determine the mutual forces acting on them under the same conditions? NM shows that, with certain qualifications stated in that paper, the answer to (a) is in the affirmative and to (b) is in the negative.*[3]

The problem of whether certain numbers that are not directly observable (in this case masses and forces) are uniquely determined by observations of the direct observables has turned out to be one of the central problems of modern statistical theory. In the statistical literature it is known as the 'identification problem'.[4] The axiomatization of NM illustrates that the identification problem is present in physics, and that it underlies the frequent question of 'when is a "law" an empirically testable statement, and when is it a tautology?' This question has often been raised not only with respect to the ·Second Law of Motion, but also with respect to the conservation of energy. The answer given in NM is that: *in celestial mechanics the second law of motion can be regarded as a tautology; but it is a physical hypothesis that, in a reference frame with respect to which the fixed stars are unaccelerated, the momentum and angular momentum of the solar system is invariant, and the masses of the sun and planets uniquely determined.* That the answer is not obvious is shown by the fact that it was disbelieved by such an eminent physicist as Filon and is questioned again in CPM.[5]

Physicists have for some time recognized the necessity, in the axiomatization of a physical theory, for 'semantic', 'operational', or 'epistemic' definitions of concepts to connect them with measurement procedures. The identification problem, with its implications for the distinction between empirical law and tautology, has usually been less completely analysed. For a discussion of these two points, see Margenau [3] , pp. 60–73, and pp. 84–94, 232–42, respectively.

## 4. OTHER AXIOM SYSTEMS

Now the axiomatization of NM is not the only possible or reasonable axiomatization of classical mechanics. Its real interest lies in showing what Newton's law's of motion mean when they are dissociated from any specific physical hypotheses about the force field. This is certainly what Mach had in mind, however imperfect his execution. When there is adjoined to the three laws of motion the inverse square law or alternatively, laws to the effect that electrical or magnetic fields of known (calculated) intensity produce a specified force field, then certain numbers that were not uniquely determined in the smaller system become so, and it is meaningful to ask whether the second law of motion is 'physically valid'.[6]

These alternative possibilities are indicated in outline in Part 5 of NM. Their chief significance is in illustrating that *whether a particular statement is a tautology or a physical hypothesis depends on the complete axiom system in which the statement occurs. Most physical systems turn out to be incompletely identified, in the statistical sense, and this incomplete identifiability gives a certain degree of choice as to which statements in the system we will treat as definitions and which as physical hypotheses.* The principal possibilities for the axiomatization of classical mechanics appear to be:

A. To treat only position as an observable (and hence a primitive notion in the formal system), mass and force as defined quantities. The Second Law is then a definition, and the main physical hypothesis that can be tested is that there exists an operationally definable reference system with respect to which the Third Law (i.e. the conservation of momentum and angular momentum) holds for the solar system. This is the axiomatization of NM.

B. To proceed as in (A), but to add a physical hypothesis in the form of the gravitational law. The conjunction of the Second Law and the gravitational law then has observable consequences, hence one has the alternative of regarding the latter as the definition of force, and the former as a physical hypothesis.

C. To proceed as in (B), but to postulate other laws of force (e.g., electromagnetic) as well as, or in place of, the gravitational law. This is the approach of Hamel mentioned in footnote 6, above. Alternatives (B) and (C) are both discussed in Part 5 of NM.

The virtue, in all of these formulations, of making primitive terms in the formal system correspond to observables in the physical system (and hence in making mass and force defined rather than primitive terms) is that this procedure permits us, by counting variables and equations, to examine the identifiability of the numbers in the system, and hence to determine to what extent the system is purely definitional, and to what extent it can lead to testable physical hypotheses.

## NOTES

[1] The papers in question (see list of references) are McKinsey, Sugar and Suppes (CPM), and Simon (NM).

[2] As a matter of fact, the word 'axiom' in CPM appears to be a misnomer. If we first define a Euclidean geometry as a set of certain elements having the property, among others, that parallels never meet; and if we begin each theorem with 'If, in a Euclidean geometry, . . .'; then the parallel 'axiom' need never be postulated as an axiom. If, now, we are interested in physical geometry — the geometry of physical space — we introduce some such physical hypothesis as: 'The elements of physical space, with length measured as follows . . . constitute a Euclidean geometry.' This physical hypothesis is then tested by measuring large triangles, or by some such method.

[3] In particular, the remarks on pp. 270–1 of CPM as to the implications of Pendse's papers and of NM for the uniqueness of mass are quite misleading, as will be seen by reference to NM, particularly the 'Comments' on pp. 898 and 901.

[4] See Hood and Koopmans [2], especially Chapters 1–3.

[5] The following passages from Filon's paper [1] summarize his (erroneous) view: 'In other words, Newton, after talking round the question defines mass by weight . . . his definition . . . makes the laws of motion dependent upon gravity . . . , yet it has always, since Newton, been argued that the law of gravitation was something additional to, and independent of the laws of motion . . . . I believe now that Mach's argument is fallacious. . . . Mach's procedure for determining the ratio of the inertial masses . . . without introducing gravity is illusory, and we have, in fact, been brought back, by a devious route, to Newton's definition, which appears to be the only possible one. . . . I cannot today enter into the question of celestial observations, except to say that careful analysis of their implications does not apparently disturb our conclusions. . . . It seems at any rate remarkable that after all the fuss we have made about the fundamental distinction between mass and weight and the criticisms levelled at the engineer for his systematic use of $w/g$, it should turn out that the engineer was right after all.'

[6] The axiom of Hamel that the authors of CPM criticize — see their footnote 3, p. 253 — can easily be formalized along the lines indicated in this paragraph. That this is Hamel's intent is clear from the second passage quoted in CPM, footnote 15, p. 270.

## REFERENCES

(CPM) McKinsey, J. C. C., A. C. Sugar, and Patrick Suppes, 'Axiomatic Foundations of Classical Particle Mechanics', *Journal of Rational Mechanics and Analysis* 2, 253–72 (April 1953).

(NM) Simon, Herbert A., 'The Axioms of Newtonian Mechanics', *Philosophical Magazine, Ser. 7*, 38, 888–905 (December 1947) (reprinted as Chapter 6.1 in this volume).

[1]    Filon, L. N. G., 'Mass and Force in Newtonian Mechanics', *Mathematical Gazette*
       **22**, 9−16 (1938).
[2]    Hood, William and T. C. Koopmans (eds.), *Studies in Econometric Method*. (New
       York: Wiley, 1953).
[3]    Margenau, Henry, *The Nature of Physical Reality* (New York: McGraw-Hill,
       1950).

# DEFINABLE TERMS AND PRIMITIVES IN AXIOM SYSTEMS†

An axiom system may be constructed for a theory of empirical phenomena with any of a number of goals in mind. Some of these goals are identical with those that motivate the axiomatization of mathematical theories, hence relate only to the formal structure of the theory — its syntax. Other goals for axiomatizing scientific theories relate to the problems of verifying the theories empirically, hence incorporate semantic considerations.

An axiom system includes, on the one hand, entities like primitive terms, defined terms, and definitions, and on the other hand, entities like axioms, theorems, and proofs. Tarski [10, p. 296] has emphasized the parallelism between the first triplet of terms and the second. The usual goals for axiomatizing deductive systems are to insure that neither more nor less is posited by way of primitive terms and axioms than is necessary and sufficient for the formal correctness of the definitions and proofs, and hence the derivability of the defined terms and theorems. An axiom system is usually accompanied by proofs of the independence, consistency, and completeness of its axioms; and presumably should also be accompanied — although it less often is — by proofs of the independence, consistency, and completeness of its primitive terms.

Frequently a set of sentences (axioms and theorems) and terms admits alternative equivalent axiom systems; that is non-identical partitionings of the sentences into axioms and theorems, respectively; and of the terms into primitive and defined terms. Hence, a particular set of axioms and primitive terms may be thought of as a (not necessarily unique) basis for a class of equivalent axiom systems.

In constructing an axiom system for an empirical theory, we may wish to distinguish sentences that can be confronted more or less directly with evidence (e.g., 'the temperature of this water is 104°') from other sentences. We may wish to make a similar distinction between predicates, functors, and other terms that appear in such sentences (e.g., 'temperature') and those that

---

† [Henkin, Suppes and Tarski (eds.), *The Axiomatic Method*, Amsterdam: North-Holland Publishing Co., 1959, pp. 443–453].

do not. The terms 'observation sentences' and 'observables' are often used to refer to such sentences and such terms, respectively.[1]

The distinction between observables and non-observables is useful in determining how fully the sentences of a theory can be confirmed or disconfirmed by empirical evidence, and to what extent the terms of the theory are operationally defined. In addition to the formal requirements, discussed previously, we might wish to impose the following additional conditions on an axiom system for an empirical theory:

(1) that the entire system be factorable into a subsystem that is equivalent to some axiom system for a part of logic and mathematics, and a remainder;

(2) that in the remainder, axioms correspond to observation sentences, and primitive terms to observables.

Condition (2) is, of course, a semantic rather than a syntactic condition, and has no counterpart in the axiomatization of mathematical theories. The usefulness of the condition is that, if it is met, the empirical testability of observation sentences guarantees the testability of all the sentences in the system, and the operational definability of observables guarantees the operationality of all the terms. In the remainder of this paper we shall explore some problems that arise in trying to satisfy Condition (2), and some modifications in the notion of definability – as that term is used in formal systems – that are needed to solve these problems.

The question of what characteristics an axiom system should possess has been raised in the past few years [9] in connection with the definability of mass in Newtonian mechanics. In one recent axiomatization of Newtonian particle mechanics [5] particular care is taken to meet the syntactic conditions for a satisfactory axiomatization, and mass introduced as a primitive term. In another axiomatization [8] special attention is paid to semantic questions, and definitory equations for mass are introduced.

## 1. DEFINABILITY AND GENERIC DEFINABILITY

Tarski [10] has proposed a definition of the term *definability* in a deductive system, and has shown how this definition provides a theoretical foundation for the method employed by Padoa [6] to establish whether particular terms in a system are definable or primitive. In their axiomatization of classical particle mechanics, McKinsey, Sugar and Suppes [5, Paragraph 5] employ the method of Padoa to show that, by Tarski's definition, mass and force are primitive terms in their system. Application of the same method to Simon's earlier axiomatization of Newtonian mechanics [8] gives the same result — mass and force are primitives in that system.

The latter result appears to conflict with common-sense notions of definability, since in [8] the masses of the particles can (in general) be computed when their positions and accelerations are known at several points in time [8, Theorem I]. Condition (2) of the previous section is violated if masses, which are not observables, are taken as primitive terms; and it appears paradoxical that it should be possible to calculated the masses when they are neither observables nor defined terms. These difficulties suggest that Tarski's concept of definability is not the most satisfactory one to use in the axiomatization of empirical science.

A closer examination of the situation, for [8], shows that the masses are not uniquely determined in certain situations that are best regarded as special cases — e.g., the case of a single unaccelerated particle. It is by the construction of such special cases, and the application of the method of Padoa to them, that McKinsey, Sugar and Suppes show mass to be a primitive in [5], and by inference in [8]. But I shall show that if the definition of Tarski is weakened in an appropriate way to eliminate these special cases it no longer provides a justification for the method of Padoa, but does provide a better explication of the common-sense notion of definability.

## 1.1. Statement of the Problem

We shall discuss the problem here in an informal manner. The treatment can easily be formalized along the lines of Tarski's paper.[2] In Tarski's terms [10, p. 299], *the formula* $\phi(x; b', b'', \ldots)$ *defines the extra-logical constant a if, for every x, x satisfies $\phi$ if and only if x is identical with a; i.e., if:*

$$(I) \qquad (x): x = a. \equiv .\phi(x; \; b', b'', \ldots),$$

*where x is the only real variable in $\phi$, and $b'$, $b''$, ... are the members of a set of extra-logical constants (primitives and/or defined terms).*

Translated into these terms, the (attempted) definition of 'the mass of particle $i$' in [8, p. 892] proceeds thus: (1) We take as the function $\phi$ the conjunction of the six scalar equations that state the laws of conservation of momentum and conservation of angular momentum for a system of particles. (2) We take as the set $B$ the paths of the particles in some time interval. (3) We take as $x$ the set of numbers $m_i$, that satisfy $\phi$ for the given $B$.

This procedure does not satisfy Tarski's definition since the existence and uniqueness of the masses is not guaranteed. For example, in the case of a single, unaccelerated particle, *any* number, $m$, substituted in the equations for conservation of momentum and angular momentum will satisfy those equations. But Tarski shows (his Theorem 2) that if two constants satisfy a definitory formula for a particular set, $B$, they must be identical.

## 1.2. Generic Definition

To remove the difficulty, we replace Tarski's definition with a weaker one: *the formula* $\phi(x; b', b'', \ldots)$ DEFINES GENERICALLY *the extralogical constant a if, for every x if x is identical with a, x satisfies* $\phi$:

$$(I')\qquad (x): x = a. \quad \supset. \phi(x; b', b'', \ldots).$$

After the equivalence symbol in formula (I) has been replaced by an implication in this way, the three theorems of Tarski's paper are no longer provable. In particular, formula (7) in his proof of Theorem I [10, pp. 301–302] can no longer be derived from the modified forms of his formulas (3) and (6). Hence, the method of Padoa cannot be used to disqualify a proposed generic definition.

It is easy to show that in [8] mass is generically defined by means of the paths of the particles on the basis of the Third Law of Motion (more exactly, the laws of conservation of momentum and angular momentum); and that resultant force is generically defined by means of the paths of the particles and their masses on the basis of the Third and Second Laws of Motion [8, p. 901]. Similarly, we can show that in [5, p. 258] resultant force is generically defined by means of the paths of the particles and their masses on the basis of the Second Law of Motion.

The advantage of substituting generic definition for definition is that, often, a constant is not uniquely determined for all possible values of the other extra-logical constants, but experimental or observational circumstances can be devised that do guarantee *for those circumstances* the unique determination of the constant.

In the axiom system of [8], for example, the conditions under which masses exist for a system of particles and the conditions under which these masses are unique have reasonable physical interpretations. The observables are the space-time coordinates of the particles. From a physical standpoint, we would expect masses (not necessarily unique) to be calculable from the motion of a set of particles, using the principles of conservation of momentum and angular momentum, whenever this set of particles was physically isolated from other particles. Moreover, we would expect the relative masses to be uniquely determined whenever there was no proper subset of particles that was physically isolated from the rest. These are precisely the conditions for existence (Definition 3) and uniqueness (Theorem I and Definition 6) of the masses in this axiomatization. Thus, the definition of mass in [8] does not lead to a unique determination of the mass of a single star at a great distance from other stars, but does permit the calculation, uniquely up to a factor of proportionality, of the masses of the members of the solar system from observation of their paths alone, and without postulating a particular force law [8, pp. 900–901].

## 2. OTHER CONCEPTS OF DEFINABILITY

The sharp distinctions between axioms and theorems, and between primitive and defined terms have proved useful dichotomies in axiomatizing deductive systems. We have seen that difficulties arise in preserving the latter distinction in empirical systems, when the axiom system is required to meet Condition (2) – when primitive terms are identified with observables. But it has long been recognized that comparable difficulties arise from the other half of Condition (2), that is, from the identification of axioms with observation sentences. In our axiomatization of Newtonian mechanics, for example, the law of conservation of momentum, applied to an isolated system of particles, is an identity in time containing only a finite number of parameters (the masses). If time is assumed to be a continuous variable, this law comprises a nondenumerable infinity of observation sentences. Hence, the law is not itself an observation sentence nor is it derivable from a finite set of observation sentences.

The two difficulties – that with respect to axioms and that with respect to primitives – arise from analogous asymmetries. In a system of Newtonian mechanics, given the initial conditions and masses of a system of particles, we can deduce univocally their paths. Given their paths, we may or may not be able to derive unique values for the masses. Given the the laws and values of the generically defined primitives, we can deduce observation sentences; given any finite set of observation sentences, we cannot generally deduce laws. When the matter is put in this way, the asymmetry is not surprising, and it is easy to see that the thesis of naive logical positivism – essentially the thesis of Condition (2) – is untenable unless it is weakened substantially.

## 2.1. Contextual Definitions, Implicit Definitions and Reduction Sentences

Revisions of the concept of definition similar in aim to that discussed here have been proposed by a number of empiricists. Quine's [7, p. 42] notion of contextual definition, while nowhere spelled out formally, is an example:

The idea of defining a symbol in use was, as remarked, an advance over the impossible term-by-term empiricism of Locke and Hume. The statement, rather than the term, came with Frege to be recognized as the unit accountable to an empiricist critique. But what I am now urging is that even in taking the statement as unit we have drawn our grid too finely. The unit of empirical significance is the whole of science.

Braithwaite [1] carries the argument a step further by pointing out advantages of having in an empirical theory certain terms that are not uniquely determined by observations. His discussion of this point [1, pp. 76–77] is worth quoting:

We can, however, extend the sense of definition if we wish to do so. In explicit definition, which we have so far considered, the possibilities of interpreting a certain symbol occurring in a calculus are reduced to one possibility by the requirement that the symbol should be synonymous (within the calculus) with a symbol or combination of symbols which have already been given an interpretation. But the possibilities of interpreting a certain symbol occurring in a calculus may be reduced without being reduced to only one possibility by the interpretation already given of other symbols occurring in the formulae in the calculus. If we wish to stress the resemblance between the reduction of the posssibilities of interpreting a symbol to only one possibility and the reduction of these possibilities but not to only one possibility, instead of wishing to stress (as we have so far stressed) the difference between these two sorts of reduction, we shall call the second reduction as well as the first by the name of definition, qualifying the noun by such words as 'implicit' or 'by postulate'. With this extension of the meaning of definition the thesis of this chapter can be expressed by saying that, while the theoretical terms of a scientific theory are *implicitly defined* by their occurrence in initial formulae in a calculus in which there are derived formulae interpreted as empirical generalizations, the theoretical terms cannot be *explicitly defined* by means of the interpretations of the terms in these derived formulae without the theory thereby becoming incapable of growth.

As a final parallel, I will mention Carnap's concept of *reduction sentence* in his essay on *Testability and Meaning* [2, p. 442]. A reduction sentence for $Q_3$ is a sentence of the form, $Q_2 \supset (Q_1 \supset Q_3)$, where $Q_2$ is interpreted as the set of conditions under which the subsidiary implication holds, and where $Q_1$ is interpreted as a (partial) definiens for $Q_3$. Thus, let $Q_2$ be the statement that a set of particles is isolated; $Q_1$ be the statement that a certain vector, $\bar{m}$, substituted for the coefficients in the equations stating the laws of conservation of momentum and angular momentum for the particles, satisfies those equations; and $Q_3$ be the statement that the components of $\bar{m}$ are masses of the particles. Then $Q_2 \supset (Q_1 \supset Q_3)$ is essentially identical with the definition of mass in [8]. The subsidiary connective is an implication rather than an equivalence because there is no guarantee that another vector, $\bar{m}'$, may not also constitute a satisfactory set of masses, so that $Q_2 \supset (Q'_1 \supset Q'_3)$, where $Q'_1$ is derived from $Q_1$, and $Q'_3$ from $Q_3$ by substituting $\overline{m}'$, for $\overline{m}$.

## 2.2. *Definability Almost Everywhere*

In preference to either definability of generic definability, we might want to have a term midway in strength between these two — a notion of definability that would guarantee that we could 'usually' determine the defined term univocally, and that the cases in which we could not would be in some sense exceptional. Under certain conditions it is, in fact, possible to introduce such a term. *Suppose that B is a point in some space possessing a measure, and let there be a sentence of form* (I) *that holds almost everyhwere in the space of B. Then, we say that a is* DEFINED ALMOST EVERYWHERE.

If, in [8], we take $B$ as the time path of the system which satisfies the axioms in some interval $k < t < m$, and take the Lebesgue measure in the appropriate function space for the $B$'s as the measure function, then mass is defined almost everywhere, as is resultant force.

## 3. DEFINABILITY AND IDENTIFIABILITY

It has not generally been noted that the problem of definability of non-observables in axiomatizations of empirical theories is identical with what has been termed the 'identification problem' in the literature of mathematical statistics [4, p. 70; 9, pp. 341–342]. The identification problem is the problem of estimating the parameters that appear in a system of equations from observations of the values of the variables in the same system of equations.

## 3.1. *Some Types of Identifiability Problems*

Consider, for example, a system of linear equations:

$$(1) \qquad \sum_i a_{ij} x_j = b_i \quad (i = 1, \dots, n),$$

where the $x$'s are observables and the $a$'s and $b$'s are parameters. The $a$'s and $b$'s are generically defined by this system of equations, but they are not defined in Tarski's sense, for, no matter how many sets of observations of the $x$'s we have, the $a$'s and $b$'s are not uniquely determined. For suppose that $A$

and $b$ are a matrix and vector, respectively, that satisfy (1) for the observed $x$'s.[3] Then $A'$ and $b'$ will also satisfy (1), where $A' = PA$ and $b' = Pb$ for any non-singular matrix $P$. To identify the $a$'s and $b$'s – that is, to make it possible to estimate them uniquely – additional constraints beyond those embodied in equations (1) must be introduced.

On the other hand, consider the system of linear difference equations:

$$(2) \qquad \sum_j a_{ij} x_j(t) = x_i(t+1), \quad (i = 1, \ldots, n),$$

where, as before, the $x$'s are observables, and the $a$'s and $b$'s constant parameters. In this case, the $a$'s are defined almost everywhere in the space of $\bar{x}(t)$. There are $n^2$ parameters to be estimated, and the number of equations of form (2) available for estimating them is $n(k-1)$, where $k$ is the number of points in time at which the $x$'s are observed. Hence, for almost all paths of the system, and for $k > n + 1$, the $a$'s will be determined uniquely.[4]

We see that the system of Equations (2) is quite analogous to the system of equations used in [8] to define mass. In the latter system, for $n$ particles, having $3n$ position coordinates, there are 6 second order differential equations (three for conservation of momentum, three for conservation of angular momentum) that are homogeneous in the $m$'s, and that must hold identically in $t$. There are $(n-1)$ parameters to be estimated – the number of mass-ratios of the particles, referred to a particular one of them as unit. Hence, for almost all paths of the system, the mass-ratios can be estimated uniquely from observations of the positions of the particles at $[(n/6) + 2]$ points in time.

Correspondingly, the system of Equations (1) is analogous to the system of equations used in [8, p. 901] to define the component forces between pairs of particles. Component forces are only generically defined. Hence, although the masses of particles in a system and the resultant forces acting upon them can, in general, be estimated if there is a sufficient number of observations of the positions of the particles; the component forces cannot be so estimated unless additional identifying assumptions are introduced. Such additional assumptions might, for example, take the form of a particular force law, like the inverse square law of gravitational attraction.

## 3.2. *Over-Identification and Testability*

When a scientific theory is axiomatized with a view to clarifying the problems of testing the theory, a number of considerations are present that do not appear in axiomatizing deductive systems. Hence, it may be undesirable to imitate too closely the canons usually prescribed for the latter type of axiomatization. In addition to distinguishing primitive from defined terms, it may be advantageous to subdivide the former class as so to distinguish terms that are defined almost everywhere or that are only generically defined.

More fundamentally, whether particular terms are univocally determined by the system will depend not only on the specific sentences that have the form of definitions of these terms, but upon the whole set of sentences of the system. Our analysis of an actual axiom system for Newtonian particle mechanics bears out the contentions of Braithwaite and Quine that the definitions of non-observables often are, and must be, 'implicit' or 'contextual'.

What does the analysis suggest, on the positive side, as a substitute for the too strict Condition (2)? In general, there will appear in an axiom system terms that are direct observables, and terms that are not. A minimum requirement from the standpoint of empiricism is that the system as a whole be over-identified: that there be possible sets of observations that would be inconsistent, collectively, with the sentences of the system. We have seen that this condition by no means guarantees that all the non-observables of the system will be defined terms, or even defined almost-everywhere.

A more radical empiricism would require that it be possible, by making a sufficient number of observations, to determine uniquely the values of all parameters that appear in the system. To take a simple example, a strict interpretation of this condition would not permit masses to appear in the axiomatization of Newtonian mechanics, but only mass-ratios. Resultant forces would be admissible, but not component forces, unless sufficient postulates were added about the form of the force law to overdetermine them. We may borrow Quine's phrase for this requirement, and say that when it is satisfied for some set of terms, the terms are *defined contextually* by the system.[5] The condition that all non-observables be defined contextually is still much weaker, of course, than the condition that they be defined.

For reasons of elegance, we may sometimes wish to stop a little short of insisting that all terms in a system be defined contextually. We have already mentioned a suitable example of this. In [8] mass ratios are defined almost everywhere, but masses are not defined contextually, even in an almost-everywhere sense. Still, we would probably prefer the symmetry of associating a mass number with each particle to a formulation that arbitrarily selected one of these masses as a numeraire.

Braithwaite has given us another reason, from the semantic side, for not insisting on contextual definition of all terms. He observes that if we leave some degrees of freedom in the system, this freedom allows us later to add additional axioms to the system, without introducing internal inconsistencies, when we have reason to do so. Thus, since the law of conservation of energy does not determine the zero of the temperature scale, the zero may be fixed subsequently by means of the gas laws.

Regardless of what position we take on empiricism in axiomatizing scientific theories, it would be desirable to provide for any axiom system, theorems characterizing not only its syntactical properties (e.g., the independence, consistency, and completeness of the axioms), but its semantic properties (e.g., the degree of identifiability of its non-observables) as well.

## NOTES

[1] For a more extended discussion of these terms, see [2, pp. 454–456].

[2] Compare also [2, p. 439].

[3] In this entire discussion, we are disregarding errors of observation and the fact that the equations may be only approximately satisfied. For an analysis that takes into account these additional complications, the reader must refer to [3] and [4].

[4] The convenience of replacing identifiability (equivalent to Tarski's definability) by almost-everywhere identifiability (equivalent to almost-everywhere definability) has already been noted in the literature on the identification problem [4, p. 82; 3, p. 53].

[5] Braithwaite's 'implicit definition' will not do here, for he applies it specifically to the weaker condition of the previous paragraph.

## REFERENCES

[1] Braithwaite, R. B., *Scientific Explanation* (Cambridge Eng.: Cambridge Univ. Press, 1955) 376 pp.

[2] Carnap, R., 'Testability and Meaning', *Philosophy of Science* 3, 419–471 (1936), and 4, 1–40 (1937).

[3] Hood, W. and T. C. Koopmans (eds.), *Studies in Econometric Method* (New York: Wiley, 1953), 323 pp.

[4] Koopmans, T. C. (ed.), *Statistical Inference in Dynamic Economic Models* (New York: Wiley, 1950), 439 pp.

[5] McKinsey, J. C. C., A. C. Sugar, and P. Suppes, 'Axiomatic Foundations of Classical Particle Mechanics', *Journal of Rational Mechanics and Analysis* 2, 253–272 (1953).

[6] Padoa, A., 'Essai d'une théorie algébrique des nombres entiers, précédé d'une introduction logique à une théorie déductive quelconque', *Bibliothèque du Congrès International de Philosophie* 3, (1900).

[7] Quine, W., *From a Logical Point of View* (Cambridge, Mass.: Harvard Univ. Press, 1953), 184 pp.

[8]  Simon, H. A., 'The Axioms of Newtonian Mechanics, *Philsophical Magazine*, ser. 7,
     **33**, 888–905 (1947), (reprinted as Chapter 6.1 of this volume).
[9]  Simon, H. A., 'Discussion: the Axiomatization of Classical Mechanics', *Philosophy
     of Science* **21**, 340–343 (1954) (reprinted as Chapter 6.2 of this volume).
[10] Tarski, A., 'Some Methodological Investigations on the Definability of Concepts',
     Chapter 10 in *Logic, Semantics, Metamathematics*, (Oxford, Eng.: Clarendon
     Press, 1956) 467 pp.

# A NOTE ON ALMOST-EVERYWHERE DEFINABILITY†

This paper develops a notion of *almost-everywhere definability*, first published in [1], that appears more suitable, for certain purposes of axiomatizing scientific theories, than the stronger notion of definability formalized by Tarski [2, Chapter X].

Let there exist a set of sentences $X'$, and a subset $X$, $X \subseteq X'$. Let $M$ be a set of models of $X$, and $\mu$ a measure defined on sets in $M$. Let $M'$ be the corresponding set of models of $X'$. Then $M' \subseteq M$. Suppose that the measure, $\mu$, is such that $\mu(M) > 0$, and $\mu(M - M') = 0$. Let '$a$' be an extra-logical constant that is definable, in the sense of Tarski, on the basis of $X'$, is not definable on the basis of $X$, and does not occur in $X' - X$. Then we shall say that '$a$' *is definable almost-everywhere* in $M$ on the basis of $X$ and with respect to $\mu$.

The method of Padoa for showing that a constant is not definable in a theory cannot be used to show it is not almost-everywhere definable. In particular, in several axiomatizations of classical particle mechanics [3 and 4], the concept of mass, while undefinable in the sense of Tarski, is definable almost-everywhere.

## REFERENCES

[1] Simon, Herbert A., 'Definable Terms and Primitives in Axiom Systems', in Henkin, Suppes and Tarski (eds.), *Symposium on the Axiomatic Method* (Amsterdam: North-Holland Publ. Co., 1959), pp. 443–453.
[2] Tarski, A., *Logic, Semantics, Metamathematics* (Oxford: Clarendon Press, 1956).
[3] Simon, Herbert A., 'The Axioms of Newtonian Mechanics', *Philosophical Magazine*, Ser. 7, 33, 888–905 (1947).
[4] McKinsey, J. C. C., A. C. Sugar, and P. Suppes, 'Axiomatic Foundations of Classical Particle Mechanics', *Journal of Rational Mechanics and Analysis* 2, 253–272 (1953).

† [*Journal of Symbolic Logic* 31, 705–706 (1966)].

# THE AXIOMATIZATION OF PHYSICAL THEORIES† *

The task of axiomatizing physical theories has attracted, in recent years, some interest among both empirical scientists and logicians. However, the axiomatizations produced by either one of these two groups seldom appear satisfactory to the members of the other.[1] It is the purpose of this paper to develop an approach that will satisfy the criteria of both, hence permit us to construct axiomatizations that will meet simultaneously the standards and needs of logicians and of empirical scientists.

Since the foundations of Newtonian mechanics have been studied more extensively than those of any other branch of natural science, it is desirable to test any proposed approach to axiomatization by comparing the axiom system it generates for mechanics with the systems already in the literature. However, the underlying methodological issues are more transparent when they are examined in the simpler context of Ohm's law. Hence, Sections 1–3 of this paper will be devoted to an axiomatization of Ohm's law and a discussion of the issues to which it gives rise. The results of this discussion are applied to the axiomatization of Newtonian mechanics in Section 4.

## 1. EXPERIMENTAL BASIS

It is desirable to describe with some care the empirical situation that the theory purports to handle. This can be done by referring to the experiment in which Ohm first established (1826) the law that now bears his name.[2]

Let us recall the state of knowledge of electromagnetism at the time Ohm performed his experiments:

(a) The invention of the electric battery by Volta (1800) provided, for the first time, more or less continuous flows of electricity, and turned scientific attention from electrostatic to electrodynamic phenomena.

(b) The discovery by Oersted (1820) of electromagnetic induction led in turn, to the invention by Ampere and others of a current-measuring device, or ammeter. This ammeter was essentially a magnetic needle suspended by a thin

† [*Philosophy of Science* 37, 16–26 (1970)].

wire mounted as a torsion balance. The force of a magnetic field on the needle could be measured by the torsion exerted on the wire. By a further link of reasoning, if the magnetic field was induced by a steady flow of electricity, a current intensity proportional to the induced field (i.e. to the force exerted on the needle, and balanced by the twist of wire) could be attributed to the electrical flow.

Note that at least two physical laws are assumed implicitly in this method of measuring current: (a) Hooke's law, and (b) the law that the force exerted on the magnet is proportional to the electric current. Ohm was aware of these assumptions, treating them as justified by previous experimental work. Hence, he measured current by the angle through which the pointer of the torsion balance had to be turned in order to balance exactly the force exerted by the current on the magnet.

(c) The current produced by a voltaic pile fluctuated too widely for Ohm's pruposes. He therefore used a thermoelectric battery, invented shortly before (1822) by Seebeck, involving essentially a circle of two semicircles of different metals, each of the two junction points being maintained at a different temperature. To keep the temperature differential, hence the potential, constant, Ohm immersed the one junction in steam, the other in ice.

Ohm's scheme took, then, the form shown abstractly in Figure 1.

The electrodes of a thermoelectric battery are connected by a uniform plated copper wire, the resistance, that can be of any desired length. The length is taken as the measurement of the amount of resistance ($r$). The ammeter is placed in a fixed relation to the circuit; the rotation of the torsion balance is taken as the measurement of current intensity ($c$). The experimental results are then reported as a set of ordered pairs, $\{\langle r, c \rangle\}$. We shall use

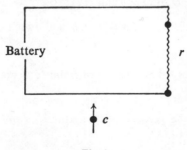

Fig. 1.

these ordered pairs directly in the axiomatization, hence will not have to incorporate the details of the measurement scheme. We have described those details to make clear what degree of abstraction from the empirical reality is already involved in regarding resistance and current as 'observables'.[3]

## 2. AXIOMS FOR OHM'S LAW

We now wish to propose an axiomatization of Ohm's law that will both be satisfactory from a formal point of view and congruous with his experiment and measurements, as we have described them. We should like the observables, resistance and current, to appear as primitive terms in the system. On the other hand, we should like to be able to compute the values of theoretical constants that are not directly observable from the values of the observables – that is to say, we should like the theoretical constants to be defined on the basis of the axioms by means of the observables.[4]

In the system to be proposed, there will be two theoretical constants: the first, $v$, may be interpreted as the voltage of the circuit; the second, $b$, as the internal resistance – that is, the resistance of the entire circuit less the resistance of the measured copper wire introduced into it.

*Ohm's Law*

$\Gamma$ is a system of *Ohmic observations* if there exist $D, r, c$ such that:

(1)        $\Gamma = \langle D, r, c \rangle$;

(2)        $D$ is a finite, nonempty set;

(3)        $r$ and $c$ are functions from $D$ into the real numbers;

(4)        for $X \in D$, $r(x) > 0$ and $c(x) \geqslant 0$.

$\Gamma$ is an *Ohmic circuit* if there exist $D, r, c, b$, and $v$ such that:

(5)        $\Gamma' = \langle D, r, c, b, v \rangle$;

(6)        $\Gamma = \langle D, r, c \rangle$ is a system of Ohmic observations;

(7)        $v$ and $b$ are real numbers

(8)        for all $X \in D$,

($\alpha$)        $c(x) = \dfrac{v}{b + r(x)}$

Perhaps the first question that would occur to a statistician or an empirical scientist regarding the axiomatizations of a system of Ohmic observations or an Ohmic circuit is whether they permit values of the theoretical terms, $v$ and $b$, to be calculated from the values of the observables — the $r$'s and $c$'s. If $v$ and $b$ are not uniquely determined by means of the observables on the basis of the axioms (($\alpha$) has more than one solution), the statistician would call them 'unidentified' or 'underidentified'. If they are uniquely determined, the statistician would call them 'just-identified'. If they can be evaluated (possibly inconsistently) in more than one way, he might call them 'overidentified'.[5]

By the axioms for a system of Ohmic observations, $D$ may not be empty. However, if $D$ contains a single element, $X$, with functions $r(x_1)$ and $c(x_1)$, then there exists an infinite set of ordered pairs $\langle v, b \rangle$ defined by:

$$(\beta) \qquad v = (b + r_1)c_1 .$$

If $D$ contains two members with distinct $r$'s and $c$'s, say $\langle r_1, c_1 \rangle$ and $\langle r_2 \, c_2 \rangle$ respectively, then the two equations comprising ($\alpha$) can be solved for unique values of $v$ and $b$:

$$(\gamma) \qquad \bar{b} = \frac{c_2 r_2 - c_1 r_1}{c_1 - c_2}; \qquad \bar{v} = c_1 c_2 \frac{r_2 - r_1}{c_1 - c_2} .$$

If $D$ contains more than two distinct members, then there will not exist a $\langle v, b \rangle$ satisfying ($\alpha$) unless the following relation holds among the $c$'s and $r$'s.

$$(\delta) \qquad (x \in D) \quad c(x) = \frac{c_1 c_2 (r_2 - r_1)}{c_2 r_2 - c_1 r_1 + (c_1 - c_2)r(x)} .$$

We see that a statistician could not expect to calculate values for $v$ and $b$ unambiguously from a system of Ohmic observations unless $D$ contained exactly two members with distinct $c(x)$'s; or $D$ contained more than two distinct members, and the relation ($\delta$) held.

## 3. DEFINABILITY AND CREATIVITY

We now wish to introduce the term 'definition', which we have eschewed up to this point. Since the subject of definability and definition has been treated extensively by Tarski, Suppes, and others in works that are readily accessible, we will not undertake a general discussion here, but rely on known results.[6] We consider a set of sentences, $X$, in which appear extra-logical constants, $a; b', b'', \ldots; c', c'', \ldots$. We represent by '$\psi(a; b', b'', \ldots; c', c'', \ldots)$' the conjunction of the sentences of $X$.

Let $a$ be some extra-logical constant and $B$ any set of such constants. Every sentence of the form:

(I)                     $(x): x = a \cdot \equiv \cdot \phi(x; b', b'', \ldots),$

where '$\phi(x; b', b'', \ldots)$' stands for any sentential function which contains $x$ as the only real variable, and in which no extra-logical constants other than $b', b''$, of the set $B$ occur, will be called a *possible definition* or simply a *definition of the term a by means of the terms of the set B*. We shall say that the term *a is definable by means of the terms of the set B on the basis of the set X of sentences*, if $a$ and all terms of $B$ occur in the sentences of the set $X$ and if at the same time at least one possible definition of the term $a$ by means of the terms of $B$ is derivable from the sentences of $X$ ([7], p. 299). Tarski demonstrates the important theorem:

THEOREM I.    In order that the term $a$ should be definable by means of the terms of the set $B$ on the basis of the set $X$ of sentences, it is necessary and sufficient that the formula

(II)          $(x): x = a \cdot \equiv \cdot (\exists z', z'', \ldots \cdot \psi(x; b', b'', \ldots; z', z'', \ldots)$

should be derivable from the sentences of $X$ ([7], p. 301).

### 3.1. Definability of Voltage and Internal Resistance

From our earlier discussion of the axioms for an Ohmic circuit, it follows immediately that the voltage, $v$, and internal resistance, $b$, of such a circuit could be made definable by means of the currents and resistances if we added one more condition to the definition:

(9)            $D$ contains at least two members with distinct $r$'s and $c$'s. (When this condition is satisfied, we will call the system an *identified Ohmic circuit*.)

Indeed, the formulas ($\gamma$) are a set of possible definitions for the two constants. However, the existence and uniqueness of solutions for these formulas depend on conditions (8) and (9).

It is easy to show by the method of Padoa (Tarski, *op cit.*, pp. 304–305) that $v$ and $b$ are not definable in a system consisting of conditions (1)–(8) alone, that is, in an Ohmic circuit. For let $D$ consist of the single element $X$

with $c(x) = r(x) = 1$. Then $\langle v, b \rangle$ will contain an infinite number of members, including, for example, $\langle 1, 0 \rangle$ and $\langle 2, 1 \rangle$.

## 3.2. Creativity of the Axioms

Lesniewski has proposed that definitions should satisfy two conditions, which P. Suppes describes thus:

Two criteria which make more specific ... intuitive ideas about the character of definitions are that (i) a defined symbol should always be eliminable from any formula of the theory, and (ii) a new definition does not permit the proof of relationships among the old symbols which were previously unprovable; that is, it does not function as a creative axiom ([6], p. 153).

Following Suppes, we will refer to these two criteria as *eliminability* and *noncreativity*, respectively. More formal definitions of the criteria can be given (and are given by Suppes, p. 154), but we will proceed in terms of their intuitive meaning. These criteria stem from the notion, often repeated in works on logic, that definitions are ('ought to be'?) mere notational abbreviations, allowing a theory to be stated in more compact form without changing its content in any way.

As our example of Ohm's law shows, in stating a physical theory it may be natural to introduce new defined terms simultaneously with new creative assumptions (i.e. 'natural laws'). Then the new terms may be definable in the sense of Tarski, as voltage and internal resistance are in an identified Ohmic circuit, without any of the axioms of the system constituting definitions for them. Since (8) is the only part of the system that contains the algebraic expression usually referred to as 'Ohm's law', and since by factoring this expression, it becomes the source both of the definitions in the strict sense, $(\gamma)$, and the law in the strict sense $(\delta)$, it is not surprising that $(\alpha)$ is sometimes referred to as definition, sometimes as law. Once it is established both that the new terms are definable in the system, and that the system is creative, this usage will ordinarily cause no difficulty.

Our analysis clarifies the meaning of the term 'overidentified', alluded to earlier. If $D$ has less than two members, then we have seen that $v$ and $b$ are underidentified and undefined. If $D$ has exactly two (distinct) members, then from $(\alpha)$, $v$ and $b$ will be just-identified and can be defined, but the axiom system will be non-creative. If $D$ has more than two distinct members, $v$ and $b$ will be overidentified by $(\alpha)$, and the axiom system will be creative. Overidentification, therefore, corresponds to creativity of the axiom system, or loosely (regarding ($\alpha$) as the 'definition' of $v$ and $b$), to creativity of the definition introducing the overidentified terms.

## 3.3. Definability of Current or Resistance

Tarski's formulation shows us that we must always consider definability to be relative not only to a set of sentences (the basis), but also relative to a set, $B$, of constants. We now show that the concept of creativity must be relativized in just the same way.

As we have seen, in an identified Ohmic circuit voltage and internal resistance are definable by means of current and resistance. But from ($\delta$) we see that it is equally the case that each $c_i$, except $c_1$ and $c_2$, is definable in an identified Ohmic circuit by means of $c_1, c_2, r_1, r_2$, and $r_i$. (Strictly speaking, we must add an axiom that $r_i \neq -b$.) Alternately (in this case, we require $c_i \neq 0$), each $r_i$ except $r_1$ and $r_2$ is definable in an Ohmic circuit by means of $c_1, c_2, r_1, r_2$, and $c_i$. As still other possibilities from ($\alpha$), every $c_i$ is definable by means of $v, b$, and $r_i$; and every $r_i$ by means of $v, b$, and $c_i$.

For any set, $B$, of extra-logical constants, we can ask whether the central condition of our system, condition (8), is creative relative to that set. Eliminate from ($\alpha$) all constants that are definable by means of the set $B$. Call the sentence obtained by this elimination (8)'. If any theorems are derivable from the conjunction of (8)' with the other conditions that are not derivable from the other conditions alone, then axiom (8) is creative relative to $B$; otherwise it is noncreative relative to $B$

From ($\delta$), we see that condition (8) is creative relative to the set $B$ consisting of the union of the $c$'s and $r$'s. However, it is noncreative relative to the $r$'s, $c_1$ and $c_2$; and relative to the $c$'s, $r_1$ and $r_2$. From ($\alpha$) we see it is also noncreative, relative to the $r$'s, $v$, and $b$; and relative to the $c$'s, $v$, and $b$.

If in each case we identify the set $B$ with the set of extra-logical constants that are directly observable, we see that our results make very good sense. In the case where the condition is creative, simultaneous measurements are made of current and resistance, as in Ohm's original experiment, permitting the law to be tested empirically. In the cases where the condition is noncreative, measurements are made of current but not of resistance, or of resistance but not current, and the observed variable is used to calculate the value of the unobserved. Here the Ohmic circuit is not being used to test Ohm's law, but to estimate constants on the assumption that the law holds. The four sub-cases correspond to different procedures for assigning values to the voltage and internal resistance.

### 3.4. *Alternative Forms of the Axioms*

There is a positive reason for employing ($\alpha$), rather than ($\gamma$) and ($\delta$), in the axiomatization of Ohm's law. In the axiomatization as given, no particular members of $D$ have to be singled out and named as the particular members employed in the definition of $b$ and $v$. Instead, all members of $D$ are treated symmetrically; *any* pair of members could serve for the definitions.

This symmetry accords also with the usual statistical practices for estimating the defined terms when there are 'errors of measurement' — i.e. when the laws are assumed to hold only approximately. Using the method of least squares, for example, we might replace ($\alpha$) by

$$(\alpha') \qquad (X \in D) \qquad v = c(x)(b + r(x)) + e(x)$$

together with the stipulation that $\Sigma_x \, e(x)^2$ be a minimum with respect to $v$ and $b$. With such a condition in place of (8), it is easy to see that not only do $v$ and $b$ continue to be definable by means of the $c$'s and $r$'s, but the $e_i$'s are definable as well. Moreover, the axiom system is now noncreative — it doesn't state a new physical law at all! This last result will sound less paradoxical if we restate it as follows: by introducing the error terms, $e_i$, we make it possible always to estimate a 'curve of best fit', but on the other hand, the 'best fit' may be a very bad fit. If we add to the conditions an upper bound on the mean square error, we again obtain an empirically testable theory, though a weaker one than the original 'exact' theory.

There is an additional lesson to be drawn from the axiomatization of Ohm's law. The nine conditions for an identified Ohmic circuit are highly heterogenous. The first four define a set of pairs of observations. The next four define a set of possible theoretic terms. The ninth sets a lower bound to the number of observations.

Now it does not seem entirely proper that the axioms for a physical theory should contain a specification of the number of observations. That number is after all arbitrary and whatever the experimenter chooses to make it; in no sense is it part of the phenomena the theory purports to describe. It might be more pleasing, therefore, to drop condition (8) from the system, thus defining Ohmic circuits instead of identified Ohmic circuits, but to modify slightly the notion of definability to allow for its absence.

We can see roughly how this may be done. Suppose a set of sentences contains a set, $D$, and some primitive terms, functions from $D$ into some domain, belonging to a set, $B$. Then we might speak of a term $a$ as *generally definable* by means of the terms of the set $B$ on the basis of this set of sentences if, for some finite $n$ and for every model of the set of sentences in which $D$ contains not less than $n$ sufficiently distinct elements, the term corresponding to $a$ is definable in that model. The meaning of 'sufficiently distinct' will be clear from the discussion at the end of Section 2 above.

The intuitive meaning of 'general definability' of a term is that the term can be defined if a sufficient number of observations is taken. This concept has the advantage also that $n$ (which is 2 in the present case, but will be different for different theories) need not be specified.[7]

### 3.5. Conclusion

We have perhaps carried our analysis of the axiomatization of Ohm's law as far as is profitable. Although it is as simple an instance as one can imagine of a nontrivial physical theory, it is not lacking in subtleties. In particular, it has allowed us to discover some of the differences between the criteria for axiomatizing a physical theory and the more familiar criteria, already often discussed and applied in the literature, for axiomatizing a portion of logic or mathematics. In the former case, new definable terms are likely to enter the system embedded in statements of physical laws. These statements will partake of the nature both of definitions and of laws. In conjunction with other axioms, they will permit definition of new extra-logical (theoretical) constants, but at the same time they will be creative relative to the extra-logical constants corresponding to observables.

Both a taste for symmetry with respect to the primitives that correspond to observables, and a desire not to embed assumptions about the number of observations directly in the theory may argue for incorporating such mixed definitions-cum-laws in the axiom system instead of factoring out their definition-like and law-like components, respectively.

### 4. AXIOMS FOR NEWTONIAN PARTICLE MECHANICS

We now turn to a more complex example, Newtonian particle mechanics. Since we have already unearthed the main issues with which we shall be concerned – definability of theoretical terms and creativity of laws – and since several nearly-adequate axiomatizations of Newtonian particle mechanics are already available in the literature, our discussion can be relatively brief.[8]

It is intended that the axioms be appropriate for celestial mechanics, and that the laws of gravitational attraction be introduced independently of the laws of motion.

*Newtonian Particle Mechanics*

A system $\Gamma = \langle P, T, s(p, t), m(p) \rangle$ that satisfies Axioms N1—N4 is called a *Newtonian system of particle mechanics*.

AXIOM N1. $P$ is a nonempty, finite set.

AXIOM N2. $T$ is an interval of real numbers.

AXIOM N3. If $p$ is in $P$ and $t$ is in $T$, then $s(p, t)$ is a three-dimensional vector such that $D^2 s(p, t)$ exists, where $D$ denotes differentiation with respect to $t$.

AXIOM N4. If $p$ is in $P$, then $m(p)$ is a real-valued function, $(p \in P)\ m \neq 0$, such that:

(4a)         $(t \in T)\quad \sum_{p \in P} m(p)D^2 s(p, t) = 0$;

(4b)         $(t \in T)\quad \sum_{p \in P} m(p)D^2 s(p, t) \times s(p, t) = 0$.

A Newtonian system of particle mechanics that satisfies Axiom N5 is called *holomorphic*;

AXIOM N5. If $P^* \subset P$, and if $E_a$ and $E_b$ are the statements obtained by *replacing* $P$ by $P^*$ in (4a) and (4b), respectively, then $\neg\, E_a$ and $\neg\, E_b$,

In interpretation, $P$ is a set of particles, $T$ an interval of time, the $m(p)$ the mass function, and the $s(p, t)$ the function designating the positions of the particles. Axiom N4 asserts the conservation of momentum and angular momentum; and Axiom N5 asserts that the system does not contain independent subsystems. For celestial mechanics, the observables are represented by $s$'s and their derivatives.

*4.1. Definability of Mass*

In Simon [3], it is proved that in a holomorphic Newtonian system of particle mechanics the ratios of the $m$'s (i.e. $m(p_i)/m(p_j)$) for all pairs of particles are definable in the sense of Tarski by means of the $s$'s. The result is not surprising in the light of formulas (4a) and (4b), the only delicate point (Theorem I of [3], pp. 892—893) being the role of Axiom N5.

Let $n_p$ be the number of elements in $P$. If we select $n_p - 1$ distinct elements from $T$, and assert one of the three scalar equations corresponding to the vector equation in (4a) for just those elements of $T$, then we will have exactly the right number of equations to estimate the ratios of the $m$'s uniquely.

Call N4′ the axiom obtained by replacing the full set of equations in N4 by this finite subset. Then N4′ will be a noncreative definition for the mass ratios by means of the s's, while N4 will be a creative definition relative to the s's. We have here a situation quite analogous to the one we discovered in axiomatizing Ohm's law.

The Axioms N1–N5 do not deal with the problem of selecting an appropriate inertial reference system; rather it is assumed that the s's are already measured relative to such a system. The problems that arise in including the determination of the reference frame in the axiomatization are discussed and the solutions of those problems given in [3], pp. 896–901, and they will not be taken up here.

### 4.2. Definability of Force

Some discussion is needed, however, of the hoary question of whether, in this context, the second law $- F = mD^2 s -$ is a physical law or a definition. By now we will be prepared for the answer that it may be a little of each. Again, I follow my treatment in [3], pp. 901–902.

*Newtonian Gravitational System*

A system $\Gamma' = \langle P, T, s(p, t), m(p), F(p, t) \rangle$ which satisfies Axiom N6, below, as well as N1–N5, is called a *Newtonian gravitational system*.

AXIOM N6. If $p$ is in $P$ and $t$ is in $T$, then $F(p, t)$ is a three-dimensional vector, such that

(6a)          $F(p, t) = m(p)D^2 s(p, t);$ and

(6b)          $F(p, t) = \sum_{p^* \neq p} \left\{ \frac{m(p)m(p^*)}{|s(p, t) - s(p^*, t)|^3} (s(p, t) - s(p^*, t)) \right\},$

where the expression bounded by vertical bars denotes the scalar distance of $s(p, t)$ from $s(p^*, t)$.

Equations (6a) constitute a definition of the ratios of the *resultant forces*, $F(p, t)$, by means of the masses, $m(p)$, and hence ultimately by means of the position functions, $s(p, t)$. Taken by themselves, equations (6a) are noncreative. Equations (6b) introduce no new undefined terms, hence are creative relative to the s's.

Alternatively, we can define *component forces* by the noncreative definitions:

(7a)  $$f(p, p^*, t) = \frac{m(p)m(p^*)}{|s(p, t) - s(p^*, t)|^3} (s(p, t) - s(p^*, t)).$$

Next we define the resultant forces (noncreatively) in terms of the component forces.

(7b)  $$F(p, t) = \sum_{p^* \neq p} f(p, p^*, t)$$

Taken together, Equations (7a) and (7b) are of course equivalent to (6b). Hence, if we now add (6a) to a system in which (7a) and (7b) are already incorporated, (6a) will be creative relative to the $s$'s.

In summary, we may say that Axiom N6, which consists of the conjunction of the Second Law of Motion with the Law of Gravitation, is creative with respect to the $s$'s. However, it is completely indifferent whether we regard the second law as a definition and the Law of Gravitation as a physical law; or whether, *vice versa*, we regard the Law of Gravitation as a definition (of gravitational force) and the second law as a physical law. Jointly, they are creative relative to the observables, hence perform both a definition-like and a law-like function.[9]

In terrestrial mechanics, the experimenter will often regard forces as observables. He may equate them with readings on any of a number of kinds of balances — torsion or spring balances, for example, or balances employing weights, hence the earth's gravitational force. He may reverse Ohm's experiment, using the known strength of an electric current as a measure of force inducted by the current. Wherever, or by whatever means force is treated as an observable, the Second Law of Motion becomes a creative axiom relative to the observables, that is, a physical law rather than a definition.

## 4.3. Nearly-Everywhere Definability

In the examples used in this paper, certain axioms have been introduced to guarantee that the values of extra-logical constants will be uniquely determined, hence that the constants will be definable. Condition (9) for identified Ohmic circuits was of such a character, as was Axiom N5 for a holomorphic Newtonian system. In Section 3.4, I showed how an axiom of the former sort might be dispensed with by replacing 'definability' by the weaker notion of 'general definability'. The idea underlying this weakening was that the case of a sufficiently large number of observations was the 'general' case; the case of too few observations to define the constants a 'special' case.

Similarly, inspection of Axiom N5 would suggest that a system will be *non*-holomorphic only if it satisfies a rather strong condition. Hence, it should be possible to exclude this case with only a modest weakening of the notion of 'definability'. Elsewhere,[10] I have shown how this can be done by defining a measure on the set of models satisfying an axiom system, then introducing the notion of 'almost-everywhere definability' relative to that measure (i.e. a constant is defined almost-everywhere if it is defined except in a set of measure zero in the space of models).

Suppose that the models satisfying a set of axioms can be characterized as the points of an $n$-dimensional space. We then define a measure on this space such that any subset of dimension less than $n$ have measure zero. 'Dimension' here corresponds closely to the statistician's notion of 'degrees of freedom'. Thus, if the accelerations and angular accelerations of $n$ particles are observed at $k$ points in time, the observations have $6nk - 6k + (n-1)$ degrees of freedom. For the observations consist of $6nk$ scalars, they are constrained by the $6k$ Equations (4a) and (4b) of Axiom N4, and there are $n-1$ unknown masses to be estimated from the equations.

Now if the system is not holomorphic, it will be subject to the additional $6k - (n-1)$ constraints represented by the formulas $E_a$ and $E_b$ of Axiom N5, hence will have fewer degrees of freedom. Hence, for any measure such that sets of less than $6nk - 6k + (n-1)$ degrees of freedom have measure zero, mass will be definable almost-everywhere relative to that measure.

### 4.4. Conclusion

In this section an axiom system has been proposed for classical celestial mechanics that allows mass to be defined by means of observations of the paths of the particles of a system, provided that the system is holomorphic. A definition of resultant force, noncreative relative to the same observations, can be added to the system. Alternatively, the Gravitational Law (or some other force law) can be used to define component forces noncreatively, whereupon the Second Law of Motion becomes a creative physical law.

The axiomatization, which is a formalization of one proposed earlier by the author, throws further light on the concept of definability, and illustrates the possibility of simplifying the axiom system by replacing 'definability' by weaker terms like 'almost-everywhere definability' and 'general definability'.

## NOTES

*This work was supported by Public Health Service Research Grant MH-07722, from the National Institutes of Mental Health.

I am indebted to Joseph D. Sneed for valuable comments and suggestions on an earlier draft of this paper.

[1] Much of the discussion has been focused on Newtonian mechanics as an example. A logician, in a textbook chapter dealing with the topic, refers to the attempted definitions of mass by Mach and his followers as 'Pickwickian', while a scientist, in a paper comparing two axiomatizations, charges logicians with ignoring questions of 'operational meaning'. These epithets, while lively, do not immediately reveal the root of the difficulty.

[2] A translation of the relevant part of Ohm's 1826 paper can be found in [1], pp. 465–472.

[3] It may be mentioned that the operations used by Ohm to measure resistance and current are essentially those incorporated in one of the standard systems for defining electrodynamic units. Thus the ampere is defined as one-tenth of the current that, in a certain geometric configuration. exerts a force of $2\pi$ dynes on a unit magnetic pole. The ohm is defined as the resistance to an unvarying current of a column of mercury having certain dimensions and temperature.

[4] Discussion of the exact meaning of the term 'defined' will be reserved until the formal axioms have been presented.

[5] We will return to the meaning of 'overidentified' presently.

[6] Treatments adequate for our purpose will be found in [6], Chapter 8; and [7], pp. 296–319.

[7] In another place I have introduced a notion of 'almost-everywhere definability' with the same aim as that which motivates 'general definability' above. I will have more to say about it later.

[8] Two modern axiomatizations are in [3], pp. 888–905 and [2], pp. 253–272. I shall adopt here the substance of the first, but the set-theoretic form of the second.

[9] Throughout this section I have proceeded less formally than in the early parts of the paper. The reader should have no difficulty in filling in the details, which involve the standard questions of specifying the conditions for the existence and uniqueness of solutions of systems of equations. These matters are treated more fully in [3], pp. 901 902.

[10] 'Almost-everywhere definability' is described informally in [4], p. 449. Subsequently, I have stated the definition more formally in an abstract in [5], pp. 705–706.

## REFERENCES

[1]  Magie, W. F., *A Source Book in Physics* (New York: McGraw-Hill, 1935).
[2]  McKinsey, J. C. C. *et al.*, 'Axiomatic Foundations of Classical Particle Mechanics', *Journal of Rational Mechanics and Analysis* **2** (1953).
[3]  Simon, H. A., 'The Axioms of Newtonian Mechanics', *Philosophical Magazine*, Series 7, **38** (1947) (reprinted as Chapter 6.1 in this volume).
[4]  Simon, H. A., 'Definable Terms and Primitives in Axiom Systems', in *The Axiomatic Method*, eds. L. Henkin *et al.*, (Amsterdam: North-Holland, 1959), (reprinted as Chapter 6.3 in this volume).

[5]  Simon, H. A., 'A Note on Almost-Everywhere Definability', abstract, in *Journal of Symbolic Logic* **31** (1966) (reprinted as Chapter 6.4 in this volume).
[6]  Suppes, P., *Introduction to Logic* (Princeton: Van Nostrand, 1957).
[7]  Tarski, A., 'Some Methodological Investigations on the Definability of Concepts', in *Logic, Semantics and Metamathematics* (Oxford: The Clarendon Press: 1956).

# RAMSEY ELIMINABILITY AND THE TESTABILITY OF SCIENTIFIC THEORIES†*

(with Guy J. Groen)

## 1. INTRODUCTION

The role in scientific theories of theoretical terms, which do not correspond directly with observables, continues to be a matter of discussion and some puzzlement. If a theoretical term in a particular theory is definable, it can, of course, be eliminated directly without altering the semantic content of the theory. In order to make room for theoretical terms that are not definable, Ramsey (1931, Chapter IX), introduced the notion of eliminability. Roughly speaking, a theoretical term is eliminable, in the sense of Ramsey, if all the empirical claims of the theory can be made without invoking it. Ramsey apparently believed that in a properly formulated scientific theory all theoretical terms would be eliminable, but that not all need be definable. Sneed (1971), however, has produced examples of simple theory-like systems containing theoretical terms that are not eliminable in the Ramsey sense.

Closely related to this issue is the question of what role a theoretical term can play in a scientific theory if it is neither definable nor Ramsey-eliminable. To admit into scientific theories terms that do not correspond to observables yet which are required in order to make the full set of empirical claims of the theory would seem to run counter to the requirements of operationalism. Of course, if there were no such terms, there would be no problem, but Sneed's examples would seem to suggest that there are.

The main aim of this paper is to show that the theoretical terms appearing in 'well-formulated' scientific theories will always be at least Ramsey-eliminable even when they are not definable. We will introduce some well-motivated restrictions on the class of systems that are to be regarded as well formulated, thereby defining a class of FIT (finitely and irrevocably testable) theories. We will show that the theories of Sneed's examples are not FIT, and that theoretical terms are always Ramsey-eliminable from FIT

† [*British Journal for the Philosophy of Science* **24**, 357–408 (1973)].

theories. Our analysis will also show that the FITness conditions provide an explanation for an often-observed asymmetry between existentially and universally quantified claims of a theory.

## 2. THE FORMALISATION

We will proceed as though the scientific theories we are interested in were axiomatised in the first-order predicate calculus with equality $\langle L, = \rangle$. Of course, no complete axiomatisations of significant scientific theories have actually been constructed in this formalisation, but Sneed has shown that the interesting methodological issues can be raised and discussed in this context.

We will be concerned with a theory that contains one or more theoretical function symbols or predicate symbols; and with structures of observable functions or predicates that may be expandable to models of the theory. Testing a theory, then, will consist in determining whether the structure describing an actual set of observations is or is not expandable to such a model – whether the theory 'holds' for these observations. A formalisation of these ideas may be sketched as follows.[1]

We employ a first-order language, $L$, with equality, containing certain function symbols, predicate symbols and constants (0-ary function symbols). One or more of the function and predicate symbols, $O_1, \ldots, O_k$, is drawn from a set $O$; and one or more, $T_1, \ldots, T_l$, from a set $T$. There is an infinite set, $X$, of constant symbols, $x_i$. We wish to consider a theory, $\bar{F}$, in $L$ whose axioms are the logical axioms together with the formula $F(O, T)$, which contains symbols from $O$ and $T$.

Next, we introduce a structure, $\langle D, O_M, T_M \rangle$ consisting of a set, $D$, of elements, and two sets of functions from $D$ to $D$ and predicates in $D$ (call them $O_M$ and $T_M$) corresponding to the two sets of symbols, $O$ and $T$, in $L$. To each distinct element of $D$ we assign a distinct constant symbol from $X$. (When the ambiguity will not cause confusion we will sometimes write $O$ indifferently for $O_M$ and $O$, and $T$ for $T_M$ and $T$. It will usually be clear from the context whether we are speaking of a theory or a structure.)

DEFINITION. The *observable consequences*, $H(O)$, of a theory are the members of the class of all consequences of $F$ that do not contain symbols from $T$.

Let $F_c(O, T)$ be a closed formula obtained from $F(O, T)$ by replacing each free variable in $F(O, T)$ by one of the constants that corresponds to an element of $D$. If all the $F_c(O, T)$ constructed in this way are true of $\langle D, O_M, T_M \rangle$, then this structure is a model for the theory $\bar{F}$.

We might be tempted at this point to propose that a structure $\langle D, O_M, T_M \rangle$ *disconfirms* a theory, $\bar{F}$, if the structure is not a model of the theory. But matters are a little more complicated. In distinguishing the sets $O_M$ and $T_M$, our intent is to interpret the elements, $x$, of $D$ as *observed objects*; the functions of $O_M$ as *observable functions* whose values for any $x$ can be determined by observation of $x$; and the $n$-ary predicates of $O_M$ as *observable relations* whose truth-values for any set of $n$ observations can be determined from those observations. The members of $T_M$, on the other hand, are *theoretical functions and relations*, whose values cannot be determined directly from observations.[2] Following Sneed (1971, p. 52), we deal with the problem of non-observability by considering the structure $\langle D, O_M \rangle$, obtained by removing the functions of predicates $T_M$ from $\langle D, O_M, T_M \rangle$. (The former structure is called by Shoenfield a *restriction* of the latter.) We next introduce the

DEFINITION. For a given structure, $\langle D, O_M \rangle$, if there exists a $T_M$ in $D$, and a corresponding $T$ in $L$, such that $F(O, T)$ is valid in $\langle D, O_M, T_M \rangle$ then $\langle D, O_M \rangle$ is *expandable to a model* for the theory $\bar{F}$.

Since the $T_M$'s are assumed not to be directly observable, we are free to expand $\langle D, O_M \rangle$ by choosing any $T$ that makes $F(O, T)$ valid, provided one exists. But now, whether a particular $\langle D, O_M \rangle$, is expandable to a model for $\bar{F}$ depends only on the $O_M$, hence is an observable property of the structure. We can say, therefore, that a structure (i.e. a set of observations) disconfirms a theory if it is not expandable to a model for the theory. It is with this notion of disconfirmation that we shall be concerned here.

Suppose that all of the symbols of $T$, in a theory; $\bar{F}$, are definable in terms of the symbols of $O$ in $F(O, T)$. In this case, we can simply use the definitions of the symbols of $T$ to eliminate all of them from $F(O, T)$, obtaining the formula $F'(O)$, whose observable consequences, $H'(O)$, are identical with the observable consequences, $H(O)$, of $F(O, T)$. All models $\langle D, O_M \rangle$ for $H(O)$ (or $H'(O)$) will be expandable, using the given definitions of the symbols of $T$, and the corresponding $T_M$, to models for $F(O, T)$. In this case, whether we express the theory in terms of both the $T$'s and $O$'s – as $F(O, T)$ – or in terms of the $O$'s alone – as $F'(O)$ – is a matter of convenience, not necessity. The presence of the unobservable $T_M$'s raises no issues about the operationality of the theory. We are particularly interested, therefore, in the case of theories that contain $T$'s that are *not* definable in terms of the $O$'s.

## 3. RAMSEY ELIMINABILITY

In order to introduce the concept of Ramsey-eliminability, we need one additional bit of notation. Let $M$ be a set of structures, $\langle D, O, T \rangle$. Then we will designate by $M_*$ the set of structures $\langle D, O \rangle$, obtained from $M$ by deleting the $T$ functions and relations. Thus, to each member of $M_*$ there will correspond a subset of $M$.

In $M$ consider the set of all models for $F(O, T)$. Call this set $M^T$. Restrict each member of $M^T$ by removing the $T$ relations, obtaining a set, $M_*^T$, of models in $M_*$. Clearly, all members of $M_*^T$ are expandable to models for $F(O, T)$, for we can construct these expansions by reintroducing the $T$'s that were deleted.

Next, consider the set of all models in $M$ for $H(O)$. Call this set $M^O$. Again, remove the $T$ relations to obtain a set $M_*^O$, of models in $M_*$. For the same reasons as before, all members of $M_*^O$ are expandable to models for $H(O)$. Moreover, by the method of their construction, the members of $M_*^O$ are all models for $H(O)$ in $M_*$. Since $F(O, T) \rightarrow H(O)$, we have proved the

THEOREM I. $M_*^T \subseteq M_*^O$.

The converse of Theorem I need not hold — there may be members of $M_*^O$ that are not members of $M_*^T$, as we shall see presently from examples.

However, for finite $D$, the converse of Theorem I follows directly from a well-known result of Craig & Vaught (1958), so we may assert (writing $m_k$ for a model of exactly $k$ elements):

THEOREM 2. For any finite $D$, all members of $M_*^O$ are extendable to members of $M^T$. Hence we can write $\forall k(m_k \in M_*^T \equiv m_k \in M_*^O)$.

The conclusion follows from the fact that, for finite $k$, we can describe any model extensionally in terms of the sets of elements of $D$ for which each of the members of $O$ holds, and any set of models by a disjunction of such descriptions. Hence, in particular, we can distinguish the class $M_*^T$ in terms of such a disjunction, involving only the $O$'s.

We can now introduce a formal definition of eliminability.

DEFINITION. If, for fixed $D$, $M_*^T = M_*^O$, that is, if all models in $M_*$ for $H(O)$ are expandable to models for $F(O, T)$, then we will say that the theoretical relations, $T$, are *D-Ramsey-eliminable*. If the relations, $T$, are $D$-Ramsey-eliminable for all $D$, then we say, simply, that they are *Ramsey-eliminable*.

Ramsey introduced, but did not define very exactly, the notion of eliminability. The definitions given above essentially follow Sneed (pp. 52–3). They appear to be faithful to Ramsey's original intent in introducing the concept.

If the theoretical terms of a theory are Ramsey-eliminable, then in a certain sense all of the empirical content of the theory can be expressed in terms of the observable relations, $O$. In this case, even if the theoretical terms are not definable (Shoenfield, pp. 80–1), they are present in the theory as a matter of convenience, not of necessity. Hence, if theoretical terms are always Ramsey-eliminable from theories, their introduction for reasons of convenience raises no questions of operationality.

Sneed, however, has proposed two examples of theories containing non-eliminable theoretical terms (Sneed, pp. 54–5). But close examination of his examples raises the question of whether they possess all the properties that we usually associate with scientific theories. It is our contention that they do not and that if we place appropriate restrictions on the scope of the term 'theory', it will be found that theoretical terms are always Ramsey-eliminable from theories.

## 4. FINITE AND IRREVOCABLE TESTABILITY

The conditions we shall introduce are aimed at guaranteeing that anything we call a well-formed theory will be operational or testable. We shall be mainly concerned with two such conditions: finiteness and irrevocability; and we will use these conditions to define a class of finite and irrevocable (FIT) theories.

The FITness conditions for a theory have nothing to do, directly, with whether the theory does or does not contain theoretical terms – they are not introduced *ad hoc* in order to deal with the problem of non-eliminability of theoretical terms. On the contrary, we shall see that it is quite natural to impose the requirements of FITness even on theories that are stated entirely in terms of observables – that is, theories of the form $F(O)$ – and that theories that fail to meet these requirements also fail to satisfy intuitive notions of operationality that have been employed by Popper (1959, Chapter III) and others.

As before, we are considering structures, $\langle D, O_M \rangle$, that represent sets of observations aimed at testing a scientific theory $F(O, T)$. A set of (possible) observations, then, comprises a set of observed objects, $x \in D$, and a set of functions and relations, $O_M$, on them. The set of observations can be identified with a model, $m$, that is possibly expandable to a model of the theory, $F(O, T)$, by introducing a new set of functions and relations, $T_M$, and the structure $\langle D, O_M, T_M \rangle$. When we wish to indicate that a model, $m$, has exactly $k$ elements, we will write $m_k$.

DEFINITION. Consider a model, $m_k$, and a second model, $m_{k+}$, obtained by annexing (zero or more) additional elements to $D$ and extending the $O_M$'s to encompass these new elements and their relations with the original elements. We will call the new model, $m_{k+}$ an extension of $m_k$, and will write: $m_{k+} \geqslant m_k$, or $m_k \leqslant m_{k+}$. If $m_{k+} \geqslant m_k$ and $m_{k+} \neq m_k$, we write $m_{k+} > m_k$.

Extending a model is to be interpreted as taking additional observations. Two questions now arise with respect to the testability of a theory:

(1) If the theory is false, do there always exist *finite* sets of observations on the basis of which it could definitely be disconfirmed (i.e. for every structure, $D$, not expandable to a model for $\bar{F}$ do there exist substructures $D_k$, with finite $k$, that are not in $M_*^O$, hence not expandable to $M_*^T$?

(2) Can the disconfirmation of a theory by some set of observations, $m_k$, ever be revoked by taking additional observations, so that $m_k$ is not in $M_*^O$, while the extended set, $m_{k+}, m_{k+} > m_k$, is in $M_*^O$?

If the first question can be answered in the affirmative for a theory, we say that the theory is *finitely testable*; if the second question can be answered in the negative, we say that the theory is *irrevocably testable*. More formally:

DEFINITION. A theory, $F(T, O)$, is *finitely testable* iff $\exists m (m \notin M_*^T)$ and

$$\forall m [(m \notin M_*^T) \rightarrow \exists m_k ((m_k \leqslant m) \wedge (m_k \notin M_*^T))], \text{ for finite } k.$$
$$(1)$$

DEFINITION. A theory, $F(T, O)$, is *irrevocably testable* iff

$$\forall m [\exists m_k ((m_k \leqslant m) \wedge (m_k \notin M_*^T)) \rightarrow (m \notin M_*^T)].$$
$$(2)$$

DEFINITION. A theory, $F(T, O)$, is *FIT* iff it is both finitely and irrevocably testable:

$$\forall m [\exists m_k ((m_k \leqslant m) \wedge (m_k \notin M_*^T)) \equiv (m \notin M_*^T)] \text{ and}$$
$$\exists m (m \notin M_*^T).$$
$$(3)$$

How are we to interpret the concepts of finite and irrevocable testability, and what justification do we have for equating these concepts with requirements of operationality? We may view the situation as follows: The scientist gains his knowledge of how the world is by making a sequence of observations on phenomena — that is, observations of objects, of functions of objects, and of the satisfaction or non-satisfaction of certain relations among sets of objects. Up to any given time, the total set of observations that has been made is finite, but it may be enlarged indefintely by taking new observations. Any denumerable sequence of observations whose initial segment agrees with the observations taken up to the present time describes a possible world. As new observations are made, they eliminate certain of these possible worlds.

The scientist wishes to formulate hypotheses, or theories that will hold for the actual world — not only as it has been revealed by past observations, but as it will appear in the light of future observations as well. Hume taught us that there is no way to guarantee that a theory consistent with all observations to date will not be refuted by future observations. But what of the converse: is there some way in which we can guarantee that if a theory is false (i.e. the sequence of past and future observations is not a model for it), this will become known to us sooner or later by observation? If theories cannot be confirmed, can they, at least, be disconfirmed when false? Finite and irrevocable testability are conditions that, if imposed upon the class of theories we are willing to entertain, guarantee their disconfirmability in a very natural sense.

Consider, first, what it would mean for a theory *not* to be finitely testable. Then, even if some assertions of the theory were false in the actual world, it could happen (i.e. the actual world could be such) that all of the assertions would be true for every finite set of observations that could be taken in that world. Thus, there would be no way to distinguish, by taking observations, between that actual world and a world in which the theory was true. The finite testability condition outlaws theories that are untestable in this sense. As a matter of fact, it appears to be difficult to construct an example of a theory — real or imaginary — that has any sort of surface plausibility, yet is not finitely testable. We will offer an example or two later of theories that are not finitely testable, but it will be seen that they are forced and 'artificial'.

Consider, next, what it would mean for a theory *not* to be irrevocably testable. Then, even if the theory were incompatible with the observations made to date, it might be 'saved' simply by making additional observations. Thus, we could never, by means of observations, refute a theory once and for all; its refutation would always be subject to reversal. It is as if, having taken ten observations of pairs of numbers that did not all lie on a straight line, we could now observe five more pairs and find that all fifteen did indeed lie on a straight line.[3]

It is interesting to note that requirements of testability for predicates that are quite similar in spirit to the FITness conditions have been introduced into automata theory and the theory of perceptrons. The notion of 'locally testable event' in automata theory (McNaughton and Papert, 1971) closely approximates our concept of '*FIT theory*', while a corresponding – but slightly stronger – concept of 'conjunctively local predicate' plays an important role in the theory of perceptrons (Minsky and Papert, 1969). In both cases, the motivation for the restriction is the same as ours: to insure a certain measure of (one-sided) decidability when a computational faculty that is capable of handling only finite sets of symbols is faced with a potentially infinite sequence.

To these justifications for the FITness conditions, we can add some less formal arguments buttressed by plausible examples. First, equating testability with disconfirmability or falsifiability follows the general usage, for which Popper (1959, Chapter IV) has made such a convincing case. Second, the FITness conditions provide an explanation for the asymmetry, upon which Popper (1959, especially pp. 68–72) and other have commented, between the testability of universal and existential statements.[4]

Finally, when applied to simple examples, the FITness conditions draw an intuitively plausible boundary between well-formed and ill-formed theories, as can be seen from the following illustrations. Note that none of the theories of the examples contain theoretical terms; all of the predicates are assumed to be directly observable.

*T1:*        Unicorns exist.   $(\exists x U(x))$.

*T2:*        No unicorns exist.   $(\forall x \neg U(x))$.

*T3:*        There is a finite number of sunrises.

*T4:*        There is a finite number of primes.

*T5:*        The number of stars is prime.

Theory *T1* is not irrevocably testable. A system of $k$ observations containing no observations of unicorns cannot be expanded to a model for the theory; but extension of the observations to include a unicorn observation produces a new system that is a model for the theory. Hence disconfirmation can be revoked by extension.

Theory *T2* is FIT. If unicorns exist, then observation of any single unicorn disconfirms *T2*, and no additional observations of non-unicorns can restore its validity. But 'unicorns exist' must be interpreted as meaning that there is at least one unicorn observation in the (potentially infinite) sequence of past and future observations.

Notice that, provided at least one observation is made, *T2* implies 'There exists a non-unicorn'. The latter assertion, though a consequence of the former, is non-testable, because it is not irrevocable. The apparent paradox disappears when we recall that testability means *dis*confirmability. No sequence of unicorn observations can disconfirm the proposition. Hence, a weak consequence of a strong and FIT theory may itself not be FIT.

Theory *T3* is not finitely testable. If there is *not* a finite number of sunrises, this cannot be shown by a finite set of observations. This is not to say that an assertion like *T3* may not be derivable as a theorem from a larger theory, but simply that the truth of *T3* cannot be disconfirmed by making observations of dawns to see if they are sunrises.

Theory *T4* is *disprovable*, from the definition of the primes, but it is not finitely testable for the same reason that *T3* is not finitely testable. This should not disturb us when we recognise that 'testable' is intended to mean 'empirically testable'. The proposition that there is a finite number of primes is certainly not empirically testable.

Theory *T5* is not irrevocably testable, as can be shown by extending a set of observations of $k$ stars ($k \notin$ Primes) until the size of the set equals the next larger prime number.

It is certainly not unreasonable to exclude *T3*, *T4*, and *T5* from the class of well-formed theories. Moreover, the difference between *T1* and *T2* is Popper's asymmetry, based on the existential quantifier in *T1* and the universal quantifier in *T2*. The criterion of irrevocability rules out *T1* but accepts *T2*. Hence, if we find Popper's condition to be intuitively plausible, we may take it as grounds for requiring irrevocability of a theory, and rejecting *T1*. conversely, if we find the irrevocability condition to be plausible, we may take it as grounds for accepting Popper's condition.

Let us consider a final example of FITness that is slightly more interesting than *T2*:

*T6*: $D$ is a set of objects that can be weighed in pairs on a two-pan balance. $O(x, y)$ means that when $x$ and $y$ are placed on the balance, the pan on which $x$ rests descends, and the other rises. We now hypothesise that $O$ is a transitive relation — i.e. that $(x, y, z)[O(x, y) \cdot O(y, z) \to O(x, z)]$.

*T6* is finitely testable, for if the theory is false, there exists a triplet $(x, y, z)$, which violates the transitivity. But if the triplet is taken as the set $D$, we then have a finite model that cannot be expanded to a model for the theory. *T6* is irrevocably testable, for if a triplet violates the transitivity, any extended model containing that triplet will also violate it.

Finally, it is worth remarking again that none of the examples, *T1–T6*, contain theoretical terms. Hence, the plausibility of imposing FITness conditions on the admissibility of scientific theories does not rest on any peculiarities of theories that possess such terms.

In pace of FITness, we could introduce a somewhat stronger condition of uniform FITness (UFIT). Suppose that the test for falsifying a theory involves the examination of relations among exactly *k* individuals. In the case of *T6*, above, *k* = 3. For that theory, if a particular structure of observations is not expandable to a model for the theory, then there always exists a substructure of three observations that is not so expandable; and conversely, if every triplet of observations in a structure is expandable to a model of the theory, then so is the entire set.

DEFINITION. A theory, $F(T, O)$, is *k-testable* iff it is FIT and there exists a *k* such that (3) is satisfied with the $m_k$ of size *k*.

The constant, *k*, is related to the concept of 'degrees of freedom'. That is, a *k*-testable theory may be viewed as having $(k - 1)$ degrees of freedom. Suppose we have a theory that asserts that a set of points, representing pairs of observables, lies, on a straight line:

$$z(x) = a + by(x). \tag{4}$$

This theory is 3-testable, since a set of observations disconfirms it iff some subset of three observations does not lie on a straight line. But the theory has two degrees of freedom, corresponding to the *T*-constants, *a* and *b*. An axiomatisation of Ohm's Law that is also 3-testable will be discussed in a later section.

DEFINITION. A theory, $F(O, T)$, is *uniformly FIT (UFIT)* iff it is *k*-testable for some *k*.

## 5. TESTABILITY AND ELIMINABILITY

Returning to the general case of FIT theories, we now prove the main theorem. We will use (1) and (2) as premises, instead of (3), to show that both the finiteness and irrevocability conditions play an essential role in the proof.

THEOREM 3. If a theory, $F(O, T)$, is FIT (i.e., if (1) and (2) are satisfied), then its theoretical terms, $T$, are Ramsey-eliminable; i.e.

$$\forall m [(m \notin M_*^T) \to (m \notin M_*^O)]. \tag{5}$$

*Proof:* Consider any particular $m$, $m \notin M_*^T$. If the domain of $m$ is finite, then (5) holds, hence we need consider only $m$ with infinite domain. Then, by the finite testability condition (1):

$$\exists m_k [(m_k \leqslant m) \wedge m_k \notin M_*^T], k \text{ finite}. \tag{6}$$

Designate by $S_k(O)$ the complete description of some $m_k$ satisfying (6), that is, the conjunction of formulas that state for each predicate in $O$ for which sets of elements $D_k$ this predicate holds, and for which it does not; and for each $n$-argument function of $O$, its value for each set of $n$ elements in $D_k$. Since $k$ is finite, $S_k(O)$ is of finite length; and by its construction, $S_k(O)$ does not involve $T$.

Now consider any model, $m'$, satisfying $F(O, T)$, so that $m' \in M_*^T$. Construct $S_k^*(O)$ by replacing the distinct individual symbols in $S_k(O)$ that designate different individuals in $D_k$ with distinct variables. Suppose that the following sentence, not involving $T$, were to hold for $m'$:

$$\exists x_1, \ldots, x_k(S_k^*(O)); \ x_1, \ldots, x_k \text{ in the } D \text{ of } m'. \tag{7}$$

Then any set of elements $x_1, \ldots, x_k$ satisfying (7) determine a model, $m_k'$, described by $S_k^*(O)$, that is isomorphic with the $m_k$ of equation (6). Hence, from the second conjunct of (6):

$$m_k' \notin M_*^T. \tag{8}$$

By the irrevocability condition, (2), $m_k' \notin M_*^T \to m' \notin M_*^T$, so that, from (8):

$$m' \notin M_*^T, \tag{9}$$

contradicting our assumption that $m' \in M_*^T$. Hence the latter assumption, or its equivalent – that $m'$ satisfies $F(O, T)$ – is incompatible with (7), so that

$$F(O, T) \to \forall x_1, \ldots, x_k(\neg S_k^*(O)). \tag{10}$$

But the right-hand side of (10) does not involve $T$, hence belongs to $H(O)$. By definition, $m \in M_*^O$ means that $H(O)$ is true of $m$. Since (7) holds for $m$, but contradicts the right-hand side of (10), it follows immediately that $m \notin M_*^O$. Q.E.D.

Since Sneed has provided two examples of theories from which the theoretical terms are not Ramsey-eliminable, it will be instructive to discover in what respects these theories are not FIT. His first example is this (Sneed, p. 54):

$T7:$      $F(T, O) = (i)\ \forall x\, \forall y (T(x, y) \rightarrow \exists z O(x, z) \wedge \neg \exists z O(y, z)) \wedge$

$(ii)\ \forall x (\exists z O(x, z) \rightarrow \exists y\, [T(x, y) \wedge \forall w (T(x, w) \rightarrow w = y)] \wedge$

$(iii)\ \forall x (\neg \exists z O(x, z) \rightarrow \exists y\, [T(y, x) \wedge \forall w (T(w, x) \rightarrow w = y)] )$

Of this he says: "Sentences $(i)$, $(ii)$, and $(iii)$ are true exactly in models $\langle D, T, O \rangle$ in which there is a one—one correspondence between individuals which stand in the first place in the $O$-relation and those which do not. Yet it can be shown that there is no sentence, containing only the predicate $O$ and identity which is true exactly in models $\langle D, O \rangle$ in which there is such a one—one correspondence."

Notice of $T7$ that, given any system of observations $\langle D, O \rangle$ with $O(x, y)$ such that one-half of the elements stand in an $O$-relation to some $y$, and half do not, and none of the $y$'s stand in an $O$-relation to some $z$, then this system can be extended to a model for $F(T, O)$. It is easy to see that the theory is finitely testable. However, it is not irrevocably testable. For suppose we observed an odd number of elements such that the conditions above could be satisfied by adding one more, appropriate, element. Then, since the conditions can be satisfied only by an even-numbered set of observations the initially observed set of elements disconfirms the theory, while the extended set does not, contrary to condition (2) of the previous sections.

Of this theory, Sneed says (pp. 54—5): "One might raise a question as to whether the fact that there is a one—one correspondence between individuals which stand in the first place of the $O$-relation and those which do not, is an observable fact. If one takes "observable fact" to mean "fact expressible in the observation vocabulary", then it clearly is not. This is just the force of the example. On the other hand, it is obviously a fact about the $O$-relation. It is just the same sort of fact about the $O$-relation as that $O$ is transitive. If one, in some sense, discovers by observation whether or not individuals stand in the $O$-relation, then there is no difference in the way one would check to see whether some particular $O$-relation had either of these properties. The point is that there are some facts about $O$-relations that cannot be expressed by sentences containing only the $O$-predicate."

These statements are correct if we take 'observable' to mean 'finitely testable', but not if we take it to mean 'finitely and irrevocably testable'. The theory that the $O$-relation is one—one is finitely, but not irrevocably, testable; while the theory that it is transitive is both finitely and irrevocably testable. Hence the latter theory is FIT, while the former is not.

Sneed's second example is contained in his observation (p. 55) that in "an axiomatization of the theory of ordered fields for the first-order predicate calculus with identity . . . for any sentence containing only the order-relation predicate and identity, there will always be models which cannot be . . . [expanded] . . . to produce models for the full theory. That is to say, intuitively, the notion of an ordered field cannot be fully characterized by sentences in the first-order calculus with identity, containing (besides identity) only the order-relation predicate."

The difficulty here is the same as was encountered in the first example — the condition of irrevocability fails. It is easy to construct a system that is not an ordered field, and cannot be expanded to one, but which can be extended by addition of appropriate elements into a system that can be so expanded. Take as an example of the former system a completely ordered discrete set with a least element (e.g. the positive integers).

The most appropriate way, therefore, to deal with Sneed's examples of theories from which theoretical terms are not Ramsey-eliminable, is to deny that they are admissible theories by imposing the requirement that theories be FIT. If this requirement is imposed, then the theoretical terms are always Ramsey-eliminable.

### 6. THEORIES MAKING EXISTENTIAL CLAIMS

We have not stated precisely what we mean by the distinction between theories making universal claims and theories making existential claims. Dr P. M. Williams has made an observation (in a personal communication with the authors) that permits the distinction to be drawn in simple terms. He points out that the class of structures, $M_*^T$, of Theorem 3 will satisfy the condition (1) and (2) iff $H(O)$ is equivalent to a set of universal prenex sentences. If we now say that a theory makes existential claims if the set of all its observable consequences is *not* so equivalent, then it follows immediately that a theory is FIT iff it does not make existential claims.

Our interest, however, lies not in this formal relation between FITness and the universal-existential dichotomy, but in the implications for the practice of science of excluding theories that make existential claims in this sense. If one can point to examples of such theories that are in good repute in science, then serious doubt will be cast on the appropriateness of the FITness conditions.

The most striking examples of actual theories that appear to make existential claims are the theories in physics that assert that certain kinds of elementary particles exist. The assertion that neutrinos exist is an important case, and one we shall discuss specifically. More recent examples, involving exactly the same issues, are theories asserting the existence of particles of anti-matter of various kinds.

No issue would arise if the statement 'Neutrinos exist' were simply derived as a consequence, employing theoretical terms, of some theory. The problem is that 'neutrino' is used by physicists as an observable term, not just a theoretical one. That is to say, if certain events are observed in a cloud chamber or bubble chamber experiment, these events are interpreted as equivalent to the observation of a particle of a certain kind. In experiments performed to test whether neutrinos exist, an affirmative answer would require the observation of neutrino events. The question before us is whether the failure to observe neutrino events would disconfirm the assertion that neutrinos exist. If not, it is not clear why the experiment should be performed at all. Under these circumstances, if 'Neutrinos exist' is treated as a complete theory, it is not FIT; if it is not a complete theory, but is a consequence of other propositions, then the experiment can still not disconfirm it, hence cannot disconfirm the propositions from which it is derived. If an assertion belonging to $H(O)$ is, when regarded as an independent theory, not FIT, it may be harmless, but it cannot contribute anything to the testability of the theory.

Let us turn to the celebrated experiment that was performed to test the existence of neutrinos. The critical question to raise about this experiment is what conclusion would have been drawn if no neutrinos had been detected (they were!). The experiment was carefully designed so that the density of neutrinos (if they existed *with* the properties that had been postulated of them) would be sufficiently high so that they would not remain undetected if present. If they had not been detected in the original experiment, but were subsequently detected by augmented observations, the disconfirmation would not have been revoked. On the contrary, a new theoretical problem would have been created,— to explain why they were not observed in the original set of observations. Thus, the theory being tested was a stronger theory than 'neutrinos exist.' It was more nearly "neutrinos exist in such numbers and with such properties that in any set of $k$ observations under these conditions there will be some neutrino observations." The theory reformulated in this way is FIT. It also makes a universal, not an existential, assertion.

The experiment could also be explained by arguing that what was being tested was not 'neutrinos exist', but 'no neutrinos exist'. As we have already seen from the case of the unicorns, the latter theory is FIT. The observation of neutrinos disconfirmed irrevocably the theory that 'no neutrinos exist'. However, this interpretation of the experiment appears less satisfactory than the one proposed in the previous paragraph, for it does not explain why this experiment was regarded as critical, while earlier experiments, where the (predicted) probability of detection was lower, were not so regarded.

## 7. AXIOMS FOR PHYSICAL SYSTEMS

In a previous paper, one of us (Simon, 1970) used Ohm's Law as an example to show how a physical theory could be axiomatised by defining an appropriate set-theoretical predicate, *Ohmic circuit*. The definition was given by:

$T8$: $\Gamma$ is a system of *Ohmic observations* iff there exist $D, r, c$, such that:

(1) $\quad\quad \Gamma = \langle D, r, c \rangle$;

(2) $\quad\quad D$ is a nonempty set;

(3) $\quad\quad r$ and $c$ are functions from $D$ into the real numbers;

(4) $\quad\quad$ for all $x \in D$, $r(x) > 0$ and $c(x) \geqslant 0$.

$\Gamma'$ is an *Ohmic circuit* iff there exist $D, r, c, b$, and $v$ such that:

(5) $\quad\quad \Gamma' = \langle D, r, c, b, v \rangle$;

(6) $\quad\quad \Gamma = \langle D, r, c \rangle$ is a system of Ohmic observations;

(7) $\quad\quad v$ and $b$ are real numbers;

(8) $\quad\quad$ for all $x \in D$

($\alpha$) $\quad\quad c(x) = \dfrac{v}{b + r(x)}$.

In this system, $r$ and $c$ are to be interpreted as observables; $b$ and $v$, as theoretical terms. The theory is finitely testable, since, in any structure that is not a model, there exist substructures, $m_3$, with values of $\{c_i(x), r_i(x)\}$ that do not satisfy ($\alpha$). It is irrevocably testable, for a set $\{c_i(x), r_i(x)\}$ will not satisfy ($\alpha$) if any of its subsets fail to do so. In fact, it is $k$-testable, with $k = 3$, and hence is UFIT.

In the earlier paper, it was shown (p. 20) that the theoretical terms, $v$ and *b*, could be made definable in the sense of Tarski by adding the following requirement to the definition of *Ohmic circuit*.

(9)            *D* contains at least two members with distinct *r*'s and *c*'s. (When this condition is satisfied, we call the system an *identified Ohmic circuit*.)

However, including in the axioms of a system a stipulation of the minimum number of observations is awkward. The previous paper proposed to avoid this difficulty by substituting a notion of *general definability* for Tarski's notion of definability (Simon, 1970, p. 22). We now see that if we are satisfied with the Ramsey-eliminability of theoretical terms, rather than their definability, the objectionable axiom (9) is not needed in any case. Ramsey-eliminability is weaker, however, than general definability, for the former does not require that the theoretical terms be *uniquely* determined, as is demanded by the latter.

## 8. TESTABILITY OF CLASSICAL CELESTIAL MECHANICS

Does classical celestial mechanics – the conjunction of the Three Laws of Motion and the Law of Universal Gravitation – constitute a FIT theory of the motions of the solar system? The answer depends on how we interpret the elements of the set *D*. (See Simon, 1970, pp. 23–26.)

Suppose that we interpret an element, *x*, of *D* to be a set of observations on the positions, momenta, and accelerations of a definite set of planets – namely, all the known planets at a point in time. Then we can test whether these observations satisfy the theory, e.g. whether the total momentum and angular momentum of the system is conserved, whether the inverse square law holds for accelerations, and so on. If the laws fail to hold for some set of observations then they are falsifiable by a finite subset of these observations (Simon, 1947), and no new set of observations of these same planets would revoke the falsification. Hence, interpreted in this way, classical celestial mechanics is a FIT theory.

There is, however, an alternative interpretation that has historical significance. We interpret an element, *x*, of *D*, to be a set of observations on the orbits of a fixed set of planets. Again, such an observation provides a finite test for the theory, but now a falsification can be countered not simply by extending the observations numerically but by redefining what constitutes an observation – that is, by discovery of a new planet and its orbit. As we know, the theory has in fact been 'resuscitated' several times in exactly this way.

Two points about this process should be noted. First, planets are *discovered*, not *invented*. To explain a deviation of observed from predicted orbits, one must discover and track a new point of light that itself has an appropriate orbit. The enumeration of the planets in the system may be regarded as one of the theory's auxiliary hypotheses that determine what is an observation. But these hypotheses are not arbitrary. The theory, as generally interpreted, does not allow mass to be attributed to points in space where a planet cannot be detected optically (or by some other non-gravitational means). 'Invisible' planets are outlawed. If the density of observations were sufficiently great it could even be said with assurance that no planets with mass greater than some constant $n$ exist having such and such orbits. (The inference would require that there be known limits upon the minimum luminosity and maximum density of objects.) By such means, the theory could be made to approach a condition of irrevocable testability.

Second, this analysis — and this paper in general — avoids the question of what it means for a theory to be *approximately* correct. 'Small' discrepancies between observation and theory are often regarded not as falsifying the theory but as grounds for treating it as only approximate. We cannot undertake to develop this point here, but we must not forget its relevance to the broader issues of the testability of theories (see Simon, 1968, pp. 439–443). We also eschew discussion here of issues of probability.

## 9. CONCLUSION

In this paper we have reexamined the question, raised earlier by Ramsey and Sneed, of the eliminability of theoretical terms from theories. First we imposed conditions of finite and irrevocable testability upon the class of systems to be regarded as well-formed theories. It was shown that these restrictions could be motivated quite independently of the question of eliminability of theoretical terms, for they are applicable to theories that contain no theoretical terms. We proved that theoretical terms are always eliminable from theories that are finitely and irrevocably testable; and we defined an important class of theories that are uniformly finitely and irrevocably testable. We showed that an axiomatisation of Ohm's Law previously proposed is a FIT theory. Finally, we applied our analysis to clarify two concrete situations of historical importance in physics: tests of the existence of neutrinos, and the consequences for celestial mechanics of the discovery of new planets.

## NOTES

*This work was supported in part by Public Health Service Grant MH-07722 from the National Institute of Mental Health. Also by Grant OEG 3-71-01212 from the Committee on Basic Research in Education and the Office of Education. We are deeply indebted to Professor Raimo Tuomela and Mr Ilkka Niiniluoto for valuable comments on an earlier draft of this paper. In particular, Mr Niiniluoto pointed out a serious defect in an earlier form of the proof of *Theorem* 4, which we have now corrected. We are also indebted to Dr P. M. Williams for useful advice, some of which we have followed.

[1] In general, we follow the terminology of Shoenfield (1967), Chapters 2–5, to which the reader can refer for detail.

[2] There are, of course, well-known difficulties in identifying relations and functions that can actually be regarded as 'observables' in any strict sense of the word. Nevertheless, in formulating theories it is both customary and convenient to dichotomize the relations in this way, and thus to distinguish between the theory proper, on the one hand, and the 'auxiliary hypotheses', on the other, that are required to connect the 'observables' with actual physical measurement operations. We will simply follow custom in dividing the difficulties in this way.

[3] It should be emphasised that in introducing the FITness requirements we are setting testability conditions for theories, and not prescribing what is to be done with a theory if it is falsified. In particular, to require that a theory be falsifi*able*, which is the intent of the FITness conditions, does not mean that it must be rejected forthwith if falsified. 'Irrevocability', then, does not imply that under no circumstances will we consider resuscitating a falsified theory. Rather, it implies that a falsified theory cannot be resuscitated *merely* by taking additional observations and without other alterations. Thus, the FITness requirements are compatible with what Lakatos calls 'methodological falsificationism', which permits a falsified theory to be saved, for example, by modifying the auxiliary hypotheses that connect it with observables. (See the discussions below of neutrinos and of celestial mechanics, and the much fuller treatment of these issues in Lakatos (1970).)

[4] See also Popper, p. 193 and footnote 2 for a comment on what he means by this asymmetry. We shall have more to say about it in a later section of this paper.

## REFERENCES

Lakatos, I., 'Falsification and the Methodology of Scientific Research Programmes', in I. Lakatos and A. E. Musgrove (eds.), *Criticism and the Growth of Knowledge* (London and New York: Cambridge University Press, 1970), pp. 91–195.

McNaughton, R. and Papert, S., *Counter-Free Automata* (Cambridge, Mass.: MIT Press, 1971).

Minsky, M. and Papert, S., *Perceptrons* (Cambridge, Mass.: MIT Press, 1969).

Popper, K. R., *The Logic of Scientific Discovery* (London: Hutchinson and New York: Basic Books, 1959).

Ramsey, F. P., *The Foundations of Mathematics* (London: K. Paul, Trench, & Trubner and New York: Harcourt Brace, 1931).

Shoenfield, J. R., *Mathematical Logic* (Reading, Mass.: Addison-Wesley, 1967).

Simon, H. A., 'The Axioms of Newtonian Mechanics', *Philosophical Magazine* **36**, 888–905 (1947) (reprinted as Chapter 6.1 of this volume).

Simon, H. A., 'On Judging the Plausibility of Theories', in B. Van Rootselaar and J. F. Staal (eds.), *Logic, Methodology and Philosophy of Science, III* (Amsterdam: North-Holland Publ. Co., 1968) (reprinted as Chapter 1.4 of this volume).

Simon, H. A., 'The Axiomatization of Physical Theories', *Philosophy of Science* **37**, 16–26 (1970) (reprinted as Chapter 6.5 of this volume).

Sneed, J. D., *The Logical Structure of Mathematical Physics* (Dordrecht, Holland and Boston, Mass.: D. Reidel Publ. Co., 1971).

# IDENTIFIABILITY AND THE STATUS
## OF THEORETICAL TERMS†

Much recent discussion about the structure of scientific theories has centered on the status of theoretical terms, that is, terms whose direct referents are not observables. It has been asked whether such terms are always *definable*, or if not definable, whether they are always *eliminable*. Another line of inquiry asks under what circumstances theoretical terms, or sentences containing them are *meaningful;* and still another asks under what circumstances they are *identifiable*, that is, can be estimated from observational data.

The present paper has two main objectives. The first is to clarify the relations among the four concepts mentioned above: definability, eliminability, meaningfulness, and identifiability. Since separate literatures have sprung up around each of them, it is important to observe that a single underlying theme can be found that threads through all of them. The second objective of the paper is to comment on why it is useful to employ theoretical terms in scientific theories, and how that usefulness relates to their identifiability.

Before we launch our discussion on either of these two topics, it is necessary to take care of some formal preliminaries, in particular, to say what is meant here by 'scientific theory'.

### 1. FORMAL PRELIMINARIES

The discussion in this paper will be conducted on a relatively informal level, since the fundamental issues that need to be raised and the basic distinctions that need to be made do not depend upon details of a formalism. When appropriate, reference will be made to the literature where some of these questions are treated more rigorously. Nor will the widest possible generality be sought, but rather, a sufficient generality to encompass a number of 'real life' examples of scientific practice.

† *Basic Problems in Methodology and Linguistics*, Dordrecht: D. Reidel Publishing Company, 1977, pp. 43–61.

As our formalism, we employ a first-order language, $L$, with equality, containing certain function symbols (possibly including constants). One or more of the function symbols, $O_1, ..., O_k$, is drawn from a set $O$, and one or more, $T_1, ..., T_l$, from a set $T$. There is an infinite set, $X$, of variable symbols, $x_i$. By a *theory*, $F$, in $L$, we will mean a set of formulas of $L$ comprised of the logical axioms together with a formula, $F(O, T)$, which contains symbols from $O$ and possibly $T$.

Next, we introduce a structure, $\langle D, O_M, T_M \rangle$, consisting of a set, $D$, of elements, and two sets of functions on $D$ (call them $O_M$ and $T_M$) corresponding to the two sets of function symbols, $O$ and $T$, in $L$. The ranges of all functions will be either the real numbers, or the truth values, $T$ and $F$. To each distinct element, $d$, of $D$ is assigned a constant symbol to serve as its name.

The functions of $O_M$ are to be interpreted as *observables* whose values can be determined in each instance by observing the appropriate set of objects at the appropriate times. The members of $T_M$, on the other hand, are *theoretical functions and relations*, whose values cannot be determined directly from observations. The structure, $\langle D, O_M \rangle$, obtained by removing the functions and predicates of $T_M$ from $\langle D, O_M, T_M \rangle$ is called the *restriction* of the latter (Shoenfield, 1967).

DEFINITION. The *observable consequences*, $H(O)$, of a theory are the members of the class of all consequences of $F$ that do not contain symbols from $T$.

Let $F_c(O, T)$ be a closed formula obtained from $F(O, T)$ by replacing each free variable in $F(O, T)$ by one of the constants that corresponds to an element of $D$. If all the $F_c(O, T)$ that can be constructed in this way are true of $\langle D, O_M, T_M \rangle$, then this structure is a model for the theory $F$.

In most of what follows, the elements of $D$ will be 'observations', rather than 'objects', so that we will write, for example, $c(x)$ and $r(x)$ for the values of the current and resistance, respectively, of a particular electrical circuit, observed at some instant of time. For some purposes, we may specialize the set $D$ to the product, $I \times J$, of sets, $I$, of observations ('instants') and, $J$, of objects. Then $x_{ij}$, for example, will represent object $j$ observed at time $i$. If certain functions are assumed to be constant over observations, we may also refer to them by expressions like $m(x)$, for the mass of an object, $x$. When the contrary is not stated, however, the members of $D$ should be interpreted as observations, so that extending the set, $D$, means taking additional observations.

DEFINITION. For a given structure, $\langle D, O_M \rangle$, iff there exists a $T_M$ on $D$, and a corresponding $T$ in $L$, such that $F(O, T)$ is valid in $\langle D, O_M, T_M \rangle$ then $\langle D, O_M \rangle$ is *expandable to a model* for the theory $F$.

DEFINITION. Consider a model, $m_k$, and a second model, $m_{k+}$, obtained by annexing (zero or more) elements to $D$ so as to obtain $D'$, $D \subseteq D'$, and extending the $O_M$'s to $D'$. We will call the new model, $m_{k+}$, an *extension of* $m_k$, and will write $m_{k+} \geqslant m_k$, and if $D' \supset D$, $m_{k+} > m_k$.

Expanding a model is to be interpreted as introducing new theoretical terms into it, while extending a model is to be interpreted as taking additional observations.

Some conditions will now be introduced to limit the concept of 'theory' so that anything we call a well-formed theory will be operational and testable (Simon and Groen, 1973). Let $M$ be a set of structures, $\langle D, O, T \rangle$. Then we will designate by $\mathcal{M}_*$ the restriction, $\langle D, O \rangle$, obtained from $M$ by deleting the $T$ predicates. Thus, to each member of $\mathcal{M}_*$ there will correspond a subset of $M$.

In $M$ consider the set of all models for $F(O, T)$, and call this set $M^T$. Restrict each member of $M^T$, obtaining a set, $\mathcal{M}_*^T$, of models in $\mathcal{M}_*$. Clearly, all members of $\mathcal{M}_*^T$ are expandable to models for $F(O, T)$. Next, consider the set of all models in $M$ for $H(O)$. Call this set $M^O$. Again, remove the $T$ relations to obtain a set $\mathcal{M}_*^O$, of models in $\mathcal{M}_*$. Again, all members of $\mathcal{M}_*^O$ are expandable to models for $H(O)$. Moreover, by their construction, the members of $\mathcal{M}_*^O$ are all models for $H(O)$ in $\mathcal{M}_*$.

Testability of a theory would seem to require that two conditions be satisfied:

(1)    If the theory is false, there should exist one or more *finite* sets of possible observations that would disconfirm it.

(2) If the theory is disconfirmed by some set of observations, $m_k$, it should not be possible to make additional observations of such a kind that the theory is now consistent with the extended set, $m_{k+} > m_k$. More formally:

DEFINITION. A theory, $F(T, O)$, is *finitely testable* iff $\exists m(m \notin \mathcal{M}_*^T)$ and $\forall m[(m \notin \mathcal{M}_*^T) \rightarrow \exists m_k((m_k \leqslant m) \wedge (m_k \notin \mathcal{M}_*^T))]$, for finite $k$.

DEFINITION. A theory, $F(T, O)$, is *irrevocably testable* iff $\forall m[\exists m_k((m_k \leqslant m) \wedge (m_k \notin \mathcal{M}_*^T)) \rightarrow (m \notin \mathcal{M}_*^T)1]$.

DEFINITION. A theory, $F(T, O)$ is *FIT* iff it is both finitely and irrevocably testable.

Simon and Groen (1973, pp. 371–5) have set forth a number of reasons for insisting that all scientific theories be *FIT*. This view, however, is by no means universally accepted (e.g. Sneed, 1971, pp. 57–59; Tuomela, 1973, pp. 63–64). One important objection to it is that theories incorporating certain standard mathematical axioms may not be FIT. For example, the assertion that a certain set of magnitudes is Archimedean is not finitely and irrevocably testable (see Adams *et al.*, 1970; Adams, 1974, pp. 439–444), nor are axioms of continuity, for even if a model failed to satisfy them, no finite set of observations could reveal this failure.

Adams *et al.* (1970) introduce the important notion of *data equivalence*. Two theories, $T$ and $T'$, are data equivalent iff they are consistent with exactly the same finite sets of observations. An axiom is 'technical' if removing it from a theory produces a new theory that is data equivalent to the original one. 'Technical' axioms, then, contribute nothing to the empirical (finitely testable) content of the theory. Adams *et al.*, observe that the Archimedean axiom and continuity axioms are generally technical in this sense.

The question of whether theories that are not FIT should be admitted into consideration might therefore be reformulated as a question of what useful function is performed by 'technical' axioms. We will not pursue that question here, but will limit the following discussion to FIT theories.

## 2.  Eliminability of theoretical terms

The topic of eliminability can be treated briefly by reference to the results reported by Simon and Groen (1973). The theoretical terms of a theory are *eliminable* (more precisely, *Ramsey-eliminable*) if, in a certain sense, all of the empirical content of the theory can be stated in terms of the observable relations, $O$. More formally:

DEFINITION.   If, for fixed $D$, $\mathcal{M}_*^T = \mathcal{M}_*^O$, that is, if all models in $\mathcal{M}_*$ for $H(O)$ are expandable to models for $F(O, T)$, then we will say that the theoretical relations, $T$, are *D-Ramsey-eliminable*. If the relations, $T$, are *D-Ramsey-eliminable* for all $D$, then we say, simply, that they are *Ramsey-eliminable*.

Simon and Groen proved (their Theorem 3, p. 375) that if a theory, $F(O, T)$, is *FIT*, i.e. finitely and irrevocably testable, then its theoretical terms, $T$, are Ramsey-eliminable.

This result tells us that the theoretical terms of a FIT theory are never indispensable, hence, if we wish to retain them it must be for reasons of convenience rather than necessity. To see what is involved in their elimination, it will be useful to look at a concrete example of a physical theory: an axiomatization of Ohm's Law, first proposed in Simon (1970). The theory is axiomatized by defining a set-theoretical predicate, *Ohmic circuit*, as follows:

*T1.*   $\Gamma$ is a system of *Ohmic observations* iff there exist $D$, $r$, $c$, such that:

(1)   $\Gamma = \langle D, r, c \rangle$;

(2)   $D$ is a non-empty set;

(3)   $r$ and $c$ are functions from $D$ into the real numbers;

(4)   for all $x \in D$, $r(x) > 0$ and $c(x) > 0$.

$\Gamma'$ is an *Ohmic circuit* iff there exist $D$, $r$, $c$, $b$, and $v$ such that:

(5)   $\Gamma' = \langle D, r, c, b, v \rangle$;

(6)   $\Gamma = \langle D, r, c \rangle$ is a system of Ohmic observations;

(7)   $v$ and $b$ are real numbers;

(8)   for all $x \in D$,

(a)        $c(x) = v/(b + r(x))$

In this system, $r$ and $c$ are to be interpreted as observables; $b$ and $v$ as theoretical terms. This theory is finitely testable, since, in any structure that is not a model, there exist substructures, $m_3$, with values of $\{c_i(x), r_i(x)\}$ that do not satisfy (a). It is irrevocably testable, for a set $\{c_i(x), r_i(x)\}$ will not satisfy (a) if any of its subsets fail to do so. In fact, it is $k$-testable, with $k = 3$.

Suppose, now, that three pairs of independent observations, $c_1$, $r_1$, $c_2$, $r_2$, $c_3$, $r_3$, are made of $c$ and $r$. We can use the first two pairs of observations to derive from (a) a pair of simultaneous equations that we can solve for $v$ and $b$.

$$b = (c_2 r_2 - c_1 r_1)/(c_1 - c_2)$$
$$v = c_1 c_2 (r_2 - r_1)/(c_1 - c_2)$$

If we now substitute these values for $v$ and $b$ in (a), and substitute also $c_3$ and $r_3$ for $c(x)$ and $r(x)$, respectively, we obtain a relation among three pairs of observations. But since these could be any three pairs of observations, we may write the relation, generally, thus:

(b) $\qquad c_i c_j (r_i - r_j) + c_i c_k (r_k - r_i) + c_j c_k (r_j - r_k) = 0.$

Now the members of $H(O)$, the observable consequences of $F(T, O)$, are all derivable from (b), which contains no members of $T$. In fact, the theory with the theoretical terms eliminated could be axiomatized by (1)–(4) together with (b).

What is the difference between the two axiomatizations (other than the absence of members of $T$ from the second)? In some intuitive sense, (a) is a more 'compact' and parsimonious expression than (b). In particular, (a) makes reference to only a single observation, $\{c(x), r(x)\}$, while (b) states a relation among a triplet of observations $\{c_i, r_i, c_j, r_j, c_k, r_k\}$. Finally, a point that will be taken up again later, (a) 'reifies' the voltage and internal resistance of the battery, while the battery and its properties are not mentioned at all in (b).

Hintikka (1965, 1970) and Hintikka and Tuomela (1970) have proposed a distinction between 'depth' information and 'surface' information that is illustrated by the two axiomatizations of Ohm's Law. Specifically, Hintikka (1965) has suggested 'that the intuitive meaning of the concept of depth of a sentence, $s$, is the number of individuals considered together (in their relation to each other) in the deepest part of $s$'. Translating 'individuals' as 'observations', sentence (b), without theoretical terms, is of depth 3, while sentence (a), containing such terms, is of depth 1. The depth of a theory may also be measured by the largest number of layers of nested quantifiers that appears in the sentence formalizing the theory (Tuomela, 1973, p. 46). Applying this measure to a first-order formalization of the Ohm's law axiomatization, Tuomela (1973, pp. 161–162) finds the depth of (b) to be 15 and the depth of (a) to be 5, again showing a depth reduction by a factor of three in (a) as compared with (b). Hintikka and Tuomela (1970, p. 310) regard the reduction in depth as a main advantage derivable from introducing theoretical terms into a theory.

Of course this relation between depth and the presence or absence of theoretical terms is not peculiar to the example of Ohm's Law. In general, if we have a sentence containing such terms, then, given a sufficient number of observations, we may be able to solve for the values of the theoretical terms in terms of the values of observables. In this way we replace the sentence by a new (and deeper) one from which the theoretical terms have been eliminated. Roughly, we would expect the sentence to increase by one in depth (according to the first measure mentioned above) for each theoretical term eliminated. This elimination process will be discussed more fully later under the topic of identifiability.

## 3. THE MEANINGFULNESS OF THEORETICAL TERMS

The concept of meaningfulness of theoretical terms to be proposed here is closely related to some ideas of Przełęcki (1974, p. 347). The basic notion is very simple: for a term to be meaningful, some sentences containing it (and containing it 'essentially') must make empirical statements about the world. Przełęcki limits her discussion to situations where the theoretical terms, $T$, are introduced by meaning postulates that are non-creative relative to the postulates that contain only $O$-terms. In the Ohm's Law example of the previous section, this condition is not met, for the $T$-terms are introduced there by (a), which is creative relative to the other postulates. In the present discussion, it is not assumed that the postulates introducing the $T$-terms are non-creative. There seems to be no real basis for the traditional insistence that definitions be separated sharply from empirical laws (Simon, 1970), and such a separation appears to be the exception rather than the rule in usual formulations of scientific laws.

Let us assume that in a theory, $F(O, T)$, all of the $T$-terms are constant functions, as they are in the axiomatization of Ohm's Law that we have been using as an example. For fixed values of the $T$-terms, there are, as before, models, $M^T$, for the theory, as well as a set of models, $\mathcal{M}_*^T$, obtained by restricting each member of $M^T$ by removing the $T$-terms.

Now consider a whole family of theories, obtained by taking different values for the $T$-terms of $F$. Associated with each theory of this family will be a set of models and a set of (possibly overlapping) restricted models. Consider the set union of the sets of restricted models, $\mathcal{M}_*^T$, calling it $\mathcal{M}_*$. Let $R(T)$ be the function whose domain consists of the admissible sets of values of the $T$-terms, and whose range consists of the corresponding subsets of $\mathcal{M}_*$. If there exists some member of the domain of $R$ whose value is a proper subset of $\mathcal{M}_*$, then the $T$-terms are *meaningful*. Let $S$ be a sentence that asserts that the $T$-terms lie in such a region. Then knowledge that $S$ is true provides information about the possible values of the $O$-terms. Hence the sentence, $S$, may be termed meaningful.

These definitions attribute meaningfulness to the set of $T$-terms as a whole. For some purposes, we may wish to attribute meaningfulness or meaninglessness to particular members of that set. In the Ohm's Law example, we might want to ask separately whether $v$ is meaningful and whether $b$ is meaningful, rather than simply whether the pair, $\{v, b\}$ is meaningful. The following definition meets this need:

Let $F(O, F)$ be a family of theories, as above. Construct a subfamily of $F$ by assigning particular values to all of the $T$-terms except $t_k$, say. Then, relative to this assignment, we can define the meaningfulness of $t_k$ exactly as before. Moreover, we can introduce a weaker concept of meaningfulness: the term, $t_k$, is meaningful if it is meaningful for some assignment of the remaining $T$-terms.

The central idea of all of these definitions is that, for a theoretical term to be meaningful, knowledge of the value of that term must imply some limitation on the range of the $O$-terms. All sorts of weaker or stronger concepts of meaningfulness may be introduced that share this general underlying idea.

The concept of meaningfulness induces a reciprocal relation between the $T$-terms, on the one hand, and the $O$-terms on the other. For consider the space, $O \times T$, which is the product space of the ranges of the $O$-terms and $T$-terms, respectively. Suppose that, in a given theory, it is true that $t \in T'$ implies $o \in O'$, where $T'$ and $O'$ are proper subspaces of $T$ and $O$, respectively. Then it follows that $o \in C(O')$ implies $t \in C(T')$, where $C(x)$ is the set complement of $x$. Hence, information about the $O$-terms implies a restriction on the possible values of the $T$-terms.

A definition of meaningfulness could be based upon this implication instead of the inverse implication that has been used here. In fact, the former is the path followed by Przełęcki (1974), and earlier by Suppes (1959). In particular, Przełęcki's criterion of weak meaningfulness is roughly equivalent to the requirement that $o \in O'$ implies $t \in T'$, where $O'$ and $T'$ are proper subspaces of $O$ and $T$, respectively.

The procedure followed in the present paper seems, however, to correspond more closely to the everyday intuitive meaning of the phrase 'empirically meaningful' than does the proposal mentioned in the last paragraph. It appears to be more natural to say that a term is meaningful if it conveys information about the observable world than to say that it is meaningful if something can be inferred about its value from information about the real world. In fact, as we shall see in the next section, the latter idea would seem closer to the concept of 'identifiability' than to the concept of 'meaningfulness'.

## 4. THE IDENTIFIABILITY OF THEORETICAL TERMS

From the discussion of the previous section it is apparent that identifiability is, in a certain sense, a converse of meaningfulness. Theoretical terms are meaningful to the extent that their values restrict the values of the observables; they are identifiable to the extent that their values are restricted by specification of the values of the observables.

Moreover, by the law of contraposition, the relation between the two terms is always reciprocal, as we saw above. For if restriction of $o$ to some subspace of $O$ restricts $t$ to some proper subspace of $T$, then restriction of $t$ to the complementary subspace of $T$ restricts $o$ to the complementary subspace of $O$.

Identifiability is a matter of degree, and a number of weaker and stronger forms of identifiability have been defined (Simon, 1966, 1970; Tuomela, 1968). By 'strength' is meant *how much* restriction is placed upon the possible values of $T$ by a given amount of information about $O$. Since the topic has been treated elsewhere (see Tuomela, 1968, and the paper by Sadovsky and Smirnov in this symposium), only a few comments will be made here about weak and strong identifiability.

Perhaps the most important consideration in selecting a definition of identifiability is that axiomatizations of theories may sometimes be simplified if complete identifiability of the theoretical terms is not insisted upon. For example, the terms, $v$ and $b$, in the axiomatization of Ohm's Law cannot be estimated from the values of observables unless there are at least two distinct observations. An additional axiom can be added that imposes this requirement; but alternatively, it may be satisfactory to define identifiability to mean 'unique estimatability provided there are a sufficient number of independent observations'. 'Sufficient number' here will generally mean one less than the number that measures the depth of the sentence obtained by eliminating the theoretical terms. (This number is closely related to the usual notion of *degrees of freedom*.)

A closely related issue arises when the theoretical terms of a system are estimatable from the observables except for certain special cases. For example, in a system of Newtonian particle mechanics, the mass ratios of two particles comprising an isolated system can be estimated from observations of positions and velocities at a sufficient number of distinct points in time, unless each of the particles is itself an isolated system. Concepts of *almost everywhere definability* have been proposed in order to rule out unidentifiability arising from such special circumstances (Simon, 1966, 1970).

Finally, *definability*, in the sense of Tarski, is simply the strongest form of identifiability, which admits none of the qualifications discussed in the two previous paragraphs.

While identifiability and definability are thus closely related concepts, neither has anything to do with eliminability, for the theoretical terms of a FIT theory, although always eliminable, need be neither definable nor identifiable. A simple and frequently cited example will be instructive. Consider a market for a single commodity, such that each observation consists of a quantity, $q(x)$, and a price, $p(x)$, at which the quantity is sold and bought. A theory of this market might consist of the two equations:

(c) $\qquad q(x) = a_1 p(x) + b_1$

(d) $\qquad q(x) = a_2 p(x) + b_2$

Equation (c) is the supply relation, which expresses the quantity offered in the market as a function of the price; while (d) is the demand relation, which expresses the quantity that will be purchased by buyers as a function of the price. The $a$'s and $b$'s are theoretical terms that define the hypothetical supply and demand curves. These two equations, taken together, are equivalent to the assertion that $p(x) = p_*$ and $q(x) = q_*$ are constants, independent of $x$. Since there are only two equations, but four theoretical terms, it is obvious that the latter are not identifiable.

This example also throws further light on the reciprocal relation between identifiability and meaningfulness – shows, in fact, that this relation need not be symmetric. As a set, the theoretical terms are meaningful, for assigning values to them determines the values of $p_*$ and $q_*$. If we hold any three of the theoretical terms constant, then, by our earlier definition, the fourth is meaningful, because the admissible values of $p_*$ and $q_*$ then depend on its value. In the opposite direction, however, knowledge of the values of $p_*$ and $q_*$ does not identify any of the theoretical terms, but only two functions of them (obtained by solving (c) and (d) for the observables). Some general results of this kind are derived formally by Rantala in his paper for this symposium.

## 5. IDENTIFIABILITY AND CHANGE OF STRUCTURE

It is well known, and often pointed out in the econometric literature (Koopmans, 1953), that if a theory is going to be used only to predict values of the observables, then it is of no significance whether or not the theoretical terms are identifiable, provided that they remain unchanged. Thus, in the simple market example of the last section, a single observation determines the price and quantity of the good that will be exchanged, and if the theory is correct, the same price and quantity will hold for all future observations. Unidentifiability of the *T*-terms does not interfere with the prediction.

If some change takes place in the world, however, altering the unobservable values of one or more of the theoretical terms, then the new equilibrium values of *p* and *q* will not be predictable until they are observed. Hence the possibility of prediction under such a change (called a change in *structure*) hinges on having some additional source of information about the values of the theoretical terms.

Suppose we know from some independent source that changes are taking place in the coefficients of the first (supply) equation, but not in the second (demand) equation. We might know, for example, that changes in weather cause large changes in production that are not predictable by the producers, hence cause large random shifts in supply. Then the second equation would continue to hold, but not the first, and we would observe values of *p* and *q* from which we could estimate $a_2$ and $b_2$. Similarly, if we knew that changes were taking place in the coefficients of the second equation but not the first, we could take observations to estimate the coefficients of the supply equation. The introduction of random shocks into one of the two mechanisms brings about identifiability of the coefficients of the other. If, however, random shocks are imposed on *both* mechanisms, then in order to achieve identifiability we must have information about the relations of the two sets of shocks, e.g. that they are uncorrelated.

This example shows that the individual equations that go to make up a theory may be interpreted as representing separate particular components of the system that the theory describes. We may have information about the system, not incorporated in the values of the observable functions, that enables us to identify theoretical terms that are otherwise unidentifiable.

More generally, a complex system having only a small number of observables but a large number of theoretical terms will leave most or all of the latter unidentifiable, unless the theoretical terms can be partitioned among components of the total system, and the behavior of each component observed independently of its relations with the rest of the system (i.e. independently of the remaining system equations). Partitioning of this kind is, of course, one of the basic ideas underlying the experimental method. Notice that the applicability of the method hinges on localizing particular theoretical terms to particular system components.

As a further illustration of these ideas, consider a system consisting of two Ohmic circuits, $A$ and $B$. Suppose that, by making observations on them, we estimate $v_A$, $b_A$, $v_B$, and $b_B$. If, now, we interchange the batteries of the two circuits, inserting the battery of $A$ in circuit $B$, and the battery of $B$ in circuit $A$, we will be tempted to predict (and probably correctly) that the values of the $v$'s and $b$'s that we will now estimate by new observations will be similarly interchanged. To make this prediction, we are obviously using some additional knowledge that associates particular theoretical terms with particular components (in this case, the batteries) of the systems. What is the source of this knowledge?

The only observations of which the formal axiomatization speaks are the observations of the current and the resistance. But in point of fact, the experimenter can also observe certain of his own interventions in the system: his replacement of the resistance wire with a longer or shorter one, or his interchanging of the batteries between the two circuits. The formal system could be expanded to assert that the values of certain theoretical *or* observational terms will remain constant only if certain components of the system remain undisturbed. Even more powerful would be assertions that particular theoretical terms are associated with particular components of the system, and that this association remains unchanged when the components are reassembled in a new way.

Postulates of this kind are implicit whenever, for example, the weight of an object is assigned by placing it on a balance with objects of known weight, and then the weight so determined is used to make calculations in new weighings. In this case again, derived quantities are associated with particular parts of the system, and are assumed to travel with these parts. In fact, this assumption that weights remain invariant from one weighing to another is essential to make the ratios of the weights of a set of objects identifiable. The assumption is, in fact, implicit in the usual axiomatizations of fundamental measurement (for a simple example, see Sneed, 1971, pp. 18–19), where the members of the basic sets in terms of which the systems are described are objects rather than observations.

It was suggested earlier that it is sometimes convenient to factor the space of observations into a product space of objects and observations, $I \times J$. If the identity of particular objects can be maintained from one observation to the next, then theoretical terms that denote constant properties of those objects become functions only of the object and not of the observation, thus reducing greatly the number of independent theoretical terms, and enhancing correspondingly the chances of achieving identifiability. In classical particle mechanics, for example, inertial mass is just such a theoretical term.

It is easy to see how we can apply these ideas formally to the axiomatization of Ohm's Law. We introduce sets, $B$, $W$, and $A$, whose members correspond to particular batteries, wires and ammeters, respectively. Then $r$, $c(x)$, $v$ and $b$ become functions from $W$, $A \times D$, $B$ and $B$, respectively, to the real numbers. This means that these quantities now depend upon the objects with which they are associated. (Note that the value of $c$ depends upon the observation, $x$, as well as the ammeter, $A$, with which it is associated.) Now, associated with any given observation, $x$, is a member of $A$, $A(x)$, a member of $W$, $W(x)$, and a member of $B$, $B(x)$. Corresponding to (8), we now will have:

(8′)  For all $x \in D$,

(a′)      $c(A(x), x) = v(B(x))/(b(B(x)) + r(W(x)))$

As before, $c$ and $r$ are to be regarded as observables, $v$ and $b$ as theoretical terms. However, we shall later have occasion to reconsider that classification.

The achievement of identifiability is facilitated also by knowledge that certain theoretical terms are identically equal to zero. If a theory consists of a set of $n$ linear algebraic equations among $n$ variables, then, in general, the coefficients of those equations will be unidentifiable, for there will be $n^2 + n$ such coefficients, and only $n$ independent equations from which to estimate them, no matter how many observations are taken. Suppose it is known, however, that all but $n$ of the coefficients are zero. Then the non-zero coefficients are, in general, identifiable. Whence might the information that made the identification possible be derived? If it were known that certain of the variables could not act directly upon each other, then the coefficients describing those particular interactions could be set equal to zero. For example, if the system of equations described a bridge truss, and certain nodes of the truss were not connected directly with certain other nodes by physical members, then the coefficients describing the forces with which one of those nodes acted upon the other would be zero. If the number of directly connected nodes were small enough, the stresses in the truss would be identifiable – it would form a so-called *statically determinate* structure.

The idea that runs through all of these examples is that the identifiability of theoretical terms of a system can be increased if the theory incorporates axioms (1) localizing particular theoretical terms in particular components of the system, and (2) associating particular experimental operations with corresponding observable alterations of specific components. These alterations are represented by associating variables, both observables and theoretical terms, with system components.

Let us consider an experimental program for verifying and extending Ohm's Law. In our axiomatization of that law, we treated resistance and current as observables. Of course they are only relatively so, for they are defined, in turn, in terms of more directly observable quantities. In the present discussion, we wish to take that indirectness into account. We begin, as Ohm did, with a simple circuit and two observables: the readings on the angular displacement of a magnet, and the length of a wire of specified composition and diameter inserted in the circuit. The first observable is used to define the theoretical term 'current', the second to define the theoretical term 'resistance'. Now, by inserting resistances of different lengths in the circuit, we obtain a number of independent observations of the current, and can estimate the voltage of the battery. Having done so, we can next experiment with wires of constant length but different cross-section. The term 'resistance' was originally defined only for wires of a specific cross-section, but now that the voltage and internal resistance have been estimated, we can use their values, together with the observed values of the current, to calculate the values of the new resistances. In this way we can extend the theoretical term, 'resistance', to apply to conductors of any shape or dimension or material that we can insert in the circuit. We can employ the same general method, now using known voltages and resistances, to calibrate different current-measuring devices, and in this way to extend the definition of the theoretical term 'current'.

In terms of our expanded formalism, using the sets $W$, $A$, and $B$, this experimental program can be interpreted as starting with $r$ and $c$ for subsets of $W$ and $A$, respectively, as observables, and the values of $r$ and $c$ for the remaining members of $W$ and $A$, as well as the values of $v$ and $b$ for all members of $B$ as theoretical terms. Knowledge of the values of the initial set of observables is sufficient to enable us to 'bootstrap' estimates of all of the theoretical terms by performing observations on appropriate circuits.

Once we are able to assign definite voltages and resistances to physical components that can be used to construct current-bearing systems, we can now also begin to determine the laws of composition of such components when they are organized in more complex arrangements. We can add axioms to the system, for example, for the behavior of two resistances in series or parallel, or of two batteries in series or parallel. Thus, by a procedure rather analogous to analytic continuation in the theory of complex variables, we are able to extend the domain of identifiability of theoretical terms from a small initial region to a wider and wider range of increasingly complex situations.

The comment was made in an earlier section of this paper that to identify a theoretical term is to 'reify' it. The meaning of that comment should now be clear. Even though the theoretical terms are not directly observable, if they can be associated, as invariant properties, with particular physical objects, and if these objects can be made to interact in various configurations with each other, then a high degree of identifiability may be attained even in complex systems. There is no magic in this process. The assumption that a theoretical term is an invariant property holds down the number of such terms whose values have to be estimated, while the ability to recombine the system components in different configurations increases the number of equations that they must, simultaneously, satisfy. Of course the axiomatization of a system that permits such 'analytic continuation' as a means for identifying theoretical terms must include appropriate composition laws for the configurations of components that are to be examined.

The developments proposed in this section can be interpreted as a possible answer to Sneed's (1971, p. 65) call for 'a rationale for the practice of exploiting values of theoretical functions obtained in one application of [a] theory to draw conclusions about other applications of the theory'. The requirement that particular theoretical terms be associated with specific objects, and that they retain their values when reassembled in different subsystems, would seem to correspond closely with Sneed's concept of a 'constraint' to be applied to a theoretical term when it is moved from one application to another.

## 6. CONCLUSION

This paper has undertaken to explore the relations among the concepts of 'eliminability', 'meaningfulness', 'identifiability', and 'definability' as applied to theoretical terms in axiomatized theories. Theoretical terms are always eliminable from finite and irrevocably testable theories. Hence, they are retained for reasons of convenience, and not because they are indispensable. One such reason is that the statement of the theory requires 'deeper' sentences, in the sense of Hintikka, if the theoretical terms are eliminated than if they are retained. Another reason for retaining theoretical terms is that, by attributing them to particular physical components of systems, we can conveniently bring a whole range of partial theories within a single general formulation, gaining identifiability in the process.

Meaningfulness and identifiability have been shown to be opposite sides of the same coin, though a coin that is not necessarily symmetrical. Meaningfulness involves predicting from known values of theoretical terms to values of observables; identifiability involves making estimates from values of observables to the values of theoretical terms. Both meaningfulness and identifiability are matters of degree – stronger and weaker notions of either can be introduced, and definability, in the sense of Tarski, can simply be regarded as the strongest form of identifiability. Meaningfulness of a set of theoretical terms always implies some degree of identifiability, in at least a weak sense, and vice versa.

In the final section of the paper it was argued that our knowledge about a system is usually not restricted to knowledge of the values of observables. In addition, we can label particular system components, and trace their continuity through operations that change the system configuration. Incorporating in the axiomatization postulates that associate specific theoretical terms with specific components, and that assert the invariance of the values of those terms is a powerful means for enhancing the identifiability of theoretical terms.

BIBLIOGRAPHY

Adams, E. W.: 1974, 'Model-Theoretic Aspects of Fundamental Measurement Theory', in L. Henkin (ed.), *Proceedings of the Tarski Symposium* (*Proceedings of Symposia in Pure Mathematics*, Vol. 25). American Mathematical Society, Providence, R.I., pp. 437–446.

Adams, E. W., Fagot, R. F., and Robinson, R. E.: 1970, 'On the Empirical Status of Axioms in Theories of Fundamental Measurement', *Journal of Mathematical Psychology* **7**, 379–409.

Hintikka, K. J. J.: 1965, 'Are Logical Truths Analytic?', *Philosophical Review* **74**, 178–203.

Hintikka, K. J. J.: 1970, 'Surface Information and Depth Information', in K. J. J. Hintikka and P. Suppes (eds.), *Information and Inference*, D. Reidel Publishing Company, Dordrecht, Holland, pp. 263–297.

Hintikka, K. J. J., and Tuomela, R.: 1970, 'Towards a General Theory of Auxiliary Concepts and Definability in First-Order Theories', in K. J. J. Hintikka and P. Suppes (eds.), *Information and Inference*, D. Reidel Publishing Company, Dordrecht, Holland, pp. 298–330.

Koopmans, T.: 1953, 'Identification Problems in Economic Model Construction', in W. Hood and T. Koopmans (eds.), *Studies in Econometric Method*, John Wiley & Sons, New York, pp. 27–48.

Przełęcki, M.: 1974, 'Empirical Meaningfulness of Quantitative Statements', *Synthese* **26**, 344–355.

Shoenfield, J. R.: 1967, *Mathematical Logic*, Addison-Wesley Publishing Company, Reading, Massachusetts.

Simon, H. A.: 1966, 'A Note on Almost-Everywhere Definability' (abstract), *Journal of Symbolic Logic* **31**, 705–706.

Simon, H. A.: 1970, 'The Axiomatization of Physical Theories', *Philosophy of Science* **37**, 16–26.

Simon, H. A. and Groen, G. J.: 1973, 'Ramsey Eliminability and The Testability of Scientific Theories', *British Journal of The Philosophy of Science* **24**, 367–380.

Sneed, J. D.: 1971, *The Logical Structure of Mathematical Physics*, D. Reidel Publishing Company, Dordrecht, Holland.

Suppes, P.: 1959, 'Measurement, Empirical Meaningfulness, and Three-Valued Logic', in C. W. Churchman and P. Ratoosh (eds.), *Measurement: Definitions and Theories*, John Wiley & Sons, New York, pp. 129–143.

Tuomela, R.: 1968, 'Identifiability and Definability of Theoretical Concepts,' *Ajatus* **30**, 195–220.

Tuomela, R.: 1973, *Theoretical Concepts*, Springer-Verlag, Vienna.

# NAME INDEX

Adams, E. W. 425, 439
Albert, A. A. 79
Alexander, Christopher 325
Amarel, Saul 215, 324
Ampere, Andre Marie 388
Anderson, John R. 265
Anding, E. 363, 368–9
Ando, Albert xi, 124, 131, 179, 183–213, 250, 261
Angell, R. B. 107, 131
Appell, P. 360, 368
Archea, J. 325
Aristotle xiii, 53
Aronofsky, J. 325
Arrow, Kenneth J. 175

Bacon, Francis 41
Bahadur, Raghu Raj 4
Balderston, Fred 284
Balderston, J. B. 212
Balmer, Johann Jakob 42
Banerji, R. B. 214, 243
Banet, L. 42, 44
Bartlett, Frederic 285
Bayes, Thomas xvii, 4–6, 30
Baylor, George W. 217, 230, 243
Beardsley, Elizabeth Lane 92
Belnap, N. D., Jr. 135
Blalock, H. M. 50
Bobrow, D. 322
Bocher, Maxime 79
Bode, J. E. 28
Bohr, Niels 288
Bourne, Lyle 36
Bower, Gordon H. 36–8, 44–5, 265
Boyle, Robert 26, 29
Bradie, Michael 338, 340
Braithwaite, R. B. 381, 384–5
Bridgman, Percy W. 52
Bryan, G. L. 325
Buchanan, Bruce G. 336
Burks, Arthur W. 52, 81, 91–2, 107, 131
Bush, Robert R. 284

Calvin, Melvin 249
Cannon, Walter B. 55–6, 79
Carnap, Rudolf 20, 24, 41, 92, 152, 381, 385
Chenzoff, A. P. 44–5
Chomsky, Noam 284
Clarkson, Geoffrey 284
Cohen, Robert S. xi
Colodny, Robert 268, 286
Conant, James B. 284
Courant, R. 212
Courtois, P. J. 180–1
Craig, William 406
Cyert, Richard M. 105

Dalton, John 269
Darwin, Charles 245
de Broglie, Maurice 288
de Groot, Adriaan 291, 303
Dexter, Lewis A. 92
Dorfman, Robert 153

Eastman, Charles 325
Eccles, John C. 284
Einstein, Albert 20, 33, 266, 286, 288–9
Eratosthenes 301
Ernst, George 243
Estes, William 36, 40, 45
Euclid 374

Fagot, R. F. 425, 439
Fei, J. C. H. 213
Feigenbaum, Edward A. 44–5, 214, 243, 284–5, 303
Feigl, Herbert 91
Feldman, J. 39, 45, 284–5, 303
Filon, L. N. G. 351, 364, 368, 372, 374–5
Fisher, Franklin M. 124, 131, 179, 184, 207–8, 212–3, 250, 261
Fisher, R. A. 3
Fitzgerald, G. F. 33
Frisch, Ragnar 78–79
Fuortes, M. G. F. 284

# SUBJECT INDEX

# SYNTHESE LIBRARY

Monographs on Epistemology, Logic, Methodology,
Philosophy of Science, Sociology of Science and of Knowledge, and on the
Mathematical Methods of Social and Behavioral Sciences

*Managing Editor:*
JAAKKO HINTIKKA (Academy of Finland and Stanford University)

*Editors:*

ROBERT S. COHEN (Boston University)
DONALD DAVIDSON (University of Chicago)
GABRIËL NUCHELMANS (University of Leyden)
WESLEY C. SALMON (University of Arizona)

1. J. M. Bocheński, *A Precis of Mathematical Logic.* 1959, X + 100 pp.
2. P. L. Guiraud, *Problèmes et méthodes de la statistique linguistique.* 1960, VI + 146 pp.
3. Hans Freudenthal (ed.), *The Concept and the Role of the Model in Mathematics and Natural and Social Sciences, Proceedings of a Colloquium held at Utrecht, The Netherlands, January 1960.* 1961, VI + 194 pp.
4. Evert W. Beth, *Formal Methods. An Introduction to Symbolic Logic and the Study of Effective Operations in Arithmetic and Logic.* 1962, XIV + 170 pp.
5. B. H. Kazemier and D. Vuysje (eds.), *Logic and Language. Studies Dedicated to Professor Rudolf Carnap on the Occasion of His Seventieth Birthday.* 1962, VI + 256 pp.
6. Marx W. Wartofsky (ed.), *Proceedings of the Boston Colloquium for the Philosophy of Science, 1961-1962,* Boston Studies in the Philosophy of Science (ed. by Robert S. Cohen and Marx W. Wartofsky), Volume I. 1973, VIII + 212 pp.
7. A. A. Zinov'ev, *Philosophical Problems of Many-Valued Logic.* 1963, XIV + 155 pp.
8. Georges Gurvitch, *The Spectrum of Social Time.* 1964, XXVI + 152 pp.
9. Paul Lorenzen, *Formal Logic.* 1965, VIII + 123 pp.
10. Robert S. Cohen and Marx W. Wartofsky (eds.), *In Honor of Philipp Frank,* Boston Studies in the Philosophy of Science (ed. by Robert S. Cohen and Marx W. Wartofsky), Volume II. 1965, XXXIV + 475 pp.
11. Evert W. Beth, *Mathematical Thought. An Introduction to the Philosophy of Mathematics.* 1965, XII + 208 pp.
12. Evert W. Beth and Jean Piaget, *Mathematical Epistemology and Psychology.* 1966, XII + 326 pp.
13. Guido Küng, *Ontology and the Logistic Analysis of Language. An Enquiry into the Contemporary Views on Universals.* 1967, XI + 210 pp.
14. Robert S. Cohen and Marx W. Wartofsky (eds.), *Proceedings of the Boston Colloquium for the Philosophy of Science 1964-1966, in Memory of Norwood Russell Hanson,* Boston Studies in the Philosophy of Science (ed. by Robert S. Cohen and Marx W. Wartofsky), Volume III. 1967, XLIX + 489 pp.

15. C. D. Broad, *Induction, Probability, and Causation. Selected Papers*. 1968, XI + 296 pp.
16. Günther Patzig, *Aristotle's Theory of the Syllogism. A Logical-Philosophical Study of Book A of the Prior Analytics*. 1968, XVII + 215 pp.
17. Nicholas Rescher, *Topics in Philosophical Logic*. 1968, XIV + 347 pp.
18. Robert S. Cohen and Marx W. Wartofsky (eds.), *Proceedings of the Boston Colloquium for the Philosophy of Science 1966-1968*, Boston Studies in the Philosophy of Science (ed. by Robert S. Cohen and Marx W. Wartofsky), Volume IV. 1969, VIII + 537 pp.
19. Robert S. Cohen and Marx W. Wartofsky (eds.), *Proceedings of the Boston Colloquium for the Philosophy of Science 1966-1968*, Boston Studies in the Philosophy of Science (ed. by Robert S. Cohen and Marx W. Wartofsky), Volume V. 1969, VIII + 482 pp.
20. J.W. Davis, D. J. Hockney, and W. K. Wilson (eds.), *Philosophical Logic*. 1969, VIII + 277 pp.
21. D. Davidson and J. Hintikka (eds.), *Words and Objections: Essays on the Work of W. V. Quine*. 1969, VIII + 366 pp.
22. Patrick Suppes, *Studies in the Methodology and Foundations of Science. Selected Papers from 1911 to 1969*. 1969, XII + 473 pp.
23. Jaakko Hintikka, *Models for Modalities. Selected Essays*. 1969, IX + 220 pp.
24. Nicholas Rescher *et al.* (eds.), *Essays in Honor of Carl G. Hempel. A Tribute on the Occasion of His Sixty-Fifth Birthday*. 1969, VII + 272 pp.
25. P. V. Tavanec (ed.), *Problems of the Logic of Scientific Knowledge*. 1969, XII + 429 pp.
26. Marshall Swain (ed.), *Induction, Acceptance, and Rational Belief*. 1970, VII + 232 pp.
27. Robert S. Cohen and Raymond J. Seeger (eds.), *Ernst Mach: Physicist and Philosopher*, Boston Studies in the Philosophy of Science (ed. by Robert S. Cohen and Marx W. Wartofsky), Volume VI. 1970, VIII + 295 pp.
28. Jaakko Hintikka and Patrick Suppes, *Information and Inference*. 1970, X + 336 pp.
29. Karel Lambert, *Philosophical Problems in Logic. Some Recent Developments*. 1970, VII + 176 pp.
30. Rolf A. Eberle, *Nominalistic Systems*. 1970, IX + 217 pp.
31. Paul Weingartner and Gerhard Zecha (eds.), *Induction, Physics, and Ethics: Proceedings and Discussions of the 1968 Salzburg Colloquium in the Philosophy of Science*. 1970, X + 382 pp.
32. Evert W. Beth, *Aspects of Modern Logic*. 1970, XI + 176 pp.
33. Risto Hilpinen (ed.), *Deontic Logic: Introductory and Systematic Readings*. 1971, VII + 182 pp.
34. Jean-Louis Krivine, *Introduction to Axiomatic Set Theory*. 1971, VII + 98 pp.
35. Joseph D. Sneed, *The Logical Structure of Mathematical Physics*. 1971, XV + 311 pp.
36. Carl R. Kordig, *The Justification of Scientific Change*. 1971, XIV + 119 pp.
37. Milič Čapek, *Bergson and Modern Physics*, Boston Studies in the Philosophy of Science (ed. by Robert S. Cohen and Marx W. Wartofsky), Volume VII. 1971, XV + 414 pp.

38. Norwood Russell Hanson, *What I Do Not Believe, and Other Essays* (ed. by Stephen Toulmin and Harry Woolf), 1971, XII + 390 pp.
39. Roger C. Buck and Robert S. Cohen (eds.), *PSA 1970. In Memory of Rudolf Carnap*, Boston Studies in the Philosophy of Science (ed. by Robert S. Cohen and Marx W. Wartofsky), Volume VIII. 1971, LXVI + 615 pp. Also available as paperback.
40. Donald Davidson and Gilbert Harman (eds.), *Semantics of Natural Language*. 1972, X + 769 pp. Also available as paperback.
41. Yehoshua Bar-Hillel (ed.), *Pragmatics of Natural Languages*. 1971, VII + 231 pp.
42. Sören Stenlund, *Combinators, λ-Terms and Proof Theory*. 1972, 184 pp.
43. Martin Strauss, *Modern Physics and Its Philosophy. Selected Papers in the Logic, History, and Philosophy of Science*. 1972, X + 297 pp.
44. Mario Bunge, *Method, Model and Matter*. 1973, VII + 196 pp.
45. Mario Bunge, *Philosophy of Physics*. 1973, IX + 248 pp.
46. A. A. Zinov'ev, *Foundations of the Logical Theory of Scientific Knowledge (Complex Logic)*, Boston Studies in the Philosophy of Science (ed. by Robert S. Cohen and Marx W. Wartofsky), Volume IX. Revised and enlarged English edition with an appendix, by G. A. Smirnov, E. A. Sidorenka, A. M. Fedina, and L. A. Bobrova. 1973, XXII + 301 pp. Also available as paperback.
47. Ladislav Tondl, *Scientific Procedures*, Boston Studies in the Philosophy of Science (ed. by Robert S. Cohen and Marx W. Wartofsky), Volume X. 1973, XII + 268 pp. Also available as paperback.
48. Norwood Russell Hanson, *Constellations and Conjectures* (ed. by Willard C. Humphreys, Jr.). 1973, X + 282 pp.
49. K. J. J. Hintikka, J. M. E. Moravcsik, and P. Suppes (eds.), *Approaches to Natural Language. Proceedings of the 1970 Stanford Workshop on Grammar and Semantics*. 1973, VIII + 526 pp. Also available as paperback.
50. Mario Bunge (ed.), *Exact Philosophy — Problems, Tools, and Goals*. 1973, X + 214 pp.
51. Radu J. Bogdan and Ilkka Niiniluoto (eds.), *Logic, Language, and Probability. A Selection of Papers Contributed to Sections IV, VI, and XI of the Fourth International Congress for Logic, Methodology, and Philosophy of Science, Bucharest, September 1971*. 1973, X + 323 pp.
52. Glenn Pearce and Patrick Maynard (eds.), *Conceptual Chance*. 1973, XII + 282 pp.
53. Ilkka Niiniluoto and Raimo Tuomela, *Theoretical Concepts and Hypothetico-Inductive Inference*. 1973, VII + 264 pp.
54. Roland Fraïssé, *Course of Mathematical Logic — Volume 1: Relation and Logical Formula*. 1973, XVI + 186 pp. Also available as paperback.
55. Adolf Grünbaum, *Philosophical Problems of Space and Time*. Second, enlarged edition, Boston Studies in the Philosophy of Science (ed. by Robert S. Cohen and Marx W. Wartofsky), Volume XII. 1973, XXIII + 884 pp. Also available as paperback.
56. Patrick Suppes (ed.), *Space, Time, and Geometry*. 1973, XI + 424 pp.
57. Hans Kelsen, *Essays in Legal and Moral Philosophy*, selected and introduced by Ota Weinberger. 1973, XXVIII + 300 pp.
58. R. J. Seeger and Robert S. Cohen (eds.), *Philosophical Foundations of Science. Proceedings of an AAAS Program, 1969*, Boston Studies in the Philosophy of

Science (ed. by Robert S. Cohen and Marx W. Wartofsky), Volume XI. 1974, X + 545 pp. Also available as paperback.

59. Robert S. Cohen and Marx W. Wartofsky (eds.), *Logical and Epistemological Studies in Contemporary Physics*, Boston Studies in the Philosophy of Science (ed. by Robert S. Cohen and Marx W. Wartofsky), Volume XIII. 1973, VIII + 462 pp. Also available as paperback.

60. Robert S. Cohen and Marx W. Wartofsky (eds.), *Methodological and Historical Essays in the Natural and Social Sciences. Proceedings of the Boston Colloquium for the Philosophy of Science, 1969-1972*, Boston Studies in the Philosophy of Science (ed. by Robert S. Cohen and Marx W. Wartofsky), Volume XIV. 1974, VIII + 405 pp. Also available as paperback.

61. Robert S. Cohen, J. J. Stachel and Marx W. Wartofsky (eds.), *For Dirk Struik. Scientific, Historical and Political Essays in Honor of Dirk J. Struik*, Boston Studies in the Philosophy of Science (ed. by Robert S. Cohen and Marx W. Wartofsky), Volume XV. 1974, XXVII + 652 pp. Also available as paperback.

62. Kazimierz Ajdukiewicz, *Pragmatic Logic*, transl. from the Polish by Olgierd Wojtasiewicz. 1974, XV + 460 pp.

63. Sören Stenlund (ed.), *Logical Theory and Semantic Analysis. Essays Dedicated to Stig Kanger on His Fiftieth Birthday*. 1974, V + 217 pp.

64. Kenneth F. Schaffner and Robert S. Cohen (eds.), *Proceedings of the 1972 Biennial Meeting, Philosophy of Science Association*, Boston Studies in the Philosophy of Science (ed. by Robert S. Cohen and Marx W. Wartofsky), Volume XX. 1974, IX + 444 pp. Also available as paperback.

65. Henry E. Kyburg, Jr., *The Logical Foundations of Statistical Inference*. 1974, IX + 421 pp.

66. Marjorie Grene, *The Understanding of Nature: Essays in the Philosophy of Biology*, Boston Studies in the Philosophy of Science (ed. by Robert S. Cohen and Marx W. Wartofsky), Volume XXIII. 1974, XII + 360 pp. Also available as paperback.

67. Jan M. Broekman, *Structuralism: Moscow, Prague, Paris*. 1974, IX + 117 pp.

68. Norman Geschwind, *Selected Papers on Language and the Brain*, Boston Studies in the Philosophy of Science (ed. by Robert S. Cohen and Marx W. Wartofsky), Volume XVI. 1974, XII + 549 pp. Also available as paperback.

69. Roland Fraïssé, *Course of Mathematical Logic* – Volume 2: *Model Theory*. 1974, XIX + 192 pp.

70. Andrzej Grzegorczyk, *An Outline of Mathematical Logic. Fundamental Results and Notions Explained with All Details*. 1974, X + 596 pp.

71. Franz von Kutschera, *Philosophy of Language*. 1975, VII + 305 pp.

72. Juha Manninen and Raimo Tuomela (eds.), *Essays on Explanation and Understanding. Studies in the Foundations of Humanities and Social Sciences*. 1976, VII + 440 pp.

73. Jaakko Hintikka (ed.), *Rudolf Carnap, Logical Empiricist. Materials and Perspectives*. 1975, LXVIII + 400 pp.

74. Milič Čapek (ed.), *The Concepts of Space and Time. Their Structure and Their Development*, Boston Studies in the Philosophy of Science (ed. by Robert S. Cohen and Marx W. Wartofsky), Volume XXII. 1976, LVI + 570 pp. Also available as paperback.

75. Jaakko Hintikka and Unto Remes, *The Method of Analysis. Its Geometrical Origin and Its General Significance,* Boston Studies in the Philosophy of Science (ed. by Robert S. Cohen and Marx W. Wartofsky), Volume XXV. 1974, XVIII + 144 pp. Also available as paperback.

76. John Emery Murdoch and Edith Dudley Sylla, *The Cultural Context of Medieval Learning. Proceedings of the First International Colloquium on Philosophy, Science, and Theology in the Middle Ages – September 1973,* Boston Studies in the Philosophy of Science (ed. by Robert S. Cohen and Marx W. Wartofsky), Volume XXVI. 1975, X + 566 pp. Also available as paperback.

77. Stefan Amsterdamski, *Between Experience and Metaphysics. Philosophical Problems of the Evolution of Science,* Boston Studies in the Philosophy of Science (ed. by Robert S. Cohen and Marx W. Wartofsky), Volume XXXV. 1975, XVIII + 193 pp. Also available as paperback.

78. Patrick Suppes (ed.), *Logic and Probability in Quantum Mechanics.* 1976, XV + 541 pp.

79. H. von Helmholtz, *Epistemological Writings.* (A New Selection Based upon the 1921 Volume edited by Paul Hertz and Moritz Schlick, Newly Translated and Edited by R. S. Cohen and Y. Elkana), Boston Studies in the Philosophy of Science, Volume XXXVII. 1977 (forthcoming).

80. Joseph Agassi, *Science in Flux,* Boston Studies in the Philosophy of Science (ed. by Robert S. Cohen and Marx W. Wartofsky), Volume XXVIII. 1975, XXVI + 553 pp. Also available as paperback.

81. Sandra G. Harding (ed.), *Can Theories Be Refuted? Essays on the Duhem-Quine Thesis.* 1976, XXI + 318 pp. Also available as paperback.

82. Stefan Nowak, *Methodology of Sociological Research: General Problems.* 1977, XVIII + 504 pp. (forthcoming).

83. Jean Piaget, Jean-Blaise Grize, Alina Szeminska, and Vinh Bang, *Epistemology and Psychology of Functions.* 1977 (forthcoming).

84. Marjorie Grene and Everett Mendelsohn (eds.), *Topics in the Philosophy of Biology,* Boston Studies in the Philosophy of Science (ed. by Robert S. Cohen and Marx W. Wartofsky), Volume XXVII. 1976, XIII + 454 pp. Also available as paperback.

85. E. Fischbein, *The Intuitive Sources of Probabilistic Thinking in Children.* 1975, XIII + 204 pp.

86. Ernest W. Adams, *The Logic of Conditionals. An Application of Probability to Deductive Logic.* 1975, XIII + 156 pp.

87. Marian Przełęcki and Ryszard Wójcicki (eds.), *Twenty-Five Years of Logical Methodology in Poland.* 1977, VIII + 803 pp. (forthcoming).

88. J. Topolski, *The Methodology of History.* 1976, X + 673 pp.

89. A. Kasher (ed.), *Language in Focus: Foundations, Methods and Systems. Essays Dedicated to Yehoshua Bar-Hillel,* Boston Studies in the Philosophy of Science (ed. by Robert S. Cohen and Marx W. Wartofsky), Volume XLIII. 1976, XXVIII + 679 pp. Also available as paperback.

90. Jaakko Hintikka, *The Intentions of Intentionality and Other New Models for Modalities.* 1975, XVIII + 262 pp. Also available as paperback.

91. Wolfgang Stegmüller, *Collected Papers on Epistemology, Philosophy of Science and History of Philosophy,* 2 Volumes, 1977 (forthcoming).

92. Dov M. Gabbay, *Investigations in Modal and Tense Logics with Applications to Problems in Philosophy and Linguistics.* 1976, XI + 306 pp.
93. Radu J. Bogdan, *Local Induction.* 1976, XIV + 340 pp.
94. Stefan Nowak, *Understanding and Prediction: Essays in the Methodology of Social and Behavioral Theories.* 1976, XIX + 482 pp.
95. Peter Mittelstaedt, *Philosophical Problems of Modern Physics,* Boston Studies in the Philosophy of Science (ed. by Robert S. Cohen and Marx W. Wartofsky), Volume XVIII. 1976, X + 211 pp. Also available as paperback.
96. Gerald Holton and William Blanpied (eds.), *Science and Its Public: The Changing Relationship,* Boston Studies in the Philosophy of Science (ed. by Robert S. Cohen and Marx W. Wartofsky), Volume XXXIII. 1976, XXV + 289 pp. Also available as paperback.
97. Myles Brand and Douglas Walton (eds.), *Action Theory. Proceedings of the Winnipeg Conference on Human Action, Held at Winnipeg, Manitoba, Canada, 9-11 May 1975.* 1976, VI + 345 pp.
98. Risto Hilpinen, *Knowledge and Rational Belief.* 1978 (forthcoming).
99. R. S. Cohen, P. K. Feyerabend, and M. W. Wartofsky (eds.), *Essays in Memory of Imre Lakatos,* Boston Studies in the Philosophy of Science (ed. by Robert S. Cohen and Marx W. Wartofsky), Volume XXXIX. 1976, XI + 762 pp. Also available as paperback.
100. R. S. Cohen and J. Stachel (eds.), *Leon Rosenfeld, Selected Papers.* Boston Studies in the Philosophy of Science (ed. by Robert S. Cohen and Marx W. Wartofsky), Volume XXI. 1977 (forthcoming).
101. R. S. Cohen, C. A. Hooker, A. C. Michalos, and J. W. van Evra (eds.), *PSA 1974: Proceedings of the 1974 Biennial Meeting of the Philosophy of Science Association,* Boston Studies in the Philosophy of Science (ed. by Robert S. Cohen and Marx W. Wartofsky), Volume XXXII. 1976, XIII + 734 pp. Also available as paperback.
102. Yehuda Fried and Joseph Agassi, *Paranoia: A Study in Diagnosis,* Boston Studies in the Philosophy of Science (ed. by Robert S. Cohen and Marx W. Wartofsky), Volume L. 1976, XV + 212 pp. Also available as paperback.
103. Marian Przełęcki, Klemens Szaniawski, and Ryszard Wójcicki (eds.), *Formal Methods in the Methodology of Empirical Sciences.* 1976, 455 pp.
104. John M. Vickers, *Belief and Probability.* 1976, VIII + 202 pp.
105. Kurt H. Wolff, *Surrender and Catch: Experience and Inquiry Today,* Boston Studies in the Philosophy of Science (ed. by Robert S. Cohen and Marx W. Wartofsky), Volume LI. 1976, XII + 410 pp. Also available as paperback.
106. Karel Kosík, *Dialectics of the Concrete,* Boston Studies in the Philosophy of Science (ed. by Robert S. Cohen and Marx W. Wartofsky), Volume LII. 1976, VIII + 158 pp. Also available as paperback.
107. Nelson Goodman, *The Structure of Appearance,* Boston Studies in the Philosophy of Science (ed. by Robert S. Cohen and Marx W. Wartofsky), Volume LIII. 1977 (forthcoming).
108. Jerzy Giedymin (ed.), *Kazimierz Ajdukiewicz: Scientific World-Perspective and Other Essays, 1931–1963.* 1977 (forthcoming).
109. Robert L. Causey, *Unity of Science.* 1977, VIII + 185 pp.
110. Richard Grandy, *Advanced Logic for Applications.* 1977 (forthcoming).

111. Robert P. McArthur, *Tense Logic*. 1976, VII + 84 pp.
112. Lars Lindahl, *Position and Change: A Study in Law and Logic*. 1977, IX + 299 pp.
113. Raimo Tuomela, *Dispositions*. 1977 (forthcoming).
114. Herbert A. Simon, *Models of Discovery and Other Topics in the Methods of Science*, Boston Studies in the Philosophy of Science (ed. by Robert S. Cohen and Marx W. Wartofsky), Volume LIV. 1977 (forthcoming).
115. Roger D. Rosenkrantz, *Inference, Method and Decision*. 1977 (forthcoming).
116. Raimo Tuomela, *Human Action and Its Explanation. A Study on the Philosophical Foundations of Psychology*. 1977 (forthcoming).
117. Morris Lazerowitz, *The Language of Philosophy*, Boston Studies in the Philosophy of Science (ed. by Robert S. Cohen and Marx W. Wartofsky), Volume LV. 1977 (forthcoming).
118. Tran Duc Thao, *Origins of Language and Consciousness*, Boston Studies in the Philosophy of Science (ed. by Robert S. Cohen and Marx. W. Wartofsky), Volume LVI. 1977 (forthcoming).
119. Jerzy Pelc, *Polish Semiotic Studies, 1894–1969*. 1977 (forthcoming).
120. Ingmar Pörn, *Action Theory and Social Science. Some Formal Models*. 1977 (forthcoming).
121. Joseph Margolis, *Persons and Minds*, Boston Studies in the Philosophy of Science (ed. by Robert S. Cohen and Marx W. Wartofsky), Volume LVII. 1977 (forthcoming).

# SYNTHESE HISTORICAL LIBRARY

Texts and Studies
in the History of Logic and Philosophy

*Editors:*

N. KRETZMANN (Cornell University)
G. NUCHELMANS (University of Leyden)
L. M. DE RIJK (University of Leyden)

1. M. T. Beonio-Brocchieri Fumagalli, *The Logic of Abelard*. Translated from the Italian. 1969, IX + 101 pp.
2. Gottfried Wilhelm Leibniz, *Philosophical Papers and Letters*. A selection translated and edited, with an introduction, by Leroy E. Loemker. 1969, XII + 736 pp.
3. Ernst Mally, *Logische Schriften*, ed. by Karl Wolf and Paul Weingartner. 1971, X + 340 pp.
4. Lewis White Beck (ed.), *Proceedings of the Third International Kant Congress*. 1972, XI + 718 pp.
5. Bernard Bolzano, *Theory of Science*, ed. by Jan Berg. 1973, XV + 398 pp.
6. J. M. E. Moravcsik (ed.), *Patterns in Plato's Thought. Papers Arising Out of the 1971 West Coast Greek Philosophy Conference*. 1973, VIII + 212 pp.
7. Nabil Shehaby, *The Propositional Logic of Avicenna: A Translation from al-Shifā: al-Qiyās*, with Introduction, Commentary and Glossary. 1973, XIII + 296 pp.
8. Desmond Paul Henry, *Commentary on De Grammatico: The Historical-Logical Dimensions of a Dialogue of St. Anselm's*. 1974, IX + 345 pp.
9. John Corcoran, *Ancient Logic and Its Modern Interpretations*. 1974, X + 208 pp.
10. E. M. Barth, *The Logic of the Articles in Traditional Philosophy*. 1974, XXVII + 533 pp.
11. Jaakko Hintikka, *Knowledge and the Known. Historical Perspectives in Epistemology*. 1974, XII + 243 pp.
12. E. J. Ashworth, *Language and Logic in the Post-Medieval Period*. 1974, XIII + 304 pp.
13. Aristotle, *The Nicomachean Ethics*. Translated with Commentaries and Glossary by Hypocrates G. Apostle. 1975, XXI + 372 pp.
14. R. M. Dancy, *Sense and Contradiction: A Study in Aristotle*. 1975, XII + 184 pp.
15. Wilbur Richard Knorr, *The Evolution of the Euclidean Elements. A Study of the Theory of Incommensurable Magnitudes and Its Significance for Early Greek Geometry*. 1975, IX + 374 pp.
16. Augustine, *De Dialectica*. Translated with Introduction and Notes by B. Darrell Jackson. 1975, XI + 151 pp.